D

Mental Illness
in the
Urban
Negro Community

Seymour Parker

Robert J. Kleiner

Mental Illness in the Urban Negro Community

The Free Press, *New York*

Collier-Macmillan Limited, *London*

To Fran and Hilda,
Our Gratitude

ACKNOWLEDGMENTS

The authors first wish to express their gratitude to each other for the eight stimulating years of their relationship, during which they mutually shared both the difficulties and the satisfactions involved in conducting this study.

We owe a debt to all the members of the Negro community of Philadelphia for their cooperation and critical evaluation of our investigation at every stage of its progress.

Without the sincere encouragement and assistance of many individuals in the respective institutions with which we were affiliated, this volume might never have been written. We particularly wish to mention John E. Davis, former Commissioner of Mental Health of the Pennsylvania Department of Public Welfare; Robert Matthews, late Professor and Chairman of the Department of Psychiatry, Jefferson Medical College, Philadelphia; and Abraham Waldman, Director of the Philadelphia Reception Center, State Department of Public Welfare. Our thanks also to all the psychiatrists in private practice and in various mental health facilities in Philadelphia for their aid in gathering information and obtaining interviews with a representative sample of their clients.

To our colleagues who consulted with us, argued with us, and who always kept us aware of the intellectual pitfalls and the excitement of our endeavor, we express our sincere thanks. We extend our appreciation in particular to John R. P. French, Jr., E. Franklin Frazier, Herbert Hyman, and Albert Pepitone.

For sharing with us the arduous task of organizing and administering a research project of this size, we wish to thank Hayward Taylor who directed the field operation, and William Davis who expended great effort and skill in supervising the collection of interviews with the mentally ill sample. To thank our Research Assistant, Judith Fine, for specific tasks would be to miss the essence of her contribution to this investigation. She has been a loyal friend who has successfully borne the brunt of our respective idiosyncrasies.

We wish to express our appreciation to National Analysts, Incorporated, of Philadelphia, whose fine staff helped us to select a population sample of the Philadelphia Negro community and to obtain interviews with these individuals. Finally, we gratefully acknowledge the financial assistance received from the National Institutes of Health (Grant Numbers M-3047, M-5661, and MH-07494-01) and from the Pennsylvania Mental Health Research Foundation.

FOREWORD

The American version of democratic society is based upon the belief that the state exists for the individual and functions to help him exercise his rights to life, liberty, and the pursuit of happiness. Our country has been envisioned as a land of opportunity where men may use their capacities to attain an effective and satisfying way of life. The chances for mobility are apparently greater in this country than in many other nations, although these basic values are not always honored. Many individuals who accept these values, and who invest considerable effort in striving, fail to obtain desired goals. These unsuccessful strivers suffer.

We have gradually come to realize that such straining to achieve leaves many frayed in spirit and inefficient at meeting crises. Too many individuals have a discrepancy between their aspirations and achievements, and for some this discrepancy is not of their own creation. We recognize, although reluctantly, that for many citizens this nation is not a land of opportunity, that competition against standards of excellence necessarily means that some will fall short of these standards, and that marked dissatisfaction may continue to characterize even those individuals who have attained high levels of achievement. It is not surprising, then, that striving again and again for success after repeated failures has in recent years become something less than a virtue. Writers and dramatists have vividly described how an achieving society can damage psychological well-being, and they have caused many to question whether the prize is worth the chase.

In terms of definitive data, however, there is remarkably little evidence that goal-striving determines mental illness or psychosomatic complaints. There are scattered indications of differential tendencies to become mentally ill according to variations in education, social class, neighborhood, or religion. But such taxonomic pieces of evidence have brought little order out of confusion and have neither sharpened issues nor provided explanations of the

ix

effects of society on mental health. Given our lack of agreement on concepts in social science, and the confusing language of psychiatric diagnosis, we cannot really expect a categorizing type of research to provide a unitary pattern.

The study reported in this volume represents an attempt to deal systematically with these problems. This investigation does much to create a coherent structure for relationships between social conditions and mental health. The authors originally became interested in the effects of goal striving on mental health when they observed illness differences among Negroes which appeared to result from setting unrealistic goals, failing to achieve these goals, and being unwilling to modify their aspirations. Before studying these phenomena, however, the authors developed a tentative exposition of causes and effects and planned their investigation as a test of this theoretical framework. In this respect, they went beyond the current precept of the ideal methodological approach. They sought to test explanations instead of counting events or types, and this book is the noteworthy result of their perseverance in such a strategy.

Their theoretical formulation was concerned with the nature, origins, and consequences of personal aspirations and the impact of social influences upon these goals. They made careful choices among concepts employed in experimental research on level of aspiration, social comparison, self-identity, and self-esteem. They took these concepts and the related hypotheses into the fresh air as guides for their observations of community citizens and psychiatric patients.

This study involved asking 3,000 Negroes about their plans, successes, and fears. The results of these interviews provide striking support for a relationship between striving and mental health, as specified by their theory, and are generally consistent with the findings from laboratory studies of self-esteem and aspiration setting. It is notable, for example, that in experimental studies, subjects designated as "disturbed" on the basis of various criteria choose unreasonably high or low goals (usually the former), compared to "normal" subjects. The present study reveals that mentally ill persons set higher goals than they can achieve and experience high levels of self-imposed goal-striving stress. In addition, laboratory subjects with high aspirations who do not perceive themselves as performing well compared to significant others develop a sense of low self-esteem. In this study the patients more often see themselves as less competent than their friends, and as a result devalue their own abilities.

In the current conception of the ideal social science strategy, descriptive surveys precede the development of explanations for noted events. The explanations are then experimentally tested and revised in laboratory settings, and field experiments are finally conducted to determine whether laboratory results make sense in the world of uncontrolled variables. The present investigation improves on this strategy in one important respect: it takes conclusions from level-of-aspiration and other related experiments, which are usually based on reactions to unimportant laboratory tasks, and demonstrates their presence and effects in day-to-day living. Clearly, in real-life situations disturbed and undisturbed individuals will differ considerably in their approaches to striving and in their reactions to failure, in many of the ways suggested by laboratory experiments.

The findings of this study raise further questions of profound importance for theories of mental health and experimental studies of such theories. These results indicate that certain personal attributes which are assumed to be significantly related to mental health may not be as important as is usually believed. Mentally ill persons in this study, for example, are not characterized by greater fear of failure than community individuals, a quality often taken by experimental students of goal striving as an indicator of mental ill health. The results of this study require that experimentalists reconsider which individual variables are valid indicators of mental disturbance and which ones are not.

The sociological investigation of mental illness is presently stimulating a revolution in the care of the mentally ill. Responsibility for therapeutic care and prevention of illness is being shifted from the isolated mental hospital to the local community. But many unexplained paradoxes still exist concerning the relationship between rates of mental illness and such factors as migration, mobility, socioeconomic status, etc. Some of these apparent paradoxes are relieved by the study at hand. For instance, illness rates are generally assumed to be higher among migrants than among the native born. In the present study, migrants from the South are *less* likely to be ill than either the native born or migrants from other Northern states. With respect to mobility, this investigation shows that illness is most likely to occur among persons at the upper end of the socioeconomic scale who are upwardly mobile, and among those at the lower end of the scale who are downwardly mobile. The high rates in these two different types of mobility groups appear to be contradictory but become understandable in light of the social-psychological variables of this study.

A primary social concern in the United States during recent years has been the slow advancement of Negroes. This study, which is based on an all-Negro sample, shows that those Negroes who actively participate at a level of goal striving often realizable only by their white brethren are more likely than others to become ill. A sign that Negroes are finding few opportunities available to them today is seen in the grim fact that goal striving is having eroding effects on many who could have avoided such consequences in a more restricted world and in a calmer, less achievement-oriented day.

Future programs in mental health will be more concerned with effective living than with aberrant behavior. These improved programs must be

planned in the light of the socio-cultural events and frustrated dreams strik-
ingly set forth in this volume. They will require the development of methods
and institutions for the prevention of illness and therapy at all status levels
and in all segments of our society.

—*Alvin Zander*

CONTENTS

Contents

Mental Illness
in the
Urban
Negro Community

1

INTRODUCTION AND
THEORETICAL
ORIENTATION

Introduction

The central problem of this study developed from an attempt to replicate the early studies of Malzberg and Lee (1956) on migration and mental disorder among Negroes. These investigators found that Negro migrants (predominantly from the South) to New York State during the period 1929–1939 had a significantly higher rate of mental disorder, as gauged by first admissions to public and private hospitals in the state, than those who were born in New York.

In view of Malzberg's and Lee's conclusive findings, we were surprised that the rate of first admissions of Negroes to the Pennsylvania public mental hospitals during the period 1951–1956 was significantly higher for natives than for migrants to the state, even when age and sex differences in the two populations were taken into account (Kleiner and Parker, 1959). Explanations advanced by previous studies to account for the relationship between migration and mental illness might lead one intuitively to expect a higher first admission rate for migrants (e.g., the difficulties involved in adjusting to unfamiliar surroundings; the greater propensity of maladjusted individuals to move into a new environment, etc.). However, the statistically significant findings of our study raised questions about the plausibility of such a rationale. Our perplexity and interest increased on noting that in the Philadelphia Negro community the rate of juvenile delinquency was higher among adolescents native to Philadelphia than among those born in the South (Savitz, 1960). Also, "broken homes," as measured by the rate of divorces, separations, and desertions, were more numerous among natives than migrants (Kephart and Monahan, 1952).

Although these studies reported the statistical distributions of the phenomena under consideration, they offered little rationale for understanding them. The theoretical problems posed by such findings excited our curiosity about possible explanations for the higher rates of deviant behavior (i.e., mental disorder, juvenile delinquency, and broken homes) of the Negro native to Pennsylvania. We determined that status position, often linked to such indices of deviancy, could not explain these results; in fact, using education as an index of status position, the native Negro rated considerably higher than the migrant. Were the reasons for similarity in direction of these rates of deviant behavior unrelated, or etiologically linked? Would it be possible to subsume them under a single theoretical formulation?

At about this time, Robert Kleiner and his associates completed an analysis of census data pertaining to the Negro community of Philadelphia. They found that, controlling for occupational level, the native group had significantly higher educational attainments than the migrant. Level of education was assumed to be roughly correlated with level of aspiration in significant areas of life (Tuckman and Kleiner, 1962). The suggestion that the discrepancy between achievement and aspiration might be higher among native Negroes than among migrants provided the necessary conceptual wedge. We reasoned that the Negro who spent his formative years of socialization in the semi-caste system of the South would be prone to gear his aspirations to a relatively low level at an early age in order to accommodate to his social situation (Prange and Vitols, 1962). That such adjustments are common for the southern Negro has been amply documented in the writings of Allison Davis, John Dollard, and others. However, the Negro raised in the North would be more likely to partake for a longer period in an ethos that (ideally) sanctioned high success goals for everyone. Only at a later stage in life would he realize that the available means for achieving his relatively high aspirations were severely limited because he was a Negro, and because he probably occupied a low rung on the socioeconomic-educational ladder. Keeping in mind that the occupational achievements of both groups were similar, we assumed that the Negro raised in the North would be likely to experience a relatively larger discrepancy between his aspirations and achievements than the migrant Negro. We further assumed that the effect of this larger discrepancy would be psychologically stressful, and/or that the pressure to lower one's aspirations would be accompanied by a serious loss of self-esteem and a propensity toward mental disorder.

For these reasons, we decided to focus our study on the psychopathogenic effects of goal-striving behavior. Migration and other sociological variables became subsidiary to this interest; the overall research design of the study would incorporate these variables in order to test the predictive power of our theoretical formulation of goal-striving stress. While other investigators in this area (e.g., Tuckman and Kleiner, 1962) inferred discrepancies from educational and occupational data, the present study elicited information on aspirations by means of direct interviews.

Although the relationship between goal-striving experience and mental disorder will be examined in a Negro population, it is not *specifically* a Negro problem. The reasons for selecting this population for study grew out of our early interest in Negro migration and mental disorder. Achievement and the stress-provoking qualities of discrepancies in goal-striving behavior are pervasive problems in American society. It is surprising, therefore, that no systematic investigation of this phenomenon in its relationship to mental disorder in the general population has been made. The high psychic toll of success strivings, portrayed in the novels of Theodore Dreiser and F. Scott Fitzgerald, is a prevalent theme in the American novel. Almost every elementary sociology text dealing with American society stresses the ceaseless quest for success and the widespread assumption that "getting ahead" is possible for everyone who works hard, is frugal, etc. Based on clinical experience, such psychiatric observers of the American scene as Horney (1937), Fromm (1941), and Kardiner and Ovesey (1951) have noted that patients frequently evaluate their self-worth in terms of the competition for material success and social status. The psychic burden of this striving is heavy for Americans in general, but particularly so for the Negro who battles for equality and status position in a social system that is *relatively* closed to him. Kardiner and Ovesey, in their psychiatric study of Negroes (Kardiner and Ovesey, 1951), and Max Lerner, in his analysis of American civilization (Lerner, 1957), observed that a considerable proportion of the Negro's self-hatred and frustration stemmed from his acceptance of white goals, which for him were largely unattainable. This idea was expressed cogently by Frazier (1957), and further confirmed in a recent study by Parker and Kleiner (1964). We found that the Negro's status position varied with negative attitudes toward the Negro community. Although our selection of Negro subjects in order to study goal-striving behavior and orientation was partly an historical accident, in certain respects it was a fortunate choice. The additional social barriers to advancement encountered by the Negro make his goal-striving experience extremely painful; the investigation of these experiences may show a particularly clear relationship to mental disorder. In addition, because of the different prevailing ideologies and norms in the North and the South, a Negro sample allows us to study the psychic effects of varying levels and intensities of goal striving among individuals socialized in the two environments.

It should be clarified at the outset that the decision to focus this study on goal-striving behavior does not imply a belief that mental disorder can be explained by this factor alone. Although research findings do indicate that the discrepancy between aspiration and achievement often correlates with psychological stress, it is not known whether, and to what degree, this discrepancy is actually related to mental illness. Furthermore, since "mental disorder" is such a broad, amorphous category, more must be known about how goal-striving patterns are related to its different manifestations. The evidence to date suggests that what we call mental disorder (even limiting the term to the so-called "functional disorders") does not have a single etiology. Organic and genetic, as well as social-psychological factors appear to be implicated. Our decision as social scientists to concentrate on a particular conceptual area flows from the following observations:

(1) Previous studies have shown an apparent relationship between goal striving and forms of deviant behavior (e.g., mental disorder).

(2) A considerable number of empirical studies (carried out mainly in experimental situations) have resulted in the development of a suggestive body of theory in this area.

(3) The investigation of goal striving lends itself to quantitative study.

Although the work of Robert Merton (1957: 131–160, 161–194) is presented on a sociological level of analysis, it does indicate that goal-striving behavior may provide a focal breeding-ground for various types of socially deviant and pathological reactions.

An examination (Kleiner and Parker, 1963) of some large-sample studies of the epidemiology of mental disorder (Hollingshead and Redlich, 1958; Srole et al., 1962; Langner and Michael, 1963) indicated a seeming lack of systematic theory, and strengthened our determination to sharpen the focus of our research, and to use a consistent theoretical formulation. Such a formulation would be a guide in selecting variables to be studied and in predicting their relationships. This conviction is not intended as a negative evaluation of these important epidemiological studies. In the initial investigation of a problem whose etiology and dimensions are largely unknown, research must cast a wide net, gather facts, and establish empirical relationships among them. The purpose of many past studies has been to explore numerous areas, rather than to develop any particular conceptual framework. Another practical focus of these studies has been the delineation of the mental health problem and its distribution in the community. Although these studies have made several important contributions, ". . . there has been no sustained systematic approach to the problems of the precipitating factors in psychological disorders of various kinds" (Reid, 1961).

We are presently confronted with a plethora of heterogeneous, and even contradictory, findings (Kleiner and Parker, 1963). The potential value of theory is its facilitation in selecting from a chaotic universe those variables which are potentially significant for a particular problem, and in providing a rationale for predicting relationships among them. Theory also provides a framework for grasping the conceptual unity of apparently disparate empirical facts. For example, the very different findings concerning the relationship between social status and mental disorder (Clausen and Kohn, 1960; Leighton et al., 1963; see also Hollingshead and Redlich, 1958; Srole et al., 1962; Langner and Michael, 1963) might not present such a confusing picture if more were known about the social and psychological concomitants of status position (i.e., intervening variables) in different types of community structures. From a knowledge of such factors we could perhaps predict in different situations the associations between status and mental disorder. Similar examples could be provided from studies of the relationship between mental disorder and such phenomena as migration, social mobility, and status incongruity.

Despite the probable multicausality of mental illness and the difficulties with research in this area, we felt that the time was ripe to concentrate on selectively gathering empirical data related to testable theoretical propositions and hypotheses. In examining the relevant epidemiological literature, we were impressed with particular aspects of sample design. Most of the large-scale epidemiological studies conducted in recent years have been based on interviews administered to a community population, and on simple statistical and descriptive data gathered from records or informants concerning those actually diagnosed as mentally ill. Thus, the interpretations and conclusions about mental illness reached in these studies were derived from gross statistical comparisons of illness rates and population differences in the community and ill groups, and from interviews with segments of the community population adjudged to have different levels of psychoneurotic symptoms. Although high symptom groups in the community, rated as "mentally ill" by means of symptom check-lists or psychological tests, may be similar in *some* respects to the psychiatrically diagnosed mentally ill population (both institutionalized and uninstitutionalized), the qualitative and quantitative nature of this relationship is not well known. It should be kept in mind that, despite their symptoms, for the most part these individuals are still functioning members of the community. Important psychological and sociological differences may characterize the two populations, and may not merely reflect such adventitious circumstances as attitudes toward psychiatric treatment, financial resources, or accessibility of treatment facilities. Basic personality structure, defense mechanisms, and psychological compensatory resources may also differentiate them. At this point in our understanding, it is both premature and risky to generalize findings from one sample to another.

Because of this unanswered question, and because we felt that our research design necessitated data both from a community population and from a medically diagnosed mentally ill sample, we decided to obtain personal interviews in both groups. This decision was made with the realization of the serious difficulties of such an undertaking (e.g., the reliability and validity of interview data). Further details of the problems involved in this design will be described in Chapter 2 and in Appendix A. In addition, by means of a symptom checklist we attempted to identify within the community sample a subgroup with a high level of psychopathological symptoms. This design was intended to furnish comparable data both from a medically diagnosed patient population and from undiagnosed community subsamples showing different levels of psychoneurotic symptoms. As far as we can determine, this is the first effort to interview a representative sample of the functioning members of a community *and* a large sample of the diagnosed mentally ill from that same community.

It should be noted that the concepts used in this study, and the theoretical formulation of which they are a part, were developed from social-psychological experiments with individuals and small groups.

While the laboratory can be used as a model approximating real life situations, clearly there are difficulties involved in translating theoretical formulations from one situation to another. Although the basic regularities of human behavior are similar, the stimuli that condition the responses, as well as the ability to control and understand them, differ in the two situations. The problem of translating theory from one setting to another lies not in any qualitative difference between the situations themselves, but in the complexity and variation of conditioning influences affecting subjects' responses. For example, the affect associated with striving for life goals will probably differ from that generated in the highly structured psychological laboratory situation. Also, factors extraneous to the goal-striving situation affecting the responses in the two settings may have different implications for the fears and hopes associated with goal-striving, time perspectives, the risks one is willing to take, the goal level set for the immediate and distant future, and the probabilities attached to goal attainment. The problem here is not primarily a general theoretical one, but rather hinges on the investigator's ability to understand and to control the factors influencing behavior in both settings. Although much is still unknown about the degree of response similarity in these contexts, we feel that the application of theoretical concepts developed under experimental conditions to the analysis of real life situations will be fruitful.

Historical Perspectives

HISTORICALLY, there have been a number of changes in the "level of aspiration" concept as it has been used in experimental situations. The early work of Hoppe (as cited in Lewin et al., 1944) showed that subjects allowed to work on tasks until satiation frequently resumed them spontaneously when the experimenter was called away. The question of why they did this, if their tension had been reduced, led Hoppe to differentiate between short- and long-range goals. For Hoppe, "goals" represented the individual's long-range (explicit or implicit) aspirations, rather than his immediate expectations of performance on a particular task. On the other hand, Dembo (cited in Lewin et al., 1944) considered "level of aspiration" as an intermediate goal (i.e., as a step toward a more comprehensive and long-range objective). This approach made the concept more operationally definable and more amenable to measurement in psychological experimentation. In most subsequent investigations, goal setting came to be linked to the subject's explicitly verbalized response to an immediate task. "Desired" goals, although recognized as extremely significant to the individual, were regarded as more distant points toward which his present behavior was ultimately directed. In most of this work there is a general assumption that the subject's behavior in the experimental setting provides a projective model (Frank, 1935a; 1935b; and 1935c) of how he behaves in analogous life situations; however, the validity of this assumption has not been definitely established.

In defining level of aspiration, an investigator must decide whether to elicit from the respondent the goal he *expects* to obtain at some definite point in the near future, or the goal level he *would like* to achieve.

Lewin considered this question in terms of the degree of reality or "irreality" governing goal selection (Lewin, 1940). Discussing the same issue, Escalona (1940) pointed out:

By the irreal levels of the life space we mean all the regions, the structure and state of which is determined by the person himself, by his needs and wishes, his hopes and fears rather than by the 'objective' environment.

It should be noted that all goal-related decisions involve influences from several levels of reality. The "irreal" level should in no way be regarded as relatively unimportant and without serious consequences for the individual. Ultimately, the level at which a study is conducted should be determined by an evaluation of the relative efficacy of the different types of goals in predicting the behavior under consideration. Even the most "irreal" choice may be very significant in particular situations. In her study of goal striving and mental disorder, Escalona (1940) noted:

It is generally agreed that this part of the personality ["irreal" or fantasy factors] has an important influence upon behavior. We believe it to be particularly significant for success and failure situations because these are so closely related to self-esteem which is a very important and emotionally stressed part of most people's lives.

The individual's expected goal will be greatly influenced by his perception of the realities of the more immediate operative situation (e.g., internal and external barriers and facilitating factors) in which he is involved. The level a person would like to achieve is more influenced by stable and idiosyncratic desires, and relatively less affected by the constraints of day-to-day realities. A crucial question in the present study is whether the individual's psychopathogenic life stresses and tensions are more intimately related to the aspirations he expects, or would like, to achieve. The effects of these two goal orientations on behavior differ considerably (Festinger, 1942; Irwin and Mintzer, 1942). As a person enters late adulthood, his effective tension system probably becomes more closely linked to the immediate goals he expects to obtain. However, the peak onset of schizophrenia is usually much earlier, at a time when his long-range and desired goals may not yet have been seriously compromised by the restrictions and limitations imposed by his experience.

The individual's expected and desired goals will probably deviate considerably during early and middle adulthood. The former may represent a painful compromise with the realities of his current life situation, a compromise to which he is not psychologically reconciled. If this is true, then failure or success in reaching the desired level, rather than the expected level, is the more crucial determinant of his frustration and self-esteem. This reasoning is particularly important when dealing with goal-striving stress among Negroes, who frequently are forced by discriminatory practices to reduce their expectations to a level considerably below their more ego-central desires. For this reason, we decided to use as a measure of aspirational level the goals the individual would like, rather than those he expects, to achieve. Assumptions underlying this choice are that this aspirational level is more stable, pervasive, and ego-central for the individual because it is less likely to be influenced by temporary barriers and compromises; consequently, it may provide a better index of self-evaluation and potential frustration.

Theoretical Orientation

THE THEORIES ADVANCED to explain mental disorder are numerous and varied, and the phenomenon has been studied at various conceptual levels—neurophysiological, psychological, and sociological. It is quite as valid to approach mental disorder via psycholinguistics as by means of neurophysiology. Each of these fields has its raison d'être and has made its own contributions to our understanding of the problem. An overview of such research, however, is a painful reminder of the story of the blind men excitedly describing an elephant after each has felt a different part of the animal. The ways of science are strange and wonderful; perhaps one day we shall be able to "see" the entire elephant.

The concepts to be set forth emerge from studies in the social sciences and from clinical research. They are not new concepts, but we hope to combine them in a way that will clarify some of the factors creating the potential for, and sustaining, this type of deviant behavior. Our concept of goal-striving stress incorporates two general notions frequently underlying speculations about mental disorder in the behavioral sciences:

proneness to mental disorder increases directly (1) with anticipation of, or actual, failure to reach desired goals (i.e., frustration); and (2) with unrelieved and prolonged high levels of stress involved in striving for goals. The latter implies nothing about frustration as discussed in (1). Although primary emphasis is placed on goal-striving stress, frustration is also considered. It is assumed that both of these conditions result in psychological discomfort that may become pathogenic.

An accepted principle both in the biological and psychological fields is that an organism must maintain an optimum level of need tension in order to function properly. Need tension may be defined as an internal state of an organism which impels it to strive for a goal. Without this tension level it cannot utilize sources of available energy to perform its life- and health-sustaining functions. Without a certain level of tonus or tension even the walls of the amoeba would disintegrate into an amorphous mass unable to ingest or retain food. This concept is supported by studies in experimental psychology indicating an inverted curvilinear relationship between learning efficiency and strength of drive, anxiety, or arousal. That is, there is an optimum level of motivation, above and below which learning efficiency is impaired (Hebb, 1949; Berlyne, 1960: 166; Eysenck, 1963). In a review of some of the work done with human subjects in this area, Osgood (1963) noted that at moderate drive levels, associative connections were facilitated; at increasingly higher levels, stereotypy and finally disorganization occurred. This view is supported by research in the areas of perception and cognition. Although the exact neuropsychological mechanisms are not fully known, there are indications that such interference with perception and cognitive functions is mediated through arousal of the reticular formation. This, in turn, activates the autonomic nervous system, increases sympathetic discharge, and produces a diffuse excitatory effect on the cerebral cortex (MacLean, 1949; Dell, 1958; Berlyne, 1962).

These findings from the experimental laboratory take on added relevance for understanding the relationship between mental disorder and both goal-striving stress and frustration, when viewed in light of recent clinical research on mental disorder at the Cornell Medical School (Wolff, 1955; Hinkle and Wolff, 1957; Hinkle and Wolff, 1958; Hinkle et al., 1958; Chapman et al., 1960; Wolff, 1962). In these studies the persistent high levels of motivation and striving for goals which many of the ill subjects had set for themselves constituted major sources of threat and stress.

Based on a series of studies that included detailed physiological observations of animal and human subjects and large-scale epidemiological investigations, Wolff formulated a unified theory of disease:

Hence, because of man's highly developed nervous system, evoked reactions may be wrong not only in magnitude but also in kind. Under circumstances perceived as threatening, behavioral and attitudinal reactions serving to protect in a crisis, may become inappropriate in amount and kind. When inappropriate in kind, they may block interaction and communication with other persons and distort circumstances so as to prevent an appropriate response. . . . The data from these and other studies indicate, therefore, that it is unprofitable to establish a separate category of illness to be defined as psychosomatic or to separate sharply—as regards genesis—psychiatric, medical and surgical diseases. The concept presented brings unification to human pathology (Wolff, 1962).

The experimental and clinical literature cited up to this point presents both empirical evidence and possible theoretical linkage among these factors: goal striving, maladaptive physiological reactions, psychological stress and mental disorder. Since aspects of sociological and psychological theory underlie the present study, concepts and their interrelationships will be presented at this level of analysis. Although organic factors are beyond the scope of this investigation, the reader should bear in mind the necessity to consider such links in a comprehensive explanation of mental disorder.

It is important at this point to discuss more fully how the major psychological variables of this study articulate with the broader social situation in which the American Negro functions, and how this social environment contributes to his goal-striving problem. Although goal striving per se is a deeply rooted human activity, clearly the level of striving considered appropriate (i.e., optimum level) and the psychological consequences of success or failure are largely determined by societal values and group norms. It is also apparent that the objective situation in which goal striving occurs is determined by the complex interplay of economic and cultural factors which differentially affects the opportunity structure for various subgroups in the population.

Sociological and Social-Psychological Origins

MERTON'S VIEWS on goal striving and reference group behavior (Merton, 1957: 131–160, 161–194, 225–280, 281–386) are relevant to this problem and add an important sociological dimension to the conceptual framework of the present study. In discussing the social and cultural pre-conditions of deviant behavior, Merton noted that the American ethos "extols common success goals for the population at large." There is a strong emphasis on high achievement goals and a widespread belief that hard work insures success. Hyman (1942) found that most people chose reference groups with achievements above their own. In the past, such beliefs were both realistic and functional for the individual. America has permitted upward social mobility, apparently to a greater degree than other societies; the continually striving individual has had a fairly good chance (i.e., high probability) of reaching his aspirations. Unfortunately, the striving Negro has been an exception to this "American dream" (Frazier, 1957: 153–212). Like his fellow Americans, the Negro internalizes the common success values and assumes (for varying periods of his life) that his chances of achieving his aspirations are good. He, too, is led to believe in the ethos of the open social system which permits a high rate of social mobility. Given the objective fact of the limited opportunity structure for the Negro (Haveman and West, 1952: 96; Lipset and Bendix, 1963: 106), this estimate of reality is not feasible and frequently leads to frustration (Kardiner and Ovesey, 1951: 316; Glick and Miller, 1956; Dreger and Miller, 1960). It is not simply that he fails to achieve specific valued goals, but rather that he considers himself a failure and experiences concomitant and severe loss of self-esteem because he has internalized the values of success orientation. In his discussion of reference group theory, Merton (1957: 225–280, 281–386) introduced the concept of "anticipatory socialization" by which he explained some of the sources of deviant behavior and personal maladjustment. According to this concept, the individual's role expectations and behavioral norms are geared to the anticipation that he will achieve the standards of his reference group. In a sense, he becomes partially socialized to a situation in which he *expects* to be involved. The specific values and behavioral norms involved in this anticipatory socialization are embodied in his reference group, which provides him with role models. Where the potential for social mobility is high, these anticipations will be functional and psychologically adjustive, in that they will facilitate the transition to new roles associated with higher status positions. But if social mobility is restricted, as it is for most Negroes, the consequences of anticipatory socialization may be seriously dysfunctional. The individual in this situation becomes psychologically marginal to his peers and to those at the level he aspires to reach. Thus, the consequences of high goal striving differ depending on the nature of the social structure and the reference group behavior of the individual.

Merton's discussion of the nature of the social system and the potentially dysfunctional effects of anticipatory socialization is consistent with findings reported in the experimental psychological and social-psychological literature. Rigid cognitive structures or highly reinforced habits interfere with the influence of new experiences which are inconsistent with these structures or habits (Koffka, 1935; Lewin, 1935; Kounin, 1941; Lewin, 1951; Osgood, 1953; McClosky and Schaar, 1965)—a situation analogous to a strongly held belief in the "American dream" and a failure to realize this dream. In addition, intense motivational states interfere with cognitive reorganization of relearning (Lewin, 1935; Birch, 1945; Hebb, 1949; Lewin, 1951; Hull, 1952; Osgood, 1953; Berlyne, 1960; Osgood, 1963; McClosky and Schaar, 1965—again, a situation that parallels a very strong internalization of socially valued goals and a concomitant inability to realize that the opportunity structure is not as open as initially assumed.

Some persons with insight into the system may adjust their goals to a level more congruent with the objective realities of the opportunity structure and with the maintenance of a sense of personal competence. Others will unrealistically and rigidly retain their previous goal levels, or even raise them in a defensive and futile attempt to bolster their self-esteem. These individuals experience a sustained high level of striving that remains unreduced. Still others will psychologically "give up" and drop their aspirational levels drastically, in order to relieve the pressures and anxieties associated with achievement striving and frustration. In both of these latter instances the usual (i.e., socially sanctioned) outlets for the expression of energy to master the environment are unavailable. Although these two types of adjustment do not *necessarily* lead to mental disorder, they may be associated with it (Lewin et al., 1944; Festinger, 1954; Atkinson, 1957; French and Kahn, 1962; French, 1963). Thus, there appears to be an optimum level of goal striving, and higher rates of psychopathology are apparently associated with levels above and below this optimum. In addition, this optimum level is not inherent in the biological organism but rather is a function of the social situation. This idea is exemplified by a recent large sample study of mental health in America (Gurin, 1960: 215–218) which compared three income groups in a community population; the middle-income group, which had the highest discrepancy between achievement and aspiration, was also the most optimistic about the future and showed the fewest symptoms of psychological anxiety. This implies that in a "normal" population there may exist an optimum level of goal striving at which psychopathological symptoms are minimal.

Conceptual Definitions

ACCORDING to Merton (1957: 151, f.n. 35), the concept of the discrepancy between achievement and aspiration has had a long history of use in understanding aspects of human behavior. He raised an important question which poses a central methodological problem of this study:

The critical question is whether this familiar insight [discrepancy] can be subjected to rigorous experimentation in which the contrived laboratory situation adequately reproduces the salient aspects of the real-life situation or whether disciplined observation of routines of behavior in everyday life will prove the more productive method of inquiry.

Although the Lewin–Escalona "level of aspiration" formulation (Escalona, 1940; Lewin et al., 1944; Escalona, 1948) provides some of our major variables, these are further linked to mental disorder by such intervening concepts as reference group behavior and self-esteem. These concepts will be discussed later in this chapter. One of the fundamental elements in our theoretical scheme is the "psychological stress" associated with goal-striving behavior. For purposes of this analysis, psychological stress occurs when an individual experiences a strong need tension in relation to high aspirational (goal) levels relative to current achievement. Under such circumstances, behavior designed to enable him to cope with this aroused state is elicited. The effects of the arousal depend on the nature of the coping mechanisms employed (Lazarus and Baker, 1956). The *discrepancy* between one's achievement and level of aspiration in a number of different content areas of striving is the basic element in our concept of goal-striving stress. The individual's actual level of achievement and his aspirational level were recorded on a single scale specifying progressively higher potential achievement levels, appropriate to a particular goal-content area. The number of levels or steps between his achievement and aspiration represented his discrepancy score. Clearly there can be no stress if the individual does not desire to leave a (psychological) region he perceives as negatively valent for one that is positively valent. It is assumed that the individual who chooses an aspirational level above his current achievement is discontent both with his present position and with his inability to reach his desired goal level. It is also assumed that (other things remaining equal) his dissatisfaction with his present position varies directly with the size of this discrepancy: the greater the discrepancy, the greater his dissatisfaction, or stress (Gardner, 1940; Hyman, 1942). The stated level of aspiration is the individual's evaluation of a satisfactory performance for himself—it is by this standard that he judges himself in relevant areas of life (Festinger, 1954). If this interpretation is valid, then the size of the discrepancy corresponds to the amount of thwarting and threat to self-esteem experienced in particular areas of goal striving.

This discussion has assumed that the size of the discrepancy will vary directly with stress only if other things remain equal. One cannot proceed very far in life, or in research, on such a simple assumption. Two persons with similar achievement levels *and* similar aspirations may experience markedly different amounts of discomfort or tension as a result of this configuration. In other words, the amount of arousal generated by these discrepancies will differ according to the centrality of the goal for the individual—the importance he attaches to reaching it. A goal of little importance will neither constitute serious threats to the individual upon failure, nor involve high anticipation of pleasure upon success; therefore, the affect associated with such goals will be small. We refer to the importance or centrality of a goal for the individual as the *valence* of the goal region. A particular goal is associated both with a *valence of success* and a *valence of failure*. The former refers to the amount of anticipated satisfaction associated with success, and the latter to the amount of anticipated disappointment associated with failure to attain the goal. Two other components of the tension level are the individual's estimates of his chances of reaching, and failing to reach, the goal (i.e., the *probability of success* and the *probability of failure*). If he assesses his chances as very poor (i.e., if the goal is psychologically distant), the goal will fail to arouse a great amount of tension. Both experimental evidence and clinical observation indicate that a goal has greater "driving force" when it is near attainment (Lewin, 1948: 145–158). It is reasoned that as the individual approaches a goal, the cues associated with this aspiration increase in frequency and magnitude. These signs further augment the strength of the existing motivational system. The *tension level* associated with a particular goal region is assumed to represent the interaction between the valence and probability. Our formulation of goal-striving stress consists of the discrepancy between achievement and aspiration multiplied by the tension level associated with that goal. Although the elements comprising goal-striving stress are conceptually distinct, in actual goal-striving situations they undoubtedly interact and combine in varying magnitudes. Thus, a large discrepancy may constitute little more than a fantasy involvement and may be associated with a very low tension level. However, a large discrepancy may also be associated with a high level of tension in the very confident and optimistic individual. Therefore, in the present study each of these elements has been operationally defined and measured independently.

The usefulness of the concept of tension and tension reduction for explaining and predicting behavior is illustrated by investigations of the resumption of recall of incompleted tasks. One of the earliest studies (Zeigarnik, 1938) found that a person who was oriented toward carrying out a series of tasks (i.e., in a state of tension), but who was prevented from completing them, resumed these tasks at the first opportunity (i.e., in order to reduce his tension). In another study Ovsiankina, 1928) completion of tasks was interrupted and the individual was subsequently asked to recall the tasks; he reported more of the incompleted than the completed tasks. This was attributed to his attempt to reduce the tension associated with the unfinished tasks. Later it was demonstrated that the greater recall of completed or incompleted tasks depended on the motivation induced by the experimenter. For example, a subject may be told that certain tasks he is performing will be reported in a study conducted by the experimenter. Assuming that rapport has been established, the subject usually concentrates on the tasks (i.e., a tension system or intention to help the experimenter exists). Under such conditions, the subject will recall more of the unsolved or incompleted tasks. However, if he is told that his performance is being evaluated, a tension system or intention to succeed is created. In this situation, he will tend to recall the completed tasks or successes, and forget the failures (Marrow, 1938a; 1938b; Lewis, 1944; Lewis and Franklin, 1944; Alper, 1948).

Modification and Application of the Resultant Weighted Valence Theory

THE RESEARCH RESULTING from the Resultant Weighted Valence Theory has produced experimental findings which will enable a further refinement of the concept of goal-striving stress. The Lewin–Escalona statement of the Resultant Weighted Valence Theory (Escalona, 1940; Lewin et al., 1944; Escalona, 1948) assumes that a person's goals or aspirations in any given area constitute points on a scale of increasing difficulty of attainment. When an individual selects a goal, he evaluates the pros and cons of each point on the scale and then decides toward which level he will move. The individual chooses a goal at some point of compromise between his anticipations of success and failure. He thus experiences a series of conflict situations, the resolution of which determines his selected goal level. The approach forces (valences of success and probability of success) are those situational elements which heighten his anticipation of pleasure upon goal attainment and stimulate goal striving. The avoidance forces (valence of failure and probability of failure) are anticipations of failure which build up pressures to reject the goal level, or even the entire goal region. The difference between the sum of the approach and avoidance forces may be considered the resultant force on the individual toward or away from a particular goal. The selected aspirational level is the point where the resultant force is positive (i.e., toward the goal) and of greatest magnitude. Goal levels above this point, on a scale of difficulty of attainment, will insure failure and pose a threat to self-esteem, whereas lower goal levels will not be sufficiently challenging to enhance self-esteem.

The individual has been viewed as being in a field of forces, the resultant of which determines the direction of his behavior. More specifically, when an effective force exists, he is said to be in a state of (need) tension to approach or to avoid a goal. When two or more effective forces are simultaneously operative but opposite in direction, he is in a conflict situation. The level of motivation to strive for goals is determined by the resultant or interaction of the forces in this situation. The total resultant approach or avoidance force corresponds to the magnitude of the tension to move toward or away from a given goal: the higher the resultant force, the greater the tension level. If the resultant force is positive (i.e., approach is higher than avoidance), the individual moves toward the goal, and conversely if the resultant force is negative. That goal is selected which is associated with the highest net approach force for the individual.

The intensity of the approach forces toward any goal is the product of probability of success and valence of success ($P_{succ} \times Val_{succ}$), and, for the avoidance forces, the product of probability of failure and valence of failure ($P_{fai} \times Val_{fai}$). Since the direction of the avoidance forces is away from the goal, they are assigned a negative value. The sum of the two sets of forces represents the resultant force toward the goal and the state of the individual's tension system at a particular level of aspiration. This value is referred to as the Resultant Weighted Valence (RWV).

The usefulness of the Lewin–Escalona theory (Escalona, 1940;

Lewin et al., 1944; Escalona, 1948), both in its qualitative and quantitative form, has been demonstrated in a number of studies. Alexander, Macht, and Karon (1950) took the responses of college students to questions designed to measure each component in the formulation. By direct substitution in the formula they were able to predict the occupational aspirations that these students (1) would like to realize, and (2) expected to achieve. Kleiner (1960) found that as the avoidance component was reduced (thereby increasing the relative strength of the approach motivation), the level of aspiration was raised. As the individual experienced success and perceived the task as relatively easy, he set higher goals or aspirations for himself.

At this point, our concept of goal-striving stress can be restated in terms of its components—the discrepancy between aspiration and achievement (D) and the Resultant Weighted Valence associated with a given aspirational level. It is expressed by the following formula:

$$\text{Goal-Striving Stress} = D\left[(P_{succ} \times Val_{succ}) - (P_{fai} \times Val_{fai})\right]$$

A hypothetical example may help to clarify the reasoning underlying our modification of the Resultant Weighted Valence Theory. John Doe is a semi-skilled manual worker who aspires to a middle-level managerial position in his firm. Because of his strong needs for admiration from his fellow workers and friends, he anticipates attaining this goal with a great deal of satisfaction (i.e., high valence of success). This may be expressed mathematically by the figure *three* on a scale of valences from zero to four. Since he is aware that such promotions are infrequent and have only rarely been achieved in the past, his subjective estimate of success is not high, perhaps only *three* chances out of ten (i.e., low probability of success). On the other hand, since he is also aware of the difficulties involved in obtaining a white-collar position, and he does not anticipate too much disappointment if he does not succeed, his valence of failure is low, or *one* on a four point scale. In addition, he realizes that his probability of failure is high, or *seven* chances out of ten. We assume that the discrepancy between John Doe's semi-skilled job and the position he wants to achieve is *four*, based on a scale of hierarchically arranged occupations. Substituting these values in the stress formula noted above, we can describe John Doe's goal-striving stress in the following terms:

$$\text{Goal-Striving Stress} = 4\left[(3 \times 3) - (1 \times 7)\right] = 8$$

Goal-striving stress becomes more intense with increases in the discrepancy and Resultant Weighted Valence components of the formula.

Two assumptions made about the relationship between the probability of success and failure and the valence of success and failure should be noted. For both probability and valence, success and failure are assumed to be inversely related. It is logical that as the probability of success increases, the probability of failure decreases. The matter is not as clear-cut with respect to valence. We reasoned that if goal-achievement is associated with considerable satisfaction (i.e., high valence of success), the individual will experience relatively little disappointment (i.e., low valence of failure) at not achieving it. For example, if his achievement level involves a very difficult and important goal, his valence of success will probably be very high, but the degree of disappointment at not reaching it will be low. This inverse relationship also holds for goals with a low valence of success; such goals will be associated with a high valence of failure. These assumptions determine our operational definitions of the formula values for the probability of failure and the valence of success.

Our use of the Resultant Weighted Valence Theory and the discrepancy between aspiration and achievement is analogous to the approach utilized by Vogel, Baker, and Lazarus (1958; see also Vogel, Raymond, and Lazarus, 1959). In their studies of physiological measures of anxiety, they considered anxiety a function of the interaction between a "stressor" and the individual's motive state. They specifically emphasized that in the absence of a stressor (cf. our discrepancy concept), there would be no anxiety, regardless of the motive state. Conversely, in the absence of an effective motive state (cf. our concept of tension system), there would be no anxiety, regardless of the stressor. In order to evaluate a number of physiological measures of anxiety, they induced both a motive state and a stressor.

Although the idea of conflict is involved in the Resultant Weighted Valence Theory, it differs from the use of this concept in learning theory (Miller and Dollard, 1941; Miller, 1944). According to learning theory, the individual's emotional tension or frustration is maximum when the forces to approach a particular goal region are equal and opposite to the forces acting on him to avoid that goal—that is, when the sum of these forces is zero. This view also maintains that as the intensity of each of these opposing forces increases by equal amounts, one's frustration will also increase. Miller and Dollard emphasized the psychological effects of this conflict. In the Resultant Weighted Valence Theory, the conflict between approach and avoidance forces is considered a determinant of the level of aspiration (which is taken to be the point of maximum net approach motivation). If the forces on an individual to select an aspiration are equal to the forces to avoid this goal, he will experience no goal-striving motivation.

The first hypothesis of this study is:

Hypothesis 1. *Goal-striving stress will be significantly higher in the mentally ill population than in the community population.*

Hypothesis 1 grows directly from our previous discussion which linked goal-striving stress to the development of mental disorder. Additional predictions can be derived from Hypothesis 1 by making the following assumptions. First, psychosis and neurosis are on the same illness continuum, the former being of greater severity. Second, that since the mentally ill as a group are considered to have more than the optimum level of goal-striving stress, the degree of illness will vary directly with such stress. This assumption stems from the idea that mental disorder reflects progressive interference with the organism's capacity to reorganize his cognition at stress levels above or below the optimum. Therefore, the greater inability of the psychotic to effect cognitive reorganization, or goal-directed behavior, is associated with higher levels of goal-striving stress.

Hypothesis 1a. *Within the mentally ill population, goal-striving stress will be significantly higher among patients diagnosed as psychotic than among those diagnosed as neurotic.*

Third, assuming that it is valid to evaluate mental health in the community population by means of an index of psychoneurotic symptoms, those with a lower-than-optimum level of goal-striving stress will manifest more of these symptoms than those with a stress level close to, or at, the optimum. A higher-than-optimum stress score is a function of the discrepancy and an excess of approach motivation; a lower-than-optimum score is a function of the discrepancy and extreme avoidance motivation or rigidly maintained expectations of failure. Research has shown that a high prevalence of psychoneurotic symptoms is associated with intense feelings of anxiety (Sears, 1941; Lewin et al., 1944; Atkinson and Litwin, 1960; Atkinson et al., 1960; Mahone, 1960). Such individuals severely curtail their active goal striving.

Hypothesis 1b. *Within the community population, goal-striving stress will be significantly higher in a subgroup having a low yield of psychoneurotic symptoms than in a subgroup having a high yield of such symptoms.*

The discussion up to this point has dealt with the concept of goal-striving stress, its component elements, and its relationship to mental disorder. Although hypotheses about this relationship have been presented, the issue is a complex one, and it will be necessary to consider other concepts which condition and modify the psychopathogenic effects of goal-striving stress. The first of these is *reference group behavior.* A reference group represents an existing group of people (or set of values) by means of whose performance or opinions one evaluates himself. It may constitute an actual membership group for the individual, or merely one he wishes to enter or to emulate. In the context of this study, reference group behavior is defined as the perceived discrepancy between one's achievement and that of his reference group.

While goal-striving stress may itself increase susceptibility to mental disorder (for the reasons already discussed), its effects are probably conditioned by the manner in which the individual perceives and interprets his failure to reach important goals. The individual can perceive high goal-striving stress either as a prelude to success or failure. The consequences of these different perceptions for mental health may be very different. His interpretation of goal-striving stress will also differ, depending on whether he perceives his reference group situation as threatening to his concept of self and to his interpersonal relations. We assume that the individual's reference group behavior determines to a great extent how he interprets his goal-striving experience (Lewin, 1936; Lazarus and Baker, 1956; Simpson, 1962; Zander and Quinn, 1962; Zander and Medow, 1963; Alexander and Campbell, 1964). In some cases the actual position achieved by a reference group which one aspires to enter supplies the criteria for evaluation. In other instances the values of the current reference group (or individual) determine whether feelings of success or failure are associated with a specific achievement level. Reference group behavior is also significant for this study insofar as it provides an arena for the operation of individual psychological defenses against the potentially stressful consequences of goal-striving experiences. As conceived here, the reference group functions primarily to supply evaluative criteria for one's behavior. Festinger and his associates (1954) noted that frequently "there is no objective, non-social basis for evaluating one's abilities. To the extent that such objective bases are lacking the individual again evaluates his abilities by comparing [them] with the abilities of others in groups of which he is a member." Research on reference groups indicates that their importance in determining feelings of success or failure increases (1) if the individual is a member of the group; (2) if it is attractive to him; and, (3) if the evaluative criteria it supplies are relevant or important to him. The individual will evaluate himself as a failure if, in an area relevant to his self-esteem, he perceives his performance as falling below that of a significant reference group (i.e., negative discrepancy), and he will regard himself as adequate or superior if he perceives that his performance is equal to or above it (Rasmussen and Zander, 1954; Simpson, 1962; Zander and Quinn, 1962; Zander and Medow, 1963; Alexander and Campbell, 1964). We further hypothesize that the individual who experiences such feelings of failure will be more prone to mental illness. A consideration of the concept of reference group behavior underlies the second major hypothesis of this study:

> Hypothesis 2. *The degree of negative discrepancy from a reference group will vary directly with the severity of mental illness.*

Consonant with the previous assumptions about mental disorder being on a continuum of severity, the following corollaries are presented:

> Hypothesis 2a. *Within the mentally ill population, negative discrepancy from a reference group will be higher for the psychotics than for the neurotics.*

> Hypothesis 2b. *Within the community population, negative discrepancy from a reference group will be larger for a high symptom group than for a low symptom group.*

The use of the concepts of goal-striving stress and distance from reference group as interacting elements raises some questions about their meaning and whether, in fact, they reflect similar phenomena. Is not one's own level of aspiration (used to measure goal-striving stress) already determined by the performance level of his relevant reference groups? If this is true, then considering the stress levels arising from these respective sources is tantamount to adding the same phenomenon twice. Careful consideration of these concepts, however, suggests that they overlap to some degree but are not congruent. One's level of aspiration can be regarded as the historical, but still active, precipitate of *all* his significant reference group experiences, past and present, and the degree to which he has met with success and failure in the past. Although one's personal level of aspiration *includes* norms emanating from actual reference groups in his environment, these groups do not exclusively determine such norms (Simpson, 1962; Zander and Quinn, 1962; Zander and Medow, 1963; Alexander and Campbell, 1964). Norms provided by one's existing reference group contain evaluative elements, or standards by which current performance and achievement are evaluated. According to a study by Eisenstadt (1954b), reference group norms serve "as principles of perpetual organization of the social field for the individual; i.e., with their aid various social objects could be perceived in some organized way, for instance, as conforming with given norms or deviating from them as exemplifying certain values, etc." (see also Eisenstadt, 1954a).

The final concept to be introduced in this study is that of *self-esteem*, which can be defined as the value the individual places on one or more aspects of his self-image. Self-image, in turn, consists of the individual's perception of the kind of person he *is*, and also the manner in which he interacts with others and performs his various social roles (Rogers, 1959; Simpson, 1962; Zander and Quinn, 1962). These perceptions are accompanied by corresponding self-evaluation, which can be regarded as his self-esteem. Miller (1963) regards self-esteem as the individual's evaluations of his significant subidentities, or his perception of his appearance to others and his private version of his own pattern of traits as applied to his specific social roles. In this study, an attempt will be made to analyze self-esteem by using a composite or overall index of this concept, as well as indices relevant to various subidentities of the self.

Numerous studies have indicated that self-esteem is increased by awareness of success and decreased by awareness of failure in significant areas of social role performance (Rasmussen and Zander, 1954; French and Kahn, 1962; French, 1963). The work of Rogers and Dymond (1954) suggests the importance of this concept for the etiology and progress of mental disorder. Individuals who improved during the course of psychiatric treatment also showed a reduction in the discrepancy between self-image and ideal self-image. This leads to the third major hypothesis of the present study:

Hypothesis 3. *Self-esteem will vary inversely with the severity of mental illness.*

Applying this prediction to our four mental health groupings, we anticipate that self-esteem will decrease progressively in the low symptom (community) group, the high symptom group, the neurotics, and the psychotics. These predictions are embodied in Hypotheses 3a and 3b:

Hypothesis 3a. *Within the mentally ill population, self-esteem will be lower for the psychotics than for the neurotics.*

Hypothesis 3b. *Within the community population, self-esteem will be lower for the high symptom group than for the low symptom group.*

It is possible that the relationship between success and failure in social role performance (as gauged by the discrepancy concept) and mental disorder is mediated by the effect of the former on self-esteem. However, it has been suggested (Lewin, 1940) that self-esteem will be lowered by an awareness of failure *only* if this failure is attributed by the individual to a defect in himself rather than to an external barrier in his environment. We shall explore this idea to the extent that our data permit.

We have attempted to specify the relation of three variables (goal-striving stress, reference group behavior, and self-esteem) to mental disorder. At this point, it is important to discuss the interrelationship of these variables and to present relevant hypotheses where possible. Earlier in this chapter we spoke of an optimum level of goal striving, and noted that individuals above and below this level are prone to psychopathology. We suggested that deviation from the central values of goal striving in our society induces feelings of failure and low self-esteem. A person with lower-than-optimum stress invests little or no energy in striving and thus considers himself a failure relative to values he has internalized during the socialization process. A person with high goal-striving stress feels dissatisfied with his current achievement and frustrated at his inability to reach desired goals. Both individuals are likely to define themselves as failures and to experience lowered self-esteem. The following hypothesis is based on this reasoning:

Hypothesis 4. *The degree of deviation from the optimum level of goal-striving stress (in either direction) will be inversely related to level of self-esteem.*

The prediction of the relationship between reference group behavior and self-esteem is less complex. Since one's reference group provides criteria for self-evaluation, we expect that negative discrepancy from this group will result in feelings of failure and loss of self-esteem. This interpretation is embodied in the following hypothesis:

Hypothesis 5. *The degree of negative discrepancy from reference group will be inversely related to self-esteem.*

Although Hypotheses 4 and 5 flow from the rationale offered above, they are also logically derivable from Hypotheses 1, 2, and 3. The latter contain the idea that as goal-striving stress and discrepancy from one's reference group increase, the likelihood of mental disorder also increases. We assume that self-esteem is affected both by goal-striving stress and discrepancy from reference group. If goal-striving stress varies directly, and self-esteem inversely, with mental disorder, stress and self-esteem must be inversely related to each other (Hypothesis 4). Similarly, if discrepancy from reference group varies directly, and self-esteem inversely, with mental disorder, the discrepancy and self-esteem must also be related inversely to each other (Hypothesis 5).

No prediction will be made about the relationship between goal-striving stress and discrepancy from reference group. Nevertheless, we assume that the cumulative effect of both these variables will enable us to predict the nature of self-esteem and the yield of mental disorder with greater accuracy than either goal-striving stress or discrepancy from reference group taken alone.

In summary, our conceptual scheme consists of the notion that goal-striving stress and reference group behavior contribute to self-esteem which, in turn, influences susceptibility to mental illness.

Atkinson's Revision of the Resultant Weighted Valence Theory

IN OUR APPLICATION of the Resultant Weighted Valence Theory we have been concerned with the valence of success and failure, and the probability of success and failure. The responses used as measures of these factors were based on the individual's assessment of his immediate situation. Atkinson (1957) took issue with the Lewin–Escalona approach because he felt it did not include that aspect of the individual's motivational state based on past experience, as reflected in the personality. In Atkinson's opinion, one must consider the individual's orientation toward goal striving in general (i.e., his need for achievement [nAch]), and his orientation toward failure (i.e., his need to avoid failure [nAvF]). He felt, in addition, that Lewin's interpretation of valence of success was a function of the individual's need for achievement and his incentive to strive for a given goal ($Val_{succ} = Inc_s \times nAch$), and similarly, that valence of failure should be redefined as the interaction between fear of failure and the incentive to avoid failure ($Val_{fai} = Inc_f \times nAvF$). Lewin's original formulation would be modified by Atkinson as follows:

$$[P_{succ} \times Inc_s \times nAch] - [P_{fai} \times Inc_f \times nAvF]$$

In the present study, in addition to the regular interview, Atkinson's Need Achievement Test was administered to all respondents between twenty-five and twenty-nine years of age, in the ill and community populations. These data will not be discussed in the context of the present volume.

Controlling for Illness Effect

IN PRECEDING SECTIONS we have predicted systematic differences between the community and ill populations with respect to certain variables. For example, we predict a progressive decrease in self-esteem as the degree of illness increases. Such predictions are essentially correlations; they tell us little about whether the variables under consideration are causally related. A significant correlation between low self-esteem and mental disorder provides no definite answer to the question of whether lowered self-esteem is antecedent to, or a manifestation of, mental disorder. Although the two variables undoubtedly are closely interrelated, without additional analyses the problem of causality remains unresolved.

Faced with this situation, we developed a method to probe more deeply the causal relationship between mental disorder and the variables selected for study. This method involves (1) determining the relative yield, or rates, of mental disorder for various subgroups in the community population; and (2) ascertaining whether a high yield subgroup shows a greater prevalence of characteristics predicted for a mentally ill population than does a low yield subgroup. If, for example, males are over-represented and females under-represented in the ill population compared to their distribution in the community, we expect higher average stress scores for the males in the community population. However, if rates of mental disorder do not differ for the two sex groups, stress scores for males and females in the community population should show no variation. Wherever possible, we have applied this method of analysis to different community subgroups for each of the variables being studied.

The rationale for this procedure is based on the assumption that factors found to be characteristic of a diagnosed mentally ill population will also be associated with community subgroups having relatively high yields of mental disorder. It is also implied that individuals in the community population who manifest characteristics assumed to produce illness will be more likely to become ill than those who do not show such traits. By comparing *community* subgroups differing in yield, we reduce the possible effect of mental illness itself on responses to the questionnaire items.

This method of analysis provides some basis for resolving the question of causality, although it does not indicate with absolute certainty whether any two variables are causally, or only correlatively, related. Thus, one may readily entertain the possibility that low self-esteem is a consequence of, rather than an antecedent condition to, mental disorder. This conclusion becomes less tenable, however, if community subgroups with high yields of mental illness are also found to be characterized by low self-esteem. Under these circumstances, the assumption that low self-esteem is itself psychopathological seems more feasible.

2

METHODS AND
PROCEDURES

In the preceding chapter we presented the general goals and the theoretical orientation of this study. In order to accomplish these objectives, it was necessary to translate the various aspects of the theoretical framework into operationally defined variables, and to develop methods for testing hypothesized relationships among these variables. In this chapter we shall describe the overall research design and specify the various technical definitions and procedures utilized in the execution of the research plan. In order not to divert the more general reader with minutiae, some of the relevant detailed information (which is necessary for a proper evaluation and replication of the study) has been placed in appropriate appendices.

The basic research design involved the comparison of two populations, both drawn from the Philadelphia Negro community: a representative sample of the community population, and a representative sample of individuals diagnosed as mentally ill. In order to determine with a high degree of confidence any significant differences between these two populations on any of the variables under consideration, the samples had to be large enough to permit comparisons when such factors as age, sex, achievement level, etc., were controlled, or held constant.

The sophisticated reader might question the implication that individuals in the community sample were necessarily "healthy" from a psychiatric viewpoint. Everyday observation, confirmed by Srole et al. (1962) and Langner and Michael (1963), indicates that such an assumption is untenable. Clearly, a certain proportion of individuals in any community population will be afflicted with emotional symptoms of varying severity. Therefore, we included in our mentally ill sample all those from the community sample who reported being treated by a physician for "nervous or mental trouble" at the time of, or during the year preceding, the interview ($N = 99$). This procedure removed from the community sample only current or recently treated cases; undoubtedly individuals remained who were not then in treatment but who probably required psychiatric care. Fifty-six (3.7 per cent) of the 1489 cases remaining in the community sample reported some contact with psychiatric facilities prior to the year preceding the study. We made two assumptions about our samples: (1) that the ill sample contained a significantly larger number of psychiatrically ill individuals than the community sample; and (2) that those who were psychiatrically ill in the treated sample were significantly more impaired than the untreated disturbed individuals in the community sample. These assumptions permitted us to test hypotheses concerning the relationship between particular variables and mental disorder. The questionnaire instrument administered to the community and ill samples (see Appendix B) also included a checklist of symptoms indicating the possible existence of psychopathology. This list facilitated a separation in the community sample of the relatively well and relatively ill and provided a method for confirming the hypotheses made about subgroups in the community population.

In addition to the regular interview, which lasted about 90 minutes, each respondent in the ill and community samples between twenty-five and twenty-nine years of age was asked to complete a projective test (Need Achievement Test) to determine the strength of his "achievement motive;" the administration of this test required approximately thirty minutes. The decision to confine this aspect of the data-gathering operation to the twenty-five–twenty-nine year age range was based on two considerations:

(1) Because of limited research resources, it was necessary to obtain Need Achievement protocols from a selected group.

(2) The achievement-fantasy material was believed to be particularly evident in individuals within this age range. The development of this test has been associated mainly with the names of McClelland, Atkinson, and Veroff (see Atkinson, 1958). Briefly, it entailed presenting six pictures sequentially to the respondent and asking him to create a story for each. The stories were recorded verbatim, scored according to definite

rules, and a determination made of the strength of the Need Achievement Motive (see Atkinson, 1958).

The Community Sample

THE COMMUNITY INTERVIEWS and Need Achievement protocols were
gathered during the period March–July, 1960. The initial objective of
the study was to interview a community sample of 1500. This sample was
chosen according to a five-stage proportional sample design which yielded
an overall sampling rate of 1/200 (i.e., one individual in every 200 was
selected for study). However, the following criteria had to be satisfied
for inclusion in the listing from which this sample was eventually selected: the individual had to be Negro, between twenty and sixty years
of age, a resident of Philadelphia, born (and whose parents were born)
within the continental United States, and living in the community (i.e.,
not institutionalized).

COMMUNITY SAMPLING PROCEDURES

a. *First Stage*—Thirty-six (61 per cent) of the fifty-nine voting wards
listed in the 1958 voting records for the City of Philadelphia were selected
by the following procedure. All wards with at least 800 Negro voters were
included in the selected ward group. Each of the remaining wards was
ranked according to its number of Negro votes. Fifteen hundred voters
were counted cumulatively, starting from a randomly selected name in
the first of these ranked wards. The ward in which this 1500th name was
located was added to those wards previously chosen. From this point
another 1500 voters were counted and the corresponding ward added to
the list of wards. This procedure was followed through the entire list of
ranked wards. The thirty-six wards from which the sample was drawn included 519,884 (98.2 per cent) of the 529,239 Negro residents of
Philadelphia. The unselected wards contained 9355 Negroes (1.8 per
cent).

b. *Second Stage*—All voting divisions of the thirty-six wards with at
least 300 voters were automatically included in the sample of selected
divisions. The remaining divisions were ranked according to their number
of Negro voters. Starting from a random point in the first division, 400
voters were counted; the division in which this figure was reached was
added to the sample of divisions. This procedure (comparable to that
followed in the first stage) was utilized to select the total sample of di-

visions. Three hundred and sixty (23 per cent) of the 1573 divisions in Philadelphia were chosen.

c. *Third Stage*—Members of the staff were sent into the selected divisions to eliminate blocks with all white residents. The racial character of the block was confirmed by interviews with local residents. Blocks with Negro residents were chosen in two ways.

(1) If the number of Negro households, as shown in the 1950 United States Census, equaled or exceeded a certain value determined by a sampling formula ($360 \times P_W$ [probability of ward selection] $\times P_D$ [probability of division selection]), the block was automatically included.

(2) All other blocks were ranked according to the number of Negro households. Starting from a randomly selected point in the first of these ranked blocks, the number of households equal to this ratio ($360 \times P_W \times P_D$) was counted; the block in which this figure fell was then selected. Counting from this new point, and using the procedure described for the first and second sampling stages, a final sample of 360 blocks was obtained. Groups of eight blocks were randomly assigned to each interviewer. (At the beginning of the field operation, it was assumed that 4.2 respondents would be obtained from each block [based on 1950 Census data]. Since this was an over-estimation of the actual yield, the rate of interviewing in one-third of the blocks had to be increased by 60 per cent in order to secure the 1500 interviews.)

d. *Fourth Stage*—Staff personnel recorded all households in each selected block with at least one Negro resident. This procedure necessitated interviewing neighbors about members of other households. Households for the sample were also selected according to a predetermined ratio (9/number of Negro dwelling units in the block, as shown in the 1950 Census). If this ratio was greater than 1.00, all households in the block were automatically included. This phase of the sampling yielded 3234 households, for which a total listing of Negro occupants fulfilling the study's criteria of eligibility was made. (Of these eligible households, 3003 cooperated with the study). The efficiency of this phase of the sample is shown in Table 2.1.

Table 2.1—*Efficiency of Listing Eligible Respondents*

in Selected Households

Type of Response	Frequency	Per Cent
Completed Listing	3003	93.0
Refused to Cooperate	20	0.6
No Contact Made (After Four Visits)	109	3.4
No Eligible Respondents	102	3.1
Total	3234	100.1

e. *Fifth Stage*—The rate of resident selection in each ward depended on the cumulative probabilities of selection in the first four stages of the sampling procedure. This may be illustrated by the following equation:

$$P_W \times P_D \times P_B \times P_H \times P_R = 1/200$$

where

P_W = probability of ward selection;
P_D = probability of division selection;
P_B = probability of block selection;
P_H = probability of household selection;
P_R = probability of resident selection.

As mentioned previously, the probability of selection for any given individual was always $1/200$. If, for example, in any given ward the cumulative probability of selection in the first four stages was $1/50$, every fourth eligible respondent $(1/4)$ in the ward had to be selected; if the overall probability was $1/40$, every fifth eligible respondent $(1/5)$ in the ward had to be chosen.

The total community sample consisted of 1718 eligible individuals, of whom 1588 (92.5 per cent) were successfully interviewed. Ninety-nine of these individuals, who were in psychiatric treatment during the year preceding the interview, were included with the ill sample. One hundred and forty persons (7.5 per cent) either were inaccessible after four visits, refused, or were too ill, to be interviewed. The final community sample contained 1489 individuals. Of 117 individuals between twenty-five and twenty-nine years of age, 107 (82 per cent) completed the Need Achievement Test.[1] The distribution of eligible cases is presented in Table 2.2.

Table 2.2—Response to Field Interviewer:

Community Sample

Type of Response	Frequency	Per Cent
Interviewed	1588	92.5
Refused to be Interviewed	23	1.3
Too Ill to be Interviewed	8	0.5
Never at Home (After Four Visits)	99	5.8
Total	**1718**	**100.1**

FIELD PROCEDURE

Before administering the questionnaire, the field interviewer went to one of the eight blocks randomly assigned to him. Starting from a (randomly selected) corner marked on a map by the sampling staff, he listed

1. For a more technical discussion of sampling procedures, see Appendix A.

on a prepared sheet all households in a standard sequence. On this form an "X" had been placed on a particular line to indicate the household that was to be sampled for an interview. When the interviewer came to that line, he listed in a prescribed order determined by age and sex, the potential respondents in that household. On the respondent listing form, an "X" on a certain line indicated which individual in that household should be interviewed. The interview was conducted at that time, if possible. If there was only one potential respondent in the household, that person was interviewed; if there were several potential respondents, the interviewer used a table based on random numbers to determine which person to select as a respondent. After the questionnaire was administered, the interviewer continued listing households until he came to the next "X" and then followed the identical procedure. If the selected respondent was not home at the time of the initial contact, the interviewer made a maximum of three additional visits to try to complete the questionnaire. If this failed, the case was recorded and placed with refusals in the "lost" category. At no time was the interviewer allowed to substitute another respondent in the household.

Upon contacting the potential respondent, the interviewer was instructed to say: "I am   (name)   from National Analysts, Inc., a research company. We are doing a study in Philadelphia."

At this point the interviewer presented a letter of identification which stated:

This serves to introduce   (name)   who is employed by us as a research interviewer. We are gathering information from persons like you regarding their opinions and attitudes toward their health, education, occupation, and other areas of life. We will greatly appreciate it if you will help us by allowing our interviewer to gather this information. The purpose of this interview will be only for specific research purposes and is sponsored by the Department of Welfare of Pennsylvania and Jefferson Medical College.

After presenting the letter, the interviewer continued:

We are talking to people like you about attitudes and feelings they have regarding their education, occupation, and health. We are interviewing a cross-section of people, and you were selected as part of this cross-section.

Each completed interview was given to the field supervisor, edited for quality, and checked to see that it fulfilled the requirements of the sampling procedure. In addition, a sample of interviews from each interviewer was re-checked and verified in the field by a member of the field staff.

SAMPLING ERROR

Using the sum-of-squares procedure, sampling errors were computed on four variables: sex, age, marital status, and education. The results are listed in Table 2.3.

Table 2.3—Sampling Errors

Variables	Per Cent	Sampling Error (Per Cent)
Sex		
Male	39.3	1.23
Female	60.7	1.23
Age		
20-39 (Young)	45.2	1.25
40-60 (Old)	54.8	1.25
Marital Status		
Married	67.7	1.17
Single	12.6	0.84
Widowed	5.5	0.57
Divorced	3.7	0.46
Permanently Separated	10.5	0.77
Unknown	0.1	—
Education		
0-8 years	33.6	1.18
9-12 years	58.1	1.24
13+	7.6	0.68
Unknown	0.7	—

REPRESENTATIVENESS OF THE COMMUNITY SAMPLE

Because different statistical groupings were used, it was impossible to compare our sample with the characteristics of the Negro population given in the 1960 Census on migratory status, education, and occupation; however, the age and sex distributions of the two samples could be compared. There was no significant difference between the age distribution of the community sample and the total Philadelphia Negro population in the twenty-to-sixty year age range. With respect to sex, there was a significant difference between the two distributions. The community sample included 61 per cent women and 39 per cent men, whereas the actual distribution in the city (according to the 1960 Census) was 54 per cent women and 46 per cent men. The degree of over-representation of women and under-representation of men in the two samples was the same, regardless of age. Therefore, it was necessary to analyze the two sample sex groups separately, and to assume that there were no systematic errors of representation either between the sample male group and the total male population, or between the female sample group and the total female population. Analyses which combined all sex groups might have necessitated corrections for the sex disproportion. Since the age breakdown was the same in the interviewed sample as in the total population, no such corrections were necessary when age groups were combined.

The Ill Sample

THE ILL SAMPLE consisted of Negroes from the Philadelphia area who were comparable to the community sample on eligibility requirements but who had been diagnosed by psychiatrists as needing treatment. We had decided to include in the sample only "new cases" of psychiatric illness during a specified period of time (i.e., incidence rather than prevalence[2]). During the period designated for case collection, we hoped to interview a representative sample of all such new cases with the same data-gathering instruments used in the community. Clearly, this "ideal" goal could be approached but never fully realized. A certain number of ill individuals were not lucid enough to be interviewed, and others were not cooperative. In addition, the enormous administrative problems posed by interviewing patients from all public and private in-patient facilities, clinics, and private psychiatrists made certain compromises inevitable. We attempted to minimize the potential sources of bias in our sampling procedure by training a group of interviewers to cope with the difficult task of interviewing the mentally ill.

FACILITIES FROM WHICH THE ILL SAMPLE WAS OBTAINED

The selection of facilities as sources for the ill sample posed four major problems. First, it was necessary to select facilities that would yield a sample representative of the entire diagnosed portion of the designated population. Second, only facilities where it was possible to make administrative arrangements to interview newly designated cases could be chosen. Third, a sample large enough to permit data analysis was required. Finally, in order to be certain that our interviewed sample was representative of the total eligible ill population, certain basic demographic data had to be gathered on noninterviewed cases (both in the selected facilities and in all others in the city). The facilities selected for interviewing newly designated cases included public and private in-patient and out-patient facilities, and psychiatrists in private practice. In addition, demographic data were gathered from *all* psychiatric facili-

2. A "new case" could be either a first admission, or an admission with a previous psychiatric history (i.e., readmission), during the specified period of time. Prevalence refers to the number of individuals being treated within any given period, regardless of when treatment was initiated. The term has also been used to denote the number of mentally ill (treated and untreated) individuals in a community, within a specified time period.

ties in the city (including the courts) on every new case meeting our eligibility requirements.

Our major source of psychiatric cases was the Eastern Mental Health Reception Center of the Commonwealth of Pennsylvania (hereafter referred to as the Reception Center), serving residents of Philadelphia. This institution functions primarily as a diagnostic and screening center for the admission of patients to various public and private hospitals and clinics in the area. We were particularly fortunate to obtain permission to interview here, since a large majority of Negro psychiatric patients in the city utilizes its services. We also interviewed in-patients in three public and two private psychiatric hospitals, and out-patients in one public and one private clinic. These interviews were conducted by personnel thoroughly trained by a senior member of the project staff. Finally, with the cooperation of all Negro psychiatrists in the Philadelphia area, a sample of cases being seen in private practice was interviewed (N = 47). More than half of these patients were interviewed by Project personnel; the remainder were interviewed by their own physicians, who were instructed in the use of the questionnaire by a member of the project staff.

DESCRIPTION OF THE INTERVIEWED ILL SAMPLE

The individual meeting the eligibility criteria for the interviewed ill sample had to be a Negro (1) between twenty and sixty years of age; (2) psychiatrically diagnosed as a new case in one of the selected facilities during the period March 1, 1960–May 15, 1961; (3) with a Philadelphia address at the time of diagnosis; and (4) born, and whose parents were born, in the continental United States. Any individual diagnosed as being mentally deficient, alcoholic (where this was the exclusive diagnosis), or as having organic brain damage, was excluded from the total patient population. During the interviewing period, a potentially eligible sample of 1593 individuals was obtained from all the psychiatric facilities selected as sampling sources. (It should be noted that this figure applied *only* to the facilities selected for interviewing, and not to the universe of potentially eligible patients diagnosed in all facilities in Philadelphia during this period.) Of these 1593 individuals, acceptable interviews were completed with 1324, with a loss of 269 (17 per cent). Within the interviewed group, 237 persons between the ages of twenty-five and twenty-nine were eligible for the Need Achievement Test; the test was administered successfully to 171 of these individuals (72 per cent). Table 2.4 presents the distribution of the ill sample by type of facility, and by

Table 2.4—*Distribution of Eligible and Completed Interviews in*
Selected Psychiatric Facilities

TYPE OF FACILITY	POTENTIAL CASES		COMPLETED INTERVIEWS		INCOMPLETED[1] INTERVIEWS	
	Per Cent	N	Per Cent	N	Per Cent	N
Reception Center[2]	45	724	53	708	2	16
Publicly Supported Hospitals (Inpatient)	8	129	10	129	0	0
Private Hospitals (Inpatients)	1	21	1	14	33	7
Publicly Supported Clinics	37	595	31	414	30	181
Private Clinics	5	72	1	12	83	60
Private Psychiatrists (Negro)	3	53	4	47	11	6
Total	100	1594	100	1324	17	270

1. The figures in this column represent that proportion of the potentially eligible cases not interviewed.
2. At the time of the interview, it was impossible to determine whether patients at the Reception Center would ultimately be sent to an in-patient facility or to a clinic. In all cases a diagnosis had been made, but not necessarily a disposition.

completed and incompleted interviews. At first glance it may seem unusual that the percentage of interviews completed in the in-patient facilities is higher than in the out-patient clinics. The relatively high completion rate for the in-patients can be partially explained by the procedures used in obtaining interviews in these facilities. In a sense, in-patients represented a "captive audience." If they were uncooperative or incapable of being interviewed when first contacted by a member of the interviewing staff, their names were placed on a list and they were contacted periodically in the hospital (i.e., until the termination of the interviewing period) in order to obtain the interview. This insured very low interview loss in the hospital facilities. On the other hand, the relatively high incompletion rate for out-patients reflected the frequent difficulty in administering the questionnaire when patients came for their clinic appointments; problems were also encountered in contacting out-patients at home. Of the 270 potentially eligible cases not interviewed, 70 per cent could not be contacted after an initial visit and three call-backs, 10 percent were not lucid or failed to pass an internal reliability check in the questionnaire,[3] 10 per cent refused to be interviewed, and the remainder fell into a miscellaneous category.

A high percentage of the successfully completed interviews in the ill sample came from publicly supported facilities (see Table 2.4). This percentage included patients seen at the Reception Center, the majority

3. This consisted of asking the patient on two different occasions during the interview for information on his birthplace, age, and educational level. If the responses were not the same, the entire interview was considered invalid.

of whom were eventually referred to publicly supported hospitals or clinics. Such a large percentage is not surprising when one considers the relatively low socioeconomic position of the Philadelphia Negro community.

To investigate the possibility that in the selected agencies the eligible, but noninterviewed, cases were significantly different from the interviewed cases on various demographic items, "short forms" containing information on sex, age, education, occupation, migratory status, referral source, diagnosis, and disposition were obtained for all these cases. With respect to the first five of these items, there were no statistically significant differences between interviewed and noninterviewed cases. On this basis we assumed that the eligible, but noninterviewed, cases in the selected facilities were randomly distributed (with regard to the demographic items listed above). Another closely related problem was the representativeness of the interviewed sample compared to eligible patients in *all* facilities (selected as well as unselected)[4] during the fifteen-month period. The two groups were compared on sex, age, migratory status, education, and occupation. Analyses indicated no significant differences (using .05 as a cut-off point for significance) for any of the above items except sex composition. There were approximately five per cent more males in the total eligible sample than in the interviewed sample. This difference was statistically significant at $P = <.05$; a careful examination of our referral sources supplied an explanation. The interviewed ill sample did not include any cases from the criminal courts of Philadelphia. However, "short forms" were returned on all eligible cases from this source. The fact that the vast majority of these were men accounted for the relative under-representation of males in the interviewed sample. While we make no claims regarding the random selection of our interviewed ill sample, this population did not differ from the "universe" of mentally ill meeting our eligibility requirements on any of the five major social variables except sex composition.

The process of obtaining the final interviewed ill sample should include mention of one other operation. Ninety-nine individuals who were

4. As noted previously, information on sex, age, migratory status, education, occupation, diagnosis, referral source, and disposition was requested on eligible patients from *all* psychiatric facilities in Philadelphia, including private psychiatrists. Of 299 private practitioners, 53 reported that they had eligible patients and sent the requested information; 230 reported no eligible patients; 16 either refused to cooperate or did not reply. We obtained "short forms" for 69 private patients, of whom only 47 were considered eligible. "Short forms" were obtained for a final total of 1168 patients.

interviewed as part of the community sample, but who had been treated for a psychiatric illness during the year preceding the interview, were added to the 1324 interviewed patients. The addition of these cases yielded a final interviewed ill sample of 1423.

Table 2.5—Summary of Sample Frequencies

	Frequency (N)
Total Interviewed Population (Community and Ill)	2912
Total Interviewed Community Sample	1588
Reclassified Community Sample (Placed in Ill Sample)	99
Final Interviewed Community Sample	1489
Total Interviewed Ill Sample	1324
Private Interviewed Patients	47
Final Interviewed Ill Sample (Includes 99 Reclassified Cases from Community Sample)	1423
Demographic Information on Noninterviewed Potentially Eligible Patients	1168

An Independent Measure of Illness

IN THIS STUDY, an individual has been classified as "mentally ill" if a psychiatrist has judged him *in need* of psychiatric treatment. Much has been written about the possible influence of sociological and psychological factors on the diagnostic and treatment processes, factors with little relevance to manifest symptoms. Hollingshead and Redlich (1958) considered the effects of such factors on patients from different socioeconomic classes. They noted (1) that the "psychotic" diagnosis was applied more frequently to those in the lower classes, and the "neurotic" diagnosis to those in the upper classes; (2) that lower-class patients tended to be admitted to public hospitals, while those from the upper classes tended to enter private hospitals and private psychiatric treatment; and (3) that patients from the lower classes tended to be given somatic and drug therapies, whereas patients from the upper classes received more individualized psychotherapy and/or group therapy. Because of the possible influence of such factors on psychiatric evaluation, diagnostic labels are often treated lightly and considered very tenuous. In view of this general attitude toward diagnosis, we felt that a measure of illness apart from psychiatric judgment was necessary in the present study, a measure that would differentiate our ill and community populations on the basis of the symptoms they manifested. A psychosomatic symptom scale (a modification of the Cornell Medical Index; Appendix B, Questions 111–125) was used for this purpose.

Thirteen of these questions (Appendix B, Questions 111–123) required each respondent to evaluate the frequency with which he manifested certain symptoms. The four precoded response choices ranged from "Almost never, rarely" (assigned a value of one), to "Very often, almost always" (assigned a value of four). A mean psychosomatic score was computed for each respondent—this score indicated the average frequency with which he manifested these 13 symptoms. The distribution of these scores within the community population indicated that as the average frequency of symptoms increased, the number of respondents with these higher scores decreased. Specifically, there were few individuals in the community population with average scores above 1.69. Therefore, 1.70 was arbitrarily selected as the cut-off point to demarcate "low" and "high" psychosomatic symptom groups within the community population. It is possible that some respondents with low scores were more disturbed than many high-scorers; however, we felt that an individual in the high symptom group was more likely to be seriously ill. Evidence from other research supports this supposition (Rennie, 1953; Macmillan, 1957).

The cut-off point (1.70) was superimposed on the distribution of average symptom scores for the ill population to see what proportion of the patients fell above this point. Fifty per cent of the diagnosed ill population, compared to only 12 per cent of the community population, had average scores above 1.70 ($P = < .001$). Within the ill population, 49 per cent of those diagnosed as psychotic, and 51 per cent of those classified as neurotic, had high scores. Within these diagnostic groupings there were no significant differences between the distributions of high and low scores.

We concluded that our illness measure (i.e., average symptom score, measured independently of psychiatric evaluation) did differentiate significantly between the ill and community populations.

Interviewer Selection and Training

SELECTION OF INTERVIEWERS

We intended originally to utilize the same personnel for both samples, but this was not feasible. Interviewers for the community and ill samples were selected according to identical criteria. The first three criteria were the same as those for eligibility in the community and in the ill populations; an interviewer had to be Negro, between twenty and sixty years of age, and born within the continental limits of the United States. Because the questionnaire was very extensive and complex and dealt with some emotional material, it was hoped that both groups of interviewers would be college graduates. Sixty-two per cent of the interviewers for the community and 58 per cent of those for the ill population fulfilled this criterion. The satisfaction of the final two criteria depended on the evaluation of the individual hiring the interviewers. Prospective interviewers were judged on their ability to establish rapport quickly, and also to control a stressful interview situation and record responses simultaneously. The latter quality was particularly important for the ill-sample interviewers.

Since we were not going to use the same interviewers for the community and ill samples, we were concerned with the comparability of the two groups of interviewers on such demographic variables as sex distribution, age, education, occupation, and migratory status. The interviewers for the ill sample ($N = 31$) showed a disproportionately higher number of males than the interviewers for the community ($N = 33$). Despite this difference, the proportion of men and women interviewed by male and female interviewers respectively were the same in the community and ill samples. There were no significant differences between the two groups of interviewers with respect to age, education, occupation, and migratory status.

INTERVIEWER TRAINING—COMMUNITY SAMPLE

Each community-sample interviewer was given a copy of the questionnaire to be used in the field. He was asked to answer the questions as if he were a respondent, and to study the instrument in preparation for the three-day training institute attended by all interviewers. This institute was conducted jointly by the representatives of a private research organization[5] and by the senior project personnel. On the first day, interviewers were oriented by project personnel to the broad purposes of the study, to the sponsoring institutions, and were given detailed explanations of the intent of specific questionnaire items. In addition, the research organization's supervisory staff reviewed in considerable detail the interviewer's functions in identifying the households, listing eligible respondents, and selecting the individuals to be interviewed. On the second day, the interviewers went into the field and completed sample

5. National Analysts, Inc., Philadelphia, Pennsylvania, contracted to hire interviewers and to supervise the field operation necessary for obtaining the community sample.

interviews. On the third day, they reviewed with the project directors and the organization's supervisory personnel any problems they had experienced in carrying out their tasks. In this way many difficulties were resolved, and considerable feedback was available about the clarity of the questions, the community's acceptance of the interviewers, and the level of understanding and training of the field personnel. Subsequent to the training institute, each interviewer met periodically with his field supervisor for individual supervision. There were also regular meetings between the corps of interviewers and the supervisory staff to review and discuss problems that arose in the field.

INTERVIEWER TRAINING—ILL SAMPLE

All interviewers for the ill sample were subject to a uniform training procedure. Each trainee was oriented to the broad objectives of the project and asked to complete the questionnaire form himself. After the field supervisor discussed in detail the intent of the questions and the procedure to be followed in the interview situation, the trainee was assigned a noneligible Negro psychiatric patient with whom he conducted an interview. After this "trial run," he met again with the field supervisor to discuss any problems he had encountered in administering the questionnaire or in establishing rapport in this difficult interview situation. Subsequently, the trainee administered the questionnaire to another (noneligible) patient. This interview situation was observed through a one-way mirror by the supervisor, who later discussed his impressions with the trainee. In most cases this comprised the entire training procedure. Occasionally, however, further trial interviews were conducted.

A number of interviewers were eliminated during the training period, either because they could not grasp the purpose of the interview, or because they had difficulty in handling some of the necessary role demands made by the project staff. Failures were usually of two kinds. Some trainees assumed a therapeutic role, established good rapport, and put the patient at ease, but they failed to obtain the desired information. They found it difficult to balance the nurturent and directive role demands of the situation. At the other extreme, some unsuccessful trainees tended to assume authoritarian roles, became involved in minor arguments with the patients, and/or were upset by occasional digressions. We feel that the thorough training procedure was largely responsible for reducing the number of refusals and unsuccessful interviews which one might anticipate with a psychiatrically ill population.

Description of the Questionnaire

THE FINAL FORM of the questionnaire (see Appendix B) represented many months of work, during which the instrument was revised to eliminate possible misinterpretations of questions by respondents. Many of these revisions were stimulated by problems encountered during pretests with the community and patient samples. At every point in the construction and revision process, we were concerned with the relevance of each question for exploring and testing the specific theoretical issues that underlay the investigation. The purpose of the questionnaire instrument was to explore the relationship of a limited number of variables to mental disorder, rather than all potentially relevant social–psychological factors. In order to obtain sufficient detailed information on the issues of central importance, it was necessary to eliminate items dealing with numerous intriguing research bypaths.

The questionnaire consisted of 206 items, approximately 15 per cent of which were open-ended. Although there is no definitive answer to the relative merits of open-ended and precoded questions, our desire to deal with the data quantitatively determined the decision to weight the questionnaire in favor of precoded questions. Another element influencing this decision was that the large number of different interviews necessary for obtaining the two samples made the problem of response comparability a crucial one; it was felt that "fixed" questions and precoded responses would facilitate such comparability.

In all cases the interviewer placed the questionnaire in a position where it would be visible to the respondent and then read each question to him. This enabled the interviewee to hear, as well as to read, the questions and to see his recorded responses. With few exceptions, respondents in the ill and community samples were asked identical questions. However, a few items dealing with the respondent's perception of various examples of pathological behavior and his hypothetical handling of them in given situations were omitted with the ill sample (see Appendix B). It was felt that such questions might be particularly upsetting for newly admitted psychiatric patients.

The questionnaire was primarily concerned with obtaining data about discrepancies between the respondent's achievements and aspirations in various areas of goal striving. Where appropriate, information was also obtained about the respondent's aspirations for the head of household or for a hypothetical son. The discrepancy scores were derived from the respondent's designation of achievement and aspiration levels on precoded scales for these specific phenomena: education, occupation, income, self- and ideal self-image, and the racial context of some of the social situations in which he found himself (i.e., housing, membership in organization, etc.). The respondent was also presented with a diagrammatic representation of a flight of ten steps, the top (step 10) labeled the "best possible way of life," and the bottom (step 1) the "worst possible way of life." He was instructed to select the step on this subjective "striving scale" that he had already attained, and the step to which he aspired. It was felt that this might yield data on his subjective appraisal of the discrepancy between his overall life achievements and aspirations. As part of the general plan of the questionnaire, the respondent was asked after each statement of aspiration to estimate both his probability of attaining that goal and its importance (i.e., valence) to him. Aside from these major areas, additional questions were asked about selected values, racial identification, migratory history, and other demographic items.

Occupational Status Scale

THERE ARE a number of occupational scales in use which presumably reflect how the general population would order occupations in terms of prestige. Since most of these scales were developed on predominantly white populations or according to the professional insights of social scientists, we were not certain that these existing scales reflected occupational prestige for the Negro population. This question was particularly important since one of the theoretical issues in the study dealt with the relationship between the achievement-aspiration discrepancy and psychopathology. The use of a scale untested in a Negro population would be meaningless. An occupation actually carrying high prestige among Negroes might be low on this scale, erroneously giving the impression of low aspiration levels in the Negro community. A review of the literature indicated that studies on the prestige of occupations among Negroes had been made on college or high school students. Such studies seemed limited in value because these groups were influenced by the values engendered in the school atmosphere and did not necessarily reflect the values of the larger adult population with which we were concerned. Therefore, we carried out a special study of the prestige of occupations among 125 adult Negroes from all occupational levels (see Appendix

C). Essentially, each respondent was asked to rate on a five-step scale the prestige of fifteen occupational categories. The score for any given occupation was based on the sum of the rankings it received. Since the distribution of scores suggested seven natural groupings of occupations, the original fifteen categories were collapsed into a seven-step scale.

Some of the differences between this scale and the existing ones are noteworthy. "Sales positions" were close to the bottom of our scale, whereas they are usually included in higher prestige categories. "Clerical positions," which are usually combined with "sales," were higher than "sales" on the scale we had developed; the prestige of "clerical positions" was more comparable to "skilled craftsmen." "Foremen" and similar supervisory-type positions were ranked no higher than "skilled craftsmen." Finally, musicians, dancers, and athletes ranked very high in prestige.

Social Status Index

THE NEED to utilize the concept of social status as one of our analytical variables led to some methodological difficulties. The first of these involved determining the appropriate weights to assign to the usual criteria of status position (i.e., education, income, and occupation). There were no previous studies to guide us in evaluating the importance of the criteria used by the Negro community to determine an individual's status position; we felt it would be questionable to assign the various elements equal weight or to use weighting systems based on studies of the general population.

Given this situation, we decided to obtain data from the questionnaire in order to ascertain the importance to the Negro community of various criteria of status position. The questionnaire contained a series of eight potentially relevant criteria for status position (Appendix B, Question 199). Each respondent was asked to rank three of them in their order of importance in deciding "what social class a person belongs to." The item selected as most important was given a score of three, the next a score of two, and the least important a score of one. The rank order of the total scores for each of the eight possible criteria was: education, income, family background, neighborhood, skin color, occupation, influence in the community, and organizational membership. We had included numerous questionnaire items on occupation, under the assumption that this would be an area of major concern to our population. Therefore, occupation was used as a component of the final index, although it was not selected as the third most important determinant of social status.

A group score for each of the three selected criteria (i.e., education, income, and occupation) was determined by adding their scores on all of the individual protocols. Occupation, which had the lowest total score of the three items was given a weight of one. Weights were derived for the other two items by calculating their proportional increase over the occupation score. The final weighting system was: education 4.4, income 2.5, and occupation 1.0.

After determining the weights to be used for the three status criteria, each respondent's actual educational, income, and occupational achievements were placed on scales all consisting of seven steps (see Appendix D). In the case of a housewife who was not the head of household, the income and occupation of the actual head of household were used to determine her status position. Each step number (representing the achievement for education, income, and occupation) was multiplied by its appropriate weight, and the three products were added. This total score was then divided by three to obtain an average social status score for each respondent. The average scores were grouped into a frequency distribution and divided into approximately four equal parts, yielding a four-step status scale—position 1 being the lowest and 4 the highest (see Appendix D).

An additional status scale was developed to measure the individual's social mobility, using the social position of his parents as the base of comparison. Since income reported for parent was likely to be unreliable, the respondent and his parents were compared by using a social status score based only on education and occupation (derived in the same way as the original social status index). In calculating this index, the occupation of the respondent's father, and the education of either parent (whichever was higher), was used.

Errors Resulting from Data Processing

ALL QUESTIONNAIRE ITEMS, including precoded and open-ended questions, were scored and transferred to IBM cards. In order to control coding errors, weekly reliability checks were made among the coders, and between the coders and the project coordinator. In the former procedure, the reliability estimates varied between 90 and 99 per cent, with an average of 96 per cent. In the latter, the estimates varied between

90 and 97 per cent, with an average of 93 per cent. Eleven open-ended questions, for which the coders could not establish a satisfactory reliability level, were coded by the principal investigators themselves; the reliability of their coding averaged 92 per cent. The principal investigators also coded the Need Achievement protocols. The average reliability of all coding classifications in this test was 88 per cent. On each of the questionnaire items, the IBM card punching error was less than 1 per cent.

Levels of Significance

THE CRITERIA used to evaluate the significance of differences between groups in this study should be specified at this point. We considered all differences significant that occurred by chance no more than five times out of a hundred. In any situation where specific predictions were made, the one-tailed test was used (Snedecor, 1946; Walker and Lev, 1953).

3

GOAL-STRIVING STRESS
AND MENTAL
DISORDER

In Chapter 1 we set forth in some detail the theoretical framework that has guided this study and the hypotheses to be tested and evaluated in the following chapters of the volume. The present chapter focuses primarily on the relationship between each of the goal-striving stress scores and mental illness. We deal specifically with Hypothesis 1 (which predicts higher stress scores for the ill than for the community population), 1a (higher stress scores for the psychotics than for the neurotics), and 1b (lower stress scores for the high symptom group in the community than for the low symptom group).

Since this discussion does not concentrate solely on stress scores, the rationale underlying our treatment of the data and the sequence of presentation may be helpful at this point. Our basic hypothesis (Hypothesis 1) predicted that the ill population would manifest greater goal-striving motivation and orientation than the community population. In our search for social and social–psychological antecedents to high goal striving we asked, "What does a Negro individual with high aspirations assume about the nature of the social system?" A likely alternative would be his assumption of an open social system in which goal attainment was readily accessible; in reality, however, the system would be relatively closed to him. Within this context arose the important problem of whether our respondents perceived the social system in the same way as the investigators. In light of this problem we shall consider first in this chapter the perception of the social system by the mentally ill and the

community samples, as well as by subgroups within these two populations.

The goal-striving stress scores were analyzed with respect to three
issues:

(1) The stress scores of the ill and community samples were compared in order to test directly our predictions about differences between
these two populations.

(2) Chapter 1 pointed out that a correlation between any two
variables did not necessarily imply a specific temporal sequence. In
order to investigate which of any two given variables was the antecedent, and which the consequent, condition, we compared subgroups
within the community population to determine whether those groups
with high yields, or rates, of mental illness had higher stress scores than
those with low yields. Presumably, the high yield subgroups contained
individuals functioning in the community who had not been diagnosed
as needing treatment. Such persons were probably not manifesting
psychotic or neurotic processes; thus, their responses in the interview
situation should have been relatively independent of any illness effects
and might reflect their condition prior to a possible breakdown.

(3) We divided our ill sample into subgroups diagnosed as "psychotic" or "neurotic," and our community sample into a "high psychiatric symptom" and a "low psychiatric symptom" group. Although
we made no formal prediction about whether these four mental health
groupings formed an illness continuum, we entertained this idea in
subsequent discussions of the data. On this basis we dealt with relationships among these four groupings, with respect to perception of
the social system and differences in stress scores. These three issues (i.e.,
comparisons between the ill and community populations, analyses based
on the yield issue, and the relationship among the four mental health
groupings) form the core of all discussions in the present, and the four
following, chapters.

Since the goal areas we analyzed were only samples of the universe
in which goal striving occurred, we also investigated the intercorrelations
of these scores with one another to determine whether each score was
measuring something completely discrete, or whether generalized high
or low goal striving was reflected in all areas of behavior. In addition, we
were interested in the correlation of each stress score with the four
mental health groupings derived from the ill and community populations, and in determining the extent of linear or nonlinear relationships
between these scores and our mental illness continuum. Linearity in-

volves the problem of whether the stress scores increase at a constant rate as one moves from the low symptom, to the high symptom, to the neurotic, and finally to the psychotic grouping. Nonlinearity involves the problem of whether these stress scores increase in differing amounts from the low symptom group to the psychotics. For example, the stress scores may decrease from the low to the high symptom group, but then begin to increase in the neurotic and psychotic groupings. The reverse is also possible: an increase in scores from the low to the high symptom group, and a decrease from the neurotics to the psychotics. The specific procedures employed to answer those questions are described at a later point in this chapter.

In analyzing these intercorrelations, we defined illness not only in terms of the patient-community dichotomy and our four-step mental health continuum, but also in terms of scores on a psychosomatic symptom inventory. Each respondent was asked a series of nineteen questions concerned with the frequency with which he manifested given symptoms (a modification of the Cornell Medical Index; Appendix B, Questions 111–125). The various stress scores were correlated with scores on the psychosomatic symptom inventory of the combined ill and community samples.

Perception of the Opportunity Structure

WE MAINTAIN that the greater goal-striving stress predicted for the ill population occurs in the context of a relatively closed social system. We make this evaluation as "objective" observers rather than as participants in the social situation itself. How can one experience strong goal-striving orientation within a closed social system? Perhaps ill individuals, to a greater extent than respondents from the community sample, believe that the system is in fact open to them. A person who thinks that the paths to goal achievement are accessible to him and that the social system will allow him to move toward his goals will probably set high aspirations for himself and experience excessive motivation or goal-striving stress. Therefore we must deal with the possible discrepancy between the actual nature of the social system and its character as perceived by some of its participants. It is the existence of this discrepancy that provides the contextual environment most conducive to psychopathology.

In order to test the validity of our assumption about ill-community differences on perception of the opportunity structure or social system, we considered each subject's statement on the degree to which he felt that success actually resulted from working hard, saving money, and being ambitious (Appendix B, Question 198). Precoded responses ranged from "Very often" (i.e., perception of an open opportunity structure) to "Hardly at all" (i.e., perception of a closed social system). The percentage distribution of responses to this question is presented in Table 3.1. A greater proportion of the total ill than community population believes that the conditions described in this question occur "Very often" ($P =$

Table 3.1—Perception of the Opportunity Structure by Illness Status, Sex, and Age in Percentages.[1]

	TOTAL		MALES		FEMALES		YOUNG		OLD					
	Ill	Comm.	Ill	Comm.	Ill	Comm.	Ill	Comm.	Ill	Comm.	Psych.	Neur.	High Symp.	Low Symp.
Very Often	33	24	33	27	33	22	33	23	33	26	34	29	30	24
Often	23	32	22	30	23	34	24	34	21	30	22	25	32	32
Occasionally	36	36	35	34	37	38	36	36	37	36	34	41	34	36
Hardly at all	8	7	10	9	7	6	8	7	10	8	9	4	4	8
	100	99	100	100	100	100	101	100	101	100	99	100	100	100
Total N	1400	1464	564	593	836	871	993	788	407	673	1053	347	173	1291

1. Question 198 – It has been said that if a man works hard, saves his money, and is ambitious, he will get ahead. How often do you think this really happens?

<.005). This table also presents ill-community sample differences, controlling for sex and age. When male, female, young, and older respondents are analyzed separately, the mentally ill continue to manifest a significantly higher frequency of "Very often" responses.

Because the ill tended to have lower achievement levels than the community population, we wondered whether the perception of the social system was a function of the class or status position of ill individuals. We would logically expect those with higher achievement (the community respondents) to perceive the social system as being more open than the low achievers (the patients). Although our data had already shown trends opposite to this expectation, we controlled for social class position and compared the ill and community groups (class, or multi-status position, is discussed in Appendix D). For each of four class groups considered, the ill sample, to a greater degree than its community counterpart, perceives the social system as open. Our data clearly support the assumption that the ill subjects see the social system as more open than do the community respondents.

In Chapter 1 we emphasized the importance of comparing subgroups within the community differing in yield of mental disorder. This procedure necessitated selecting several types of subgroup memberships which could be compared on their yield of illness. In this and the four subsequent chapters, the discussion is limited to sex and age differences.

Table 3.1 notes that the males are overly represented in the ill population by 5 per cent ($P = <.005$). On the basis of this observation we predict that a greater percentage of males than females in the community will reply "Very often" to the question on the open system. The males and females in the community sample differ as expected on the responses "Very often" and "Hardly at all" taken together (see Table 3.1). If we evaluate the "Very often" category alone, this difference is not significant. Similarly, there is no significant difference between the sex groups for the response "Hardly at all" analyzed separately. There is little evidence to support our expectations of differences in illness yield for community sex subgroups.

Table 3.1 also shows that the young respondents are overly represented in the mentally ill population by 17 per cent ($P = < .005$). Consequently, we predict that a greater proportion of young than of older community respondents will answer "Very often" to the question on the nature of the social system. Our data disclose no differences between the age subgroups in the community, however.

The mentally ill population clearly perceives the opportunity structure as open, in contrast to the community sample, but our expectations of differences between sex and age subgroups in the community population are not supported. Although differences in perception of the opportunity structure, or social system, apparently characterize the mentally ill and community populations, the lack of differences between subgroups in the community suggests that perceiving the social system as open is not necessarily an antecedent of psychopathology. Such a perception may rather be a concomitant or consequence of illness.

The data on the perception of the social system were examined within each of the four mental health groupings (low symptom group, high symptom group, neurotics, and psychotics) as part of our evaluation of these groups as an illness continuum. A greater percentage of the psychotics than of the neurotics answers both "Very often" ($P = <.05$) and, at the opposite extreme, "Hardly at all" to the "open system" question; the former response is the more prevalent one, however (see Table 3.1). The direction of the difference between these two groupings provides the context for Hypothesis 1a: since the psychotics perceive a more open opportunity structure, we expect them also to manifest higher goal-striving stress scores. In addition, because the answers of the psychotics fall more frequently into *both* extreme response categories on the "open system" question, we predict greater variance in their stress scores, compared to those of the neurotics.

In the two community population mental health groupings there are no significant differences on any of the response categories to this questionnaire item. On the basis of these findings we predict similar stress scores for the high and low symptom subgroups. However, this expectation is inconsistent with Hypothesis 1b, which predicts *lower* stress scores for the high symptom than for the low symptom group. This inconsistency is discussed more fully at a later point in this chapter.

In order to deal with the problem of a mental health continuum, the four groupings were compared with one another on their perception of the opportunity structure to determine (1) where there were significant differences between groupings; and (2) whether the sequence of such differences followed a specific order. The psychotics were compared to each of the other groupings—in every comparison a significantly greater proportion of "Very often" responses to Question 198 occurs in the psychotic groupings ($P = < .01$ or less in every instance; see Table 3.1). The largest proportion of "Hardly at all" responses also occurs in the psychotic grouping in all comparisons.

The neurotics were compared with the two mental health groupings in the community; no significant differences emerge between the neurotics and the high symptom group. However, significantly more neurotics than low symptom individuals answer "Very often" ($P = < .01$) to Question 198. There is also a greater proportion of "Hardly at all" responses in the low system group than among the neurotics.

The analyses involving our mental health continuum and perception of the social system reveal a tendency for a larger percentage of "Very often" responses (i.e., perception of an open system) as one moves from the low symptom group, to the high symptom group, to the neurotics, and finally to the psychotics. It should be noted that there is no real distinction between the high symptom group and the neurotics on the "open system" variable. This question is considered again in the discussion of the stress scores.

The Goal-Striving Stress Scores

IN CHAPTER 1 we predicted higher average stress scores for the mentally ill than for the community population (Hypothesis 1). A consideration of these scores allows us to test the generality of Hypothesis 1 in specific goal areas.

USE OF ACHIEVEMENT CONTROLS

In the following presentation not only are the stress scores for ill and community respondents compared (for the total samples and for age and sex subgroups), but there is also an attempt to evaluate the differences in mean stress scores between the ill and community samples at each of several achievement levels. An integral part of the stress score is the discrepancy between one's level of aspiration and his achievement; a person with a high achievement level in a given area is less likely than a person with a low level to show a large discrepancy. For example, two individuals at different achievement levels may show dissimilar numerical discrepancies only because of the physical limitations of the scale. This scale problem must be taken into account, since the discrepancy score for two such individuals will differentially influence the magnitude of their respective stress scores.

Another problem involved in analyzing stress scores without considering one's relevant achievement levels is whether the same discrepancy from two different points on the achievement scale has similar psychological implications for the respondents. For example, if Subject A has achieved four years of education and would like to have completed eight years, his discrepancy is four. However, Subject B, who has completed twelve years of education and who would like to have attained sixteen, also has a discrepancy of four. If we consider these subjects' discrepancies independent of their achievements, we assume that their positions on the achievement scale do not affect their goal-striving stress. We cannot assume, however, that the psychological impact of Subject A's situation is identical to that of Subject B, who aspired to a college diploma. On the basis of this reasoning, we decided to control for achievement wherever possible in analyzing the data (i.e., when achievement breakdowns in the ill and community samples left enough cases for statistical evaluation, including sex and age controls). The use of such controls allowed us to compare individuals at the same position on the achievement scale, and who therefore had the same distance on the scale within which to set their goals. We assumed that those at the same achievement level would also be more homogeneous in their perception of the distance breakdown their own and higher levels on the achievement scale.

Although the occupation scale was divided into seven categories, there were only enough cases for statistical evaluation, including age and sex controls, at levels 1 (lowest), 2, and 3 (see Appendix C for a detailed description of occupations at these levels). It should be noted that the relatively few individuals at occupation levels 4, 5, 6, and 7 were not included in the control group analyses of the occupation stress scores. However, they were considered in the evaluation of the total populations, in which achievement level was ignored. As a result, analysis of occupation stress scores for the total samples involved a larger number of cases than did the control group analyses. This problem was not encountered with income stress scores: the income scale was subdivided into three achievement categories which included all cases (level 1 = no income to $2000; level 2 = $2001 to $4000; level 3 = $4001 and over). In evaluating striving scale stress scores, analyses for only two of the three control groups were possible (striving scale steps 4–6, and steps 7–10; those with striving-scale step 1–3 were omitted). As was the case for occupation control groups 4, 5, 6, and 7, the omitted striving scale achievement category was included when analyses involving the total samples were made in this content area. The control categories used in analyzing the occupation–hypothetical son stress score were identical to those used for the occupation–self stress score. Five achievement levels were utilized in the area of the education–hypothetical son stress score: level 1 = no education to four years; level 2 = five to eight years; level 3 = nine to eleven years; level 4 = high school graduation; level 5 = one or more years of college. However, the small number of cases at levels 1 and 5 necessitated their omission from the control group analyses. These categories were replaced for analyses involving the total samples.

Table 3.2 presents stress score data for the five content areas itemized above. These analyses were made prior to a consideration of achievement control groups. The table indicates significant differences between the

Table 3.2—Mean Stress Scores for Ill and Community Populations

	TOTAL		MALES		FEMALES		YOUNG		OLD	
	Ill	Comm.	Ill	Comm.	Ill	Comm.	Ill	Comm.	Ill	Comm.
Occupation-Self	8.16	5.26[2]	8.25	7.34	8.08	3.70[3]	9.19	6.54[1]	5.54	3.77
Income-Self	22.05	16.07[2]	22.11	17.21[1]	22.01	15.28[2]	23.10	18.63[1]	19.45	12.96[1]
Striving Scale-Self	16.42	14.48	21.16	16.54	13.19	13.07	16.19	15.73	16.97	13.04
Occupation-Hypothetical Son	46.88	45.08	43.30	47.55	51.60	44.68[1]	49.54	44.29[1]	45.13	47.75
Education-Hypothetical Son	66.45	59.66[1]	59.41	65.90	63.89	57.52	58.17	46.74[2]	72.55	77.70

(Pairs of means are significant, by "t" test (one-tailed test) at the level indicated by the footnote notation.)

1. P=<.05
2. P=<.01
3. P=<.001

total ill and community groups when the male, female, young, and old subgroups are treated separately.

OCCUPATION-SELF STRESS SCORES

The ill show higher occupation stress scores than the community sample in comparisons of total distributions and in all sex and age control group comparisons. Three of the five possible comparisons are statistically significant (see Table 3.2). Thus, occupation stress scores for comparisons between the ill and community populations and between sex and age subgroups, ignoring achievement level, confirm Hypothesis 1.

What is the effect of controlling for achievement level? Do systematic changes in the differences between the ill and the community samples emerge at different points on the achievement scale? Since there are five tests of the significance of differences between the ill and the community groups (cf. Table 3.2) in each of the three occupation control groups, analyses involving achievement controls provide fifteen additional tests of differences between the two populations. The ill have higher goal-striving stress than the community subjects in fourteen of these fifteen comparisons (by sign test, $P = < .001$). The one exception is not statistically significant and occurs in the highest occupation achievement control group (level 3). Since this exception was in the highest control category, an additional comparison was made between all those in the ill and community samples with an occupational achievement level above this one (i.e., levels 4 through 7 combined). In this comparison the community sample shows significantly higher stress than the ill population ($P = < .005$). These two findings indicate that the generality of our prediction may break down at high achievement levels. In general we conclude that the occupation–self stress score shows a high degree of consistency in the predicted direction, and that the sizable number of significant differences further supports Hypothesis 1.

INCOME-SELF STRESS SCORES

A summary of the differences between the ill and the community populations on income stress scores, disregarding achievement level, is presented in Table 3.2. In each of the five comparisons (between total samples and with sex and age controls), the average stress score for the ill is significantly larger than the score for the community population. Thus, regardless of sex or age, the differences between the two populations in the income area are all in the predicted direction and statistically significant, further supporting Hypothesis 1.

The three income achievement control groups again provide fifteen additional tests of Hypothesis 1. Ten of these fifteen comparisons are in the predicted direction, but the degree of consistency is not statistically significant. None of the five exceptions to the prediction is significant; four of these exceptions occur in the highest income achievement group, reaffirming our earlier observation of diminished predictive power at very high achievement levels.

The reader may ask how the mean income stress scores for the total ill and community populations can differ significantly, along with a particular control group analysis yielding opposite results (although this trend is not statistically significant). Since the number of cases in the high income control group constitutes only a small proportion of the total ill or community populations, it has relatively little effect on the mean scores for the total populations. Most of the cases in the ill and community samples are concentrated at income achievement levels 1 and 2, and it is at these levels that the significant differences are obtained. The weight of the evidence for income stress scores shows significant differences between the ill and community populations, regardless of sex or age. Differences between the ill and community subgroups occur at the lower income achievement levels but begin to break down at higher levels. The analysis of income stress scores, then, also supports Hypothesis 1.

STRIVING SCALE-SELF STRESS SCORE

The third stress score is based on the individual's global goal-striving behavior, a measure of which we call the "striving scale." During the interview each respondent was shown a diagram of a flight of ten steps, the top one labeled "the best possible way of life," and the bottom one "the worst possible way of life." He was asked first to define his own idea of the "best" and "worst" possible way of life (Appendix B, Questions 178 and 179), and then to indicate where on this scale he would locate his present position, with respect to his specified anchor points (Appendix B, Question 180). Essentially, the individual defined the extreme points on this scale and then placed himself somewhere between these limits—that is, he created a self-anchored scale. Each subject was also asked to indicate the step he would like to attain in a "few years" (Appendix B, Question 183), his chances of reaching this step (Appendix B, Question 184), and his degree of disappointment if he failed (Appendix B, Question 185). In computing a person's striving scale stress score, the discrepancy between achievement and level of aspiration was taken to be the value of Question 183 minus Question 180. The respondent's specified estimate of success and degree of disappointment on failure constituted the tension component in the stress formula (discussed in Chapter 1).

Table 3.2 summarizes the comparisons made between the ill and community populations on this derived striving scale stress score. In all five comparisons, the average stress scores for the ill are higher than for the community sample, but none of these differences is significant. The consistency of the direction is significant (by sign test, $P = < .03$).

It has already been noted that only two striving scale control groups could be formed. Considering the five comparisons between the ill and community samples and subgroups within each of these control groups, we have ten separate tests of Hypothesis 1. Nine of these ten comparisons are in the predicted direction (by sign test, $P = < .01$). Although the consistency of the direction is significant, only two of the nine comparisons are significant; however, two others approach significance ($P = < .10 > .05$). Thus, there is a higher consistency in the direction of the differences between the two populations, but relatively few of the individual comparisons yield significant differences. We conclude that the differentiating ability of this stress score is not as great as the occupation or income stress score. The consistency of the findings for the striving scale score does provide some additional confirmation of Hypothesis 1.

SUMMARY OF STRESS SCORES IN
SELF-ACHIEVEMENT CONTENT AREAS

In analyzing occupation, income, and striving scale stress scores, fifteen possible comparisons can be made between the ill and community populations, considering total samples and sex and age subgroups. In all fifteen comparisons the ill show higher stress scores than the community subjects; eight of these fifteen are statistically significant. A consideration of achievement control groups (three control categories for occupation and three for income, two for striving scale) provides forty additional comparisons between the two populations. Thirty-three of these forty are in the predicted direction. Fourteen of these thirty-three are significant, and two others approach significance. None of the seven exceptions is significant, and all of them occur in the higher achievement level groups.

We conclude that the data on these stress scores heavily favor Hypothesis 1 (i.e., the mentally ill are under greater goal-striving stress than those in the community).

GOAL-STRIVING STRESS SCORES FOR A HYPOTHETICAL SON

In the content areas of the three stress scores already discussed the respondent gave information related to his own strivings. The two stress scores to be presented now are based on the respondent's striving for a hypothetical son. Each subject was asked to state his occupational and educational aspirations for a hypothetical son of "normal" intelligence (Appendix B, Questions 25 and 78), his estimate of his "son's" chances of reaching these aspiration levels (Appendix B, Questions 26 and 79), and the degree of disappointment he anticipated if this hypothetical son should fail (Appendix B, Questions 28 and 80). The computation of stress scores according to our formula demands that we substitute values for achievement, level of aspiration, the two probabilities (i.e., success and failure), and the two valences. The questions dealing with hypothetical son provide only three of the four factors necessary for computing a stress score—obviously, there is no achievement level for a hypothetical son. In order to compute the scores, the respondent's own educational and occupational achievement level was substituted in the formula, along with the aspiration level, probability, and valence estimates he gave for a hypothetical son.

We assume that in these hypothetical situations the individual projects onto the hypothetical son the goal striving which he, himself, is experiencing. On the basis of this assumption, we again predict higher stress scores for the mentally ill than for the community population.

OCCUPATION-HYPOTHETICAL SON STRESS SCORE

The data for the occupation stress scores for a hypothetical son are summarized in Table 3.2. Three of the five comparisons presented in this table go in the predicted direction, and two of these are statistically significant. The two comparisons opposite in direction are not significant. These five comparisons carried out in each of the three occupational control groups provide fifteen additional independent tests of the prediction. Seven of these fifteen comparisons confirm our prediction—the consistency of direction is not statistically significant. Four of these seven comparisons are significant. Of the eight comparisons for which the community respondents have higher average scores than the ill, only one is significant.

The absence of any overwhelming consistency in the data suggests that this hypothetical-son situation is subject to several interpretations. The three stress scores in the self-striving areas are not as ambiguous in their meaning or implication. Two tendencies seem to be operating with this hypothetical-son stress score:

(1) Those comparisons showing higher stress scores for the ill than for the community subjects suggest that the patients generalize their own high stress scores into a hypothetical situation.

(2) Those comparisons which do support Hypothesis 1 suggest that in some cases the patients may obtain high stress scores for themselves and are incapable or unwilling to project such stress onto a hypothetical son.

The findings on this stress score may be interpreted in yet another way. In some situations the community respondents may have relatively low goal striving for self and hypothetical son, compared to the ill sample. Or, the community individuals may set modest self-goals but experience high goal-striving stress for a hypothetical son. Modest stress for the self possibly reflects a realistic appraisal of one's situation. High goal-striving stress for the son may indicate either fantasy or actual expectations, a healthy adjustment to a difficult situation. The data presented up to this point do not indicate which of these possibilities is correct.

The several exceptions to Hypothesis 1 that emerge in a consideration of the occupational-hypothetical son stress score do not indicate that it is invalid to apply this hypothesis to a hypothetical son. The fact that six of the seven significant differences obtained for this stress score show higher average scores for the ill than for the community population provides some support for the hypothesis. These data also seem to support the view that the mentally ill project their own goal-striving stress onto a hypothetical son.

EDUCATION-HYPOTHETICAL SON STRESS SCORE

The final stress score to be considered is based on respondents' educational aspirations for a hypothetical son. For three of the five comparisons, the mentally ill have higher stress scores than their community counterparts (see Table 3.2); two of these are statistically significant. Neither of the two comparisons that go in an opposite direction to the prediction is significant. As was the case for the occupation-hypothetical son stress score, the weight of the evidence for the education-hypothetical son score does not overwhelmingly support Hypothesis 1. The three control categories analyzed for this score allow us to make fifteen independent tests of the hypothesis. Six of these fifteen comparisons show higher mean stress scores for the ill sample (two are statistically significant). In the other nine comparisons the community population has higher mean scores (one of these is significant). Again, the consistency of the direction is not statistically significant. The erratic nature of the data precludes any simple explanation. However, two additional analyses are possible. As mentioned earlier, educational achievement levels 1 and 5 did not contain a sufficient number of cases for analyses by sex or age breakdowns. Nevertheless, t tests could be done on the *total* number of cases in each of these two control categories. The patients at level 1 (no education to four years) have higher stress scores than the community respondents at this level ($t = 2.90$, $P = < .005$). Of those individuals at level 5 (one or more years of college), the ill also have higher scores, but the difference is not significant.

The distribution of significant differences and the inconsistency in direction of these differences permits few generalizations about variations in the education-hypothetical son stress scores for the ill and community samples.

Yield of Mental Illness and Stress Scores within the Community Population

IN THE PRECEDING CHAPTER we discussed the problem of determining whether high goal-striving stress was antecedent to mental disorder, or whether the converse was true. We mentioned that predicting differences between the ill and community populations only provided us with correlations that could not indicate the extent to which a particular response was the cause or effect of the pathological condition. We concluded that comparisons of two *community*-sample groups differing in yield of mental illness could perhaps clarify which of two variables was the antecedent, and which the consequent condition of illness. In the present context we expect a high yield community subgroup to manifest higher stress scores (i.e., show more of the characteristics of the ill population) than its low yield counterpart. A confirmation of this prediction will indicate that high goal-striving stress is probably an antecedent of mental illness. The prediction rests on the assumption that among those in the community with high goal-striving stress scores the pathological processes are either not yet operative, or are still at a low level; these high-stress individuals may eventually manifest illness.

YIELD OF MENTAL ILLNESS AND SELF-ACHIEVEMENT
GOAL-STRIVING STRESS SCORES IN THE COMMUNITY POPULATION

Table 3.1 indicates an over-representation of males (by 5 per cent) and an under-representation of females (also by 5 per cent) in the ill population. The difference is statistically significant ($P = < .001$). On this basis we predict higher stress scores for males than for females in the community sample. Table 3.3 presents the mean stress scores for males

Table 3.3—Mean Stress Scores for High and

Low Yield Community Subpopulations

	Males	Females	Young	Old
Occupation-Self	7.34	3.70[3]	6.54	3.77[2]
Income-Self	17.21	15.28	18.63	12.96[1]
Striving-Scale-Self	16.54	13.07[1]	15.73	13.04
Occupation-Hypothetical-Son	47.55	44.68	44.29	47.75
Education-Hypothetical-Son	65.90	57.52[1]	46.74	77.70[3]

(Pairs of means are significant by "t" test (one-tailed test), at the level indicated by the footnote notation.)

1. $P = < .05$
2. $P = < .01$
3. $P = < .001$ (Education-Hypothetical Son, Young vs Old, by two-tailed test)

and females in each of the three areas concerned with the respondent's own striving (occupation, income, and striving scale). In all three of these areas, males show higher scores than females, but these differences are significant only for occupation and the striving scale. All of the eight possible control group analyses for sex differences on these three scores are in the predicted direction (by sign test, $P = < .01$), and four—in the occupation and income content areas—are statistically significant. This consistency and the high percentage of significant differences support the prediction of higher stress scores for males than for females in the community sample.

Table 3.1 also indicates that the young are over-represented and the older group under-represented by 17 per cent. This percentage is statistically significant ($P = < .001$). Based on our concept of yield, we predict higher stress scores for the young than for the older respondents in the community sample. In all three areas of self-striving, the predicted direction is evident (see Table 3.3). This age difference is significant in the areas of occupation and income but not the striving scale. All of the age analyses in the eight control groups also indicate higher stress scores for the young (by sign test, $P = < .01$), and one significant difference appears in each of the three self-achievement content areas.

In an overview of the question of yield for these three stress scores, we note that the direction of the differences and the number of significant findings support our prediction about sex and age differences in the community population, regardless of achievement level. On the basis of the data and our assumption about yield of mental illness, we may seriously begin to consider high goal-striving stress as an antecedent of mental illness.

YIELD OF MENTAL ILLNESS AND HYPOTHETICAL-SON STRESS SCORES IN THE COMMUNITY POPULATION

As we have mentioned, in the two situations dealing with education and occupation for a hypothetical son we assume that the respondent projects onto this "son" his own goal-striving stress. Consequently, again we predict higher hypothetical-son stress scores for males than for females, and for young than for older subjects in the community population.

Table 3.3 shows that the average stress scores for males are higher than for females, for both of the hypothetical-son scores. This sex difference reaches statistical significance only in the area of education. In all three education control groups the average scores are again higher for males, although none of the differences reaches significance. Two of the three occupation control categories yield higher scores for females than for males, but neither is significant. In the one control group manifesting the predicted pattern, the sex difference is significant.

Although we expect higher stress scores for the young than for the older responses, the data on age differences present a contradictory picture. Both for the education and occupation scores, the older group has higher stress than the younger—these differences are significant. This pattern is maintained in all three of the education control groups and is significant for one of the categories. Thus, the direction of the differences is consistently opposite to the prediction. In two of the three occupation control groups the older respondents again have higher scores than the young, but these differences are not significant. One occupation category, however, does yield significantly higher averages for the young.

The findings for the education-hypothetical son stress score support the prediction of higher stress for males than for females. However, the data on this same score go counter to the prediction of higher stress for the young respondents. We cannot generalize about the findings for the occupation-hypothetical son stress score because: (1) the differences in stress for total male and female groups, as well as for the total young and old groups, are not significant; and (2) there is no consistent pattern within the control groups for sex or age breakdowns, although both of the significant differences obtained in these control group analyses are in the predicted direction.

Our specific prediction of age differences for these hypothetical-son scores grew out of a mechanical application of our point of view on the yield issue. Because of the over-representation of the young in the mentally ill population, we expected higher hypothetical-son stress scores for the young respondents in the community sample. However, a prediction of age differences for these scores may demand further interpretation. It is possible that those in the older group (forty to sixty years of age) recognize the improbability of reaching aspirations set in their younger years. The source of their achievement satisfaction must be their children. It is likely that they project their own unfulfilled hopes and aspirations onto a hypothetical son, and are thus characterized by high stress scores. The younger respondents (twenty to thirty-nine years of age), who are still in a position to obtain their goals with a reasonable amount of effort, need not project their strivings onto a hypothetical son. The lack of significant age differences in these hypothetical-son stress scores may be a function of the simultaneous occurrence of these two processes.

THE EFFECT OF AGE ON THE GOAL-STRIVING STRESS SCORES

We have just discussed a number of predictions about young and older community respondents, based on differences in representation of age groups in the patient population. Throughout the discussion it has been assumed that the young and older groups constitute two discrete categories. At no point have we considered the possibility that the older group represents what we may expect to happen to the younger individuals as they age and mature through experience. At this point we assume that the older group in the patient population contains individuals who, at an earlier age, manifested the characteristics of the younger patients in our sample. We make a similar assumption about young and older community sample respondents. Thus, we can compare young and older respondents in the ill and community populations to determine what effect illness or lack of it has on the stress scores of these respective samples. In view of the higher readmission rate to mental institutions among the older patients, we expect that individuals in this group will have longer histories of illness and admissions for treatment than those in the younger population. In effect, we suggest that the older patient group differs from the younger group not only in age and experience, but also in chronicity. However, the question of chronicity must be left for a future discussion when its effects can be examined more directly. In addition, we limit this presentation to a consideration of stress scores for the total populations; we are not concerned here with the details of control group analyses.

Table 3.3 shows a significant decrease in occupation-self stress scores from the young to the older group in the community population. The stress scores in the patient population also follow this pattern, but the difference is not significant. The same pattern is observed in both samples for the income-self scores: a decrease in stress as age increases, although the difference is significant only in the community population. The striving scale stress scores decrease (but not significantly) as one moves from the young to the older group in the community. In the ill population there is only a slight tendency for the stress scores to increase with age in the striving scale content area. Thus, each of the self-achievement stress scores diminishes with age in the community sample, significantly in two of the three content areas. In the ill population, the average stress levels are maintained over time for each of the three scores. The fact that the older patients maintain stress scores as high as those of the younger patients indicates the apparent inability of the mentally ill to appraise their situation more realistically as they grow older.

What are the effects of age on aspirations for a hypothetical son? In the community sample there is a significant increase in the education-hypothetical son stress scores with age. This stress score increases only slightly with age in the ill sample. With respect to the occupation-hypothetical son scores, there is a tendency for an increase in stress with age in the community population—this trend is not significant. In the ill population the scores decrease with age, again not significantly.

We have already mentioned that community subjects over forty years of age probably project their goal striving onto a hypothetical son, to a greater degree than those in the twenty-to-thirty-nine year age group. The findings do indicate a concomitant increase in age and the hypothetical-son stress scores among community respondents. There is no such tendency in the ill population. The older ill individuals tend to fluctuate above or below the norm established by the young group, and regardless of the direction of the fluctuation, there are no significant deviations from the younger group norms.

A number of general conclusions about the effect of age on the goal-striving patterns of the ill and community populations are suggested by these findings. It is apparent that, as age increases, those in the community population reduce their own goal-striving stress and at the same time become more involved (i.e., higher stress scores) in goals for their children. The pattern differs among the patients: as age increases, the ill tend to maintain both their own goal-striving stress and that which they have invested in their children. Apparently the ill are characterized by a high level of goal-striving stress which is independent of the reference person or the content area of the stress measurement. These data are also consistent with the earlier point (Chapter 1) that the mentally ill have difficulty in reorganizing their cognitions and perceptions of the social system. In usual circumstances we expect a person to lower his goal striving as he reaches the age at which his aspirations cease to be realistic. It appears that the individual who persists in maintaining high goal-striving stress for himself is potentially pathological.

The Mental Health Continuum

EARLIER in this chapter we entertained the notion that the four mental health groupings (the low symptom group, the high symptom group, the neurotics, and the psychotics) formed a continuum of progressively increasing severity of illness. To investigate this possibility, we made predictions about differences between the psychotics and neurotics, and between the low and high symptom groups. The first hypothesis (1a) stated that the psychotics would manifest higher goal-striving stress scores than the neurotics; the second hypothesis (1b), based on the concept of optimum goal-striving stress, predicted lower stress scores for the high psychiatric symptom individuals in the community than for their low symptom counterparts. We remind the reader that the concept of optimum goal-striving stress refers to that level of striving which falls within the range of potentially realizable goals in our social system, and which is also consistent with our emphasis on ambition and success as desirable attributes. Either of the alternatives to this type of adjustment— maintaining goals that are unrealistically high in view of the nature of the opportunity structure, or manifesting almost no goal striving, a deviation from societal norms—may create problems for the individual. Although we cannot specify an optimum stress level, the low symptom group in the community is assumed to reflect this "healthy" level.

Table 3.4 presents the average stress scores for each of the above four

Table 3.4—Mean Stress Scores by Illness Status

| | Ill | | Community | |
| | PSYCHOTICS | NEUROTICS | HIGH SYMP. | LOW SYMP. |
	Means		Means	
Occupation-Self	9.32	4.51[2]	4.96	5.29
Income-Self	23.18	18.68	14.17	16.30
Striving Scale-Self	19.73	6.78[3]	13.05	14.67
Occupation-Hypothetical-Son	50.70	40.55[2]	32.97	47.51[3]
Education-Hypothetical-Son	66.49	48.72[2]	45.80	62.93[1]

(Pairs of means are significant, by "t" test (one-tailed test) at the level indicated by the footnote notation. Any significant differences between non-adjacent groupings are reported in text.)

1. $P = <.05$ (For Education-Hypothetical Son, High Sympton vs Low Symptom, by two-tailed test)
2. $P = <.01$
3. $P = <.001$ (For Occupation-Hypothetical Son, High Symptom vs Low Symptom, by two-tailed test)

mental health groupings. With respect to Hypothesis 1a, the psychotics are characterized by higher stress scores than the neurotics in the three content areas related to self-striving. These differences are significant for the occupation and striving scale stress scores, but not for the income score. In all three occupation control groups the direction of the difference is as predicted and is significant for one control category. Two of the three income control groups confirm the prediction (one is significant). One group does not (not significant), but this reversal occurs in the highest achievement control group for which statistical analyses could be made (level 3). This provides additional evidence that the direction of difference for the stress scores tends to break down at higher achievement levels. Our previous discussion of differences between the ill and community populations considered only two striving-scale control groups. This was necessitated by the limited number of community population cases in one control group (level 1: striving scale steps 1–3). However, the ill population did contain enough cases to extend over the three achievement levels. Therefore, for striving scale control group analyses within the ill population, three control categories will be considered; for comparisons between the ill and community populations, or within the community population, only two control groups can be analyzed. In the three striving scale groups, the scores for the psychotics are higher than for the neurotics, with one of the three comparisons significant.

Results of the control group analyses for the three scores can be summarized as follows: eight of the nine control groups support Hypothesis 1a with respect to direction of differences (by sign test, $P = < .02$). The differences are significant for three of these control groups. We conclude that the weight of the evidence for the three self-achievement stress scores supports the prediction.

In evaluating Hypothesis 1a in light of both hypothetical-son stress scores, it should be noted (Table 3.4) that the mean scores for the psychotics are significantly higher than for the neurotics. All six education- and occupation-hypothetical son control groups show directional differences consistent with the prediction. The differences are significant for four of the categories. Clearly, the data on the hypothetical-son stress scores confirm our expectation of higher goal-striving stress for the psychotics.

Hypothesis 1b predicts higher stress scores for the low symptom than for the high symptom group in the community sample. All three of the stress scores in the self-achievement areas support the prediction (Table 3.4), although these differences are not significant. Two of the three occupation control groups show differences consistent with the prediction; one of these is significant. The one exception to the prediction is significant and again occurs in the highest occupation achievement category—further evidence that our prediction does break down at the higher achievement levels. Analyses in two of the three income control groups go in the predicted direction, but neither is significant. The exception to the prediction is also not significant. Since there is an absence of any significant differences or consistency in direction, it is difficult to draw conclusions from the control group analyses in this content area. Analyses for the two striving scale control categories go in opposite directions, and the one consistent with the prediction is significant. Thus, five of the eight possible control group analyses are in the predicted direction, and two of them are significant. One of the three opposite in direction to Hypothesis 1b is significant. Although the means for the total samples go in the predicted direction, the data for the control groups do not provide strong support for the hypothesis.

A consideration of the hypothetical-son stress scores shows higher stress for the low symptom than for the high symptom group, a trend consistent with Hypothesis 1b. In all three control group analyses for the education-hypothetical son score, the direction of differences between the symptom groups is consistent with Hypothesis 1b, with two of the categories reaching significance. For the occupation-hypothetical son stress score, the low symptom group has lower stress in each of the three control group comparisons (two are significant). When we consider the degree of stress for a hypothetical son, there are no exceptions to Hypothesis 1b with respect to direction. Furthermore, six of the eight control group comparisons are statistically significant. Clearly, the weight of the evidence supporting Hypothesis 1b is found in the analyses of the hypothetical-son stress scores. The stress scores in the self-achievement areas do not differentiate strongly between the high and low symptom groups. In the area of the hypothetical son scores, however, the low symptom individuals show greater stress than the high symptom subjects. This suggests that the mechanism of projection operates somewhat differently in subgroups within the community population. Those in the low symptom group tend to have moderate stress scores for themselves but are highly involved in striving for a hypothetical son. Those individuals characterized by a high level of psychiatric symptoms, however, have moderate stress scores both for self and hypothetical son. The projection of goal-striving stress onto one's child may act as a safety valve for the low symptom individual, who realizes that he cannot reach valued high goals himself. Instead, he projects these aspirations onto a "son" and invests considerable motivation in this child's success or failure. The low stress scores for self and son that characterize the high symptom respondents apparently provide the impetus for the development of psychosomatic symptoms. It is interesting that the high and low symptom groups vary in the same way as the neurotics and psychotics. In contrast to the psychotics, the neurotics show low stress scores for self as well as for hypothetical son.

Hypotheses 1a and 1b predict respectively lower stress scores for the neurotics than for the psychotics, and for the high symptom group relative to the low symptom group. The final question to be raised in our consideration of the mental health continuum involves differences between the neurotics and the high symptom group. The neurotics are those individuals who have been recommended for psychiatric treatment, whereas the high symptom individuals are characterized by a large number of psychosomatic symptoms but have not been recommended for treatment. We must determine whether this difference in formal definition correlates with variations in stress scores. Intuitively, one might expect higher stress scores for those being seen by psychiatrists or recommended for treatment. However, our data on the perception of the social system disclose no differences between the neurotic and the high symptom group; on this basis we predict no stress score differences between these groups.

Table 3.4 indicates that there is no significant difference between the neurotics and the high symptom group for any of the three self-achievement stress scores. Similarly, neither of the hypothetical-son stress scores differentiates significantly between the two mental health groupings. When the five stress scores are considered, fourteen control group analyses are possible. Ten of these fourteen comparisons show higher mean scores for the neurotics than for the high symptom individuals (two are significant), and four show an opposite trend (two of these four are also significant). The consistency of the difference is not significant ($P = < .09$). We conclude that there are few differences between the neurotics and the high symptom respondents. This supports our expectation, based on data gathered about respondents' perception of the social system.

A comparison of the psychotics and the low symptom subjects is important because these individuals are at opposite extremes of our continuum, and we assume that they characterize the "sickest" and the "healthiest" respondents in our samples. If this assumption is valid, differences between the ill and community populations should be most clearly illustrated in comparisons between these mental health groupings. In this context, we expect higher stress scores for the psychotics than for the low symptom respondents. For all three self-achievement stress scores, the psychotics do have significantly higher scores than the low symptom group (see Table 3.4). Seven of the eight control group analyses for these three stress scores show higher average scores for the psychotics (by sign test, $P = < .04$). The data on the hypothetical-son scores indicate almost no differences between the psychotics and the low symptom group. Although the expectation of higher scores for the psychotics is confirmed in these two content areas (see Table 3.4), the difference is not significant in either instance. Four of the six control group analyses carried out for the two hypothetical-son scores are in the predicted direction, and two comparisons yield higher scores for the low symptom group. Only one of the four analyses in the predicted direction is significant. The difference between the psychotics and the low symptom group is most clearly delineated in the three self-achievement stress scores.

We have already mentioned that the low symptom subjects (compared to high symptom respondents) project their own goal-striving stress onto a hypothetical son and have moderate or low stress associated with their own striving—that is, they compromise striving for their own aspirations. In the context of this discussion it is apparent that the psychotics maintain high goal-striving stress for self *and* for hypothetical son. They are unable to lower their own stress and project their hopes onto a child. In contrast to the psychotics and the low symptom group, the neurotics and the high symptom group are characterized by low stress, both for self and hypothetical son. Thus, individuals in these two groupings have no need to employ the "safety valve" of lowering goal-striving stress in self-achievement areas. If we relate our data on perception of the social system and our findings on stress scores we see that:

(1) The mentally ill, who perceive an open opportunity structure relative to the community subject, have higher stress scores than their community counterparts;

(2) The neurotics and the high symptom respondents perceive the social system in the same way and show similar stress scores,

(3) The psychotics, who see the social system as open relative to the low symptom respondents have the higher stress scores;

(4) The psychotics, who perceive a more open system than the neurotics, also have higher stress scores than these individuals.

The question of why high symptom subjects, who perceive a more open system than low symptom subjects, have similar stress scores in the self-achievement content areas and lower scores for a hypothetical son remains unresolved.

Linear and Nonlinear Relationships between Stress Scores and the Illness Continuum

WE HAVE DISCUSSED at some length the possibility that the four mental groupings form some type of continuum, progressively increasing in severity from the low symptom group, to the high symptom group, to the neurotics, to the psychotics. A somewhat mechanical point of view might predict an increase in stress scores along this same continuum. However, in our discussion of an optimum level of goal-striving stress (Chapter 1), we suggested that our mental health groupings and measures of stress did not constitute a linear relationship. We made certain predictions based on other assumptions which seemed to indicate a tendency toward a curvilinear relationship between the stress scores and our illness continuum. This tendency is specifically illustrated by the fact that although stress scores are generally higher for the psychotics than for the low symptom respondents, on four of the five stress measures average scores for the neurotics fall *below* those of the low symptom group. In addition, in all five areas of stress measurement, the high symptom group has lower scores than the low symptom group.

The existence of a nonlinear relationship between stress scores and the illness continuum coincides with certain other observations about differences between these mental health groupings. Whereas the neurotics and high symptom respondents are still functioning members of the community (although the neurotics are, or have been, in treatment), the psychotics are usually hospitalized. Except for the low symptom individuals, who are assumed to function at an optimum level of goal-striving stress, those in the remaining mental health groupings may react to deviations from the optimum stress level in various ways. The neurotics and high symptom individuals may either lower their aspiration levels, raise their expectations of failure, raise their valences of failure, or be characterized by any combination of these reactions. Such modes of adjustment are concomitant with their perception of the social system as open, compared to low symptom subjects. The psychotics may have very high levels of aspiration, very high probabilities and valences of success attached to their goals, or may manifest any combination of these factors. Again, the social-psychological mode of adjustment for the psychotics occurs in the context of their perception of the social system as open, relative to the low symptom group.

These differences in adjustment to the goal-striving constellation have implications for the community's attitude toward and treatment of certain of its members. For example, one may ask why the psychotic individual is hospitalized and the neurotic person is not. It is possible that the neurotics and the high symptom individuals, all of whom are characterized by low goal striving, constitute little threat to themselves and to the community. In a community setting they may be more passive and dependent than the psychotics, who may sometimes become aggressive and hostile as a result of their intense goal striving. Such behavior can be a threat, to themselves and to the community; consequently, these individuals are hospitalized. We do not intend to attribute the entire institutionalization process to these antecedent conditions, but merely to suggest that these factors contribute to the ultimate decision to hospitalize a mentally disturbed person. Of course, we are still faced with the question of why the neurotics are in treatment, or have been brought to a psychiatric facility for evaluation, and the high symptom individuals are not.

Differences in Variance

IN EXAMINING THE DIFFERENCES between the total ill and community populations, we find that the variance (i.e., variability of scores) of the former sample is significantly greater than that of the latter. This is not surprising in view of numerous level-of-aspiration experiments done in the laboratory which have reported significantly greater variance in the goal levels of highly anxious-to-mentally disturbed subjects, relative to less anxious or disturbed subjects. Why should this difference in variance occur? The ill may be more unstable and therefore less consistent in their goal-striving behavior than the "healthy" community respondents. Such an explanation only reiterates the fact of greater variance. It assumes failure to obtain "reality" feedback, in which case choices are determined by innumerable situational factors and internal states.

It is also possible that in some respects the ill population is more heterogeneous than the community population. This heterogeneity may be the result of including various diagnostic groupings in the patient sample. If we assume, for example, that a patient diagnosed as a manic-depressive adopts a different mode of adjustment to a particular situation than a paranoid schizophrenic, considering these two categories as part of one larger sample increases the variability and heterogeneity of the combined group. We have already noted a number of similarities between the neurotics and the high symptom group which tend to increase the overlap of these two subpopulations. If the neurotics and the high symptom individuals were withdrawn from the ill and community populations, respectively, the differences between the psychotics and the low symptom group should increase considerably.

Using as an illustration the striving scale stress scores, it may be noted that the inclusion of the neurotics in the patient population and the high symptom group in the community population reduces the significance of the differences between the two total populations. The mean score in this content area for the ill sample (16.42) is higher than for the community population (14.48), although this difference is not significant. The difference between the mean score for the psychotics (19.73) and the low symptom group (14.67) does reach significance, however (see Table 3.4). It should also be noted that the mean stress score for the neurotics (6.78) is the lowest of the four mental health groupings, yet this subgroup is included in the ill population along with the psychotics, who have the highest mean score. Clearly, in the context of the striving

scale stress measurement, the inclusion of the psychotics and the neurotics in the same population increases the variance of the total mentally
ill population.

For the occupation-self stress score the difference between the means
for the psychotics and the neurotics is 4.81, whereas the difference
between the mean scores for the high and low symptom groups is only
.33. For the income-self score the difference in means between the
two ill mental health groupings is 4.50, but only 2.13 between the two
community subgroups. The difference in means for the occupation-
hypothetical son stress score is 10.15 in the patient population, and 14.54
in the community, a reversal of the trend noted for the three self-
achievement scores. In the area of aspirations for a hypothetical son, the
mean psychotic-neurotic difference is 17.77, and the mean high-low
symptom group difference is 17.13. For four of the five stress scores, then,
the mean difference between the two ill mental health groupings is
greater than between the two community groupings. On this basis, we
expect significantly greater variance for the ill than for the community
sample on these four stress measurements—this expectation is confirmed.

The greater variance in the ill sample is open to more than one
interpretation. First, it is suggested that the variance within the ill population, compared to the community population, is not randomly distributed. Second, the variance in the ill population seems to result from the
inclusion of subgroups, the members of which differ markedly in their
modes of adaptation to the goal-striving situation. A final possibility
(which may be a derivative of the "mode of adjustment" explanation) is
that the greater variance in stress scores in the ill sample reflects these
individuals' concern over avoiding threats to their self-esteem. It has
been suggested that persons with low self-esteem may select either very
low levels of aspiration (thereby guaranteeing success), or goals which
are impossible to attain (thus enabling them to rationalize failure on the
basis of the difficulty of the tasks). Level of aspiration is mentioned in
this context because it is a major component of the stress formulation.

In our analysis of the differences between the four mental health
groupings, it was noted that the variance increased along our continuum
from the low symptom group to the psychotics for each of the five stress
scores, although there were no variance differences between the neurotics and the high symptom group. The reasons offered in the previous
paragraph to explain the difference in variance between the ill and
community samples do not fully account for the systematic increase
among the mental health groupings. Three other possibilities may be

considered in this context, although we do not intend to imply that these three points are necessarily discrete and independent:

(1) The change in variance along the mental health continuum may be a function of decreasing efficiency of "defensive" or "coping" responses to threatening situations.

(2) The nature of these "defensive" or "coping" responses may vary with position on the illness continuum.

(3) The differences in variance in the four mental health groupings may be a function of respondents' perception of the social system. For example, the variability of responses to the "open system" question is greater for psychotics than for neurotics, and the variance is also greater for the former than the latter subgroup. These points will be elaborated upon in subsequent chapters.

Intercorrelation of the Stress Scores and Dependent Variables

WE HAVE BEEN DISCUSSING the five stress scores as if they tap the individual's goal striving in completely discrete content areas or with respect to different reference individuals. In a sense, this approach has assumed that one's responses are a function of the particular content area about which he is questioned, rather than a function of the individual himself. The discussion has not considered whether some of the determinants of responses in the area of occupation, for instance, may be the same as those in the area of income or the striving scale. We must consider the extent to which the stress scores are a function of common factors, and the extent to which they are a function of the unique aspects of the content areas to which they refer. One approach to this problem is to determine how the stress scores in one area vary with the stress score changes in another content area. If, for instance, a given individual has high occupation-self stress scores, does he also have high striving scale or income stress scores? The degree to which an individual's stress scores vary together is referred to as their "interdependence"—the more they vary together, the greater the interdependence, and conversely. It should be emphasized that interdependence refers to the degree to which the stress scores vary together *within a given individual;* the previous discussion was concerned with the significance of differences between measures of *group* characteristics. The interdependence of any two sets of scores may be estimated by means of the Pearson Product Moment Correlation.

A consideration of the intercorrelations of the stress scores with one another will determine the extent of their interdependence. We shall also estimate the correlation between each of the stress scores, employing three procedures for ordering individuals on an "illness-wellness" continuum. The first procedure divides our total sample into a mentally ill group (based on psychiatric evaluation) and a community group (with a minimum of previous psychiatric contact). The second procedure employs the four mental health groupings as possibly constituting a continuum of severity of illness. Since there is a correlation of .54 ($P = < .01$) between our psychosomatic symptom index and the illness-community distinction, the third approach correlates each individual's stress scores and his psychosomatic score. Only four of the five stress scores were considered in these correlation procedures. The multiple correlation computer program used to analyze our data would consider only those cases for which information was available on *all* the variables we wished to examine. Because of incomplete questionnaire responses, it was often impossible to compute all five stress scores for any given respondent. Only 1670 cases of our total interviewed sample ($N = 2912$) met the criterion of having valid information on all five stress scores and on every additional variable we wished to examine. Much of the incomplete information seemed to be in the area of the education-hypothetical son stress score. When this score was excluded, the size of the total sample able to be utilized for the multiple correlation computer program increased from 1670 to 1995 cases (70 per cent of the interviewed sample). Differences between groups tend to be more reliable as the size of such groups increases. For this reason, we removed the education–hypothetical son stress score as a variable and used the sample of 1995, rather than that of 1670 cases.

Six possible correlations must be computed in order to relate each of the four stress scores to one another. Table 3.5 presents the correlation values and levels of significance for each of these comparisons. The table also includes the intercorrelations for these six comparisons within each

Table 3.5—Intercorrelations of Goal–Striving Stress Scores

	Total Interviewed Population		Psychotics		Neurotics		High Symp.		Low Sym
	r	P	r	P	r	P	r	P	r
Stress Score Comparisons									
Occupation-Self with Striving Scale-Self	.19	<.01	.21	<.01	.11	<.05	.31	<.01	.08 <
Occupation-Self with Income-Self	.23	<.01	.30	<.01	.22	<.01	.03	N.S.	.19 <
Occupation-Self with Occupation-Hyp. Son	.17	<.01	.21	<.01	.20	<.01	.16	<.05	.10 <
Striving Scale-Self with Income-Self	.14	<.01	.14	<.01	.12	<.05	.18	<.05	.15 <
Striving Scale-Self with Occupation-Hyp. Son	.21	<.01	.25	<.01	.26	<.01	.18	<.05	.13 <
Income-Self with Occupation-Hyp. Son	.16	<.01	.17	<.01	.28	<.01	.15	<.05	.10 <

of our four mental health groupings. This allows us to determine the degree to which the significance of the data observed for the total population (i.e., ill and community populations combined) also applies within each of the mental health groupings. The correlation coefficients for the total population are significant in each of the six comparisons made ($P = <.01$). Twenty of the twenty-four correlations carried out for the four mental health groupings are statistically significant. The use of the psychosomatic index as an "illness-wellness" measure would have necessitated the imposition of arbitrary grouping criteria on these scores. We felt that such a procedure contributed nothing to the analyses. We conclude, therefore, that the stress scores for any given individual tend to vary together and in the same direction, to a significant degree. This suggests that some of the determinants of the responses from which the stress scores are derived influence the individual in all the content areas, regardless of the reference person (i.e., self or hypothetical son). Since a correlation of 1.00 means perfect interdependence, however, the absolute magnitude of these correlations indicates that the common factors are by no means the major determinants of the obtained responses.

Table 3.6 presents the correlations between each of the four stress

Table 3.6— Correlations Between Stress Scores and Illness Status

	Illness-Community Dichotomy (Linear Assumption)		Four Step Illness Continuum (Linear Assumption)		Four Step Illness Continuum (Non-Linear Assumption)	
	r	P	r	P	r	P
Occupation-Self	.04	N.S.	.04	N.S.	.10	<.01
Income-Self	.05	N.S.	.05	N.S.	.03	N.S.
Striving Scale-Self	.01	N.S.	.02	N.S.	.20	<.01
Occupation-Hypothetical-Son	-.02	N.S.	-.01	N.S.	.06	<.05

scores and two of the three procedures employed to order individuals on an "illness-wellness" scale. In computing the correlation coefficients, we assume that for a given change in a person's stress score in one area there occurs a given change in his score in another area. It is further assumed that the ratio of these two given changes remains the same, regardless of the absolute magnitude of the stress scores prior to the change. In other words, we take for granted that the rate of change of any two given stress scores remains constant all along the potential range of stress scores. This is referred to as the "assumption of linearity." In our discussion of anticipated differences between the psychotics and the neurotics and between the high and low symptom groups, we assumed a nonlinear relationship— a variation in direction and rate of change with different positions on our mental health continuum. (We employed the quadratic equation formula for determining nonlinearity.) The data reported in Table 3.6 for the four mental health groupings include correlations based both on the linear and the nonlinear assumption, as an illustration of their differential effect on these correlations. If we had made the linear assumption, we would have predicted that as the magnitude of one's stress scores increased, the likelihood of his being ill also increased. Conversely, as the stress scores decreased, the likelihood of illness would also decrease. Regarding the nonlinear assumption, which is appropriate to our predictions, we expect the distribution of stress scores to fit a curve other than a straight line—that is, as one moves from the low symptom to the high symptom group, the stress scores decrease, but as one continues to move from the high symptom group to the neurotics, the scores begin to increase. Finally, as one moves from the neurotics to the psychotics, the scores increase until they are significantly higher for the psychotics than for the low symptom group.

We have already mentioned that the psychotics tend to have high goal-striving stress scores for themselves, as well as for a hypothetical son. However, those in the low symptom group ("healthiest") show quantitative differences in scores for self and for a hypothetical son. The low symptom individuals apparently adjust their own goal striving and project their past unfulfilled aspirations onto a child. Thus, the hypothetical son can be conceptualized as a "safety valve" used by the low symptom respondents to relieve high levels of stress in self-achievement areas. If we consider the neurotics and the high symptom group as intermediary groupings on the illness continuum, we predict increasing correlations between stress scores for self and hypothetical son in the area of occupation as we move from the low symptom group to the psychotics. Such increasing correlations would indicate progressively greater interdependence of scores for self and son as one moves along the continuum. This expectation is confirmed (see Table 3.6). The correlation coefficients between these two stress scores for the four mental health groupings are .10, .16, .20, and .21: as one moves from the "healthiest" to the "sickest" group on the illness continuum, there is an increasing tendency to find simultaneously high stress for self and hypothetical son.

It should be noted that none of the correlations (based on a linear assumption) between the stress scores and the ill-community division of our population, or between the stress scores and the four-step mental health continuum, is significant (see Table 3.6, first and second columns). Clearly, if we did not consider the influence of diagnosis within the mentally ill population, or the effect of differential psychiatric symptom scores within the two community groupings, we would erroneously conclude that our stress scores were unrelated to illness. Both on theoretical and empirical grounds, there is reason to suspect the linear assumption between the stress scores and mental illness. When the nonlinear assumption is applied to the relationship between the stress scores and the four mental health groupings (Table 3.6, third column), three of the four scores are significantly related to the illness continuum. Although the psychosomatic index scores correlate highly with mental illness, they do not correlate strongly with the stress scores (two of the four comparisons are significant, but only at the .05 level of confidence). We must conclude that the scores on this psychosomatic symptom inventory cannot substitute for the mental health groupings we have used. In addition, it should be noted that an individual with relatively high scores on the inventory may not be classified as mentally ill, although there is often a joint occurrence. In view of these comparatively weak correlations, this index of illness will not be employed in discussions of the component elements of the stress scores (Chapter 4).

We must now consider whether the higher correlations obtained between the stress scores and the illness continuum, using the nonlinear (as opposed to the linear) assumption, is a function of the characteristics of the stress scores themselves, or of the four groups constituting our mental health continuum. The distances on the continuum between the four mental health groupings are, in fact, probably unequal; however, the linear assumption implies that these intervals are equal. It also implies that for a given change in illness status there will be a concomitant given change in stress scores—that is, a constant ratio between the two measures.

In order to determine whether the problems underlying the linear assumption applied to the stress scores or to the illness continuum, we intercorrelated the stress scores with one another, using both the linear and nonlinear assumptions. We reasoned that if the correlations based on the linear assumption were higher, we could attribute the assumptions associated with the linear procedure to stress scores. In addition, we could propose that the higher correlations obtained for the nonlinear assumption were a function of problems inherent in our conception of the illness continuum.

The coefficients for the six possible intercorrelations, using the nonlinear assumption, are .09, .12, .13, .01, .13, and .08. The corresponding coefficients based on the linear assumption are .19, .23, .17, .14, .21, and

.16—higher in all instances than the coefficients based on the nonlinear assumption. Thus, the distribution of stress scores tends to conform more closely to the linear assumption, indicating that the observed nonlinearity is more a function of the four illness groupings than of the stress scores. Additional support for this conclusion may be derived from the earlier observation that the neurotics and the high symptom group do not differ on their perception of the social system or on stress scores. We may speculate that if we had applied the linear assumption to a mental health continuum composed of three groupings (i.e., the low symptom group, a combination of the high symptom group and the neurotics, and the psychotics), we could have expected higher correlations between the stress scores and the illness continuum.

CHARACTERISTICS OF SUBGROUPS WITHIN THE
MENTALLY ILL POPULATION

In the discussion presented up to this point, we have been primarily concerned with differences between the ill and community populations, differences between subgroups in the community population, and findings relating to our mental health continuum. We have not dealt with differences between subgroups in the mentally ill population for two reasons. First, we have no specific expectations or hypotheses to test about anticipated differences between males and females or between young and older ill respondents. In general, we feel that once an individual becomes mentally ill he has passed the critical point where the antecedent conditions to mental illness have already crystallized; it makes no difference how far beyond this critical point he has moved.

Second, if we had discussed this problem in the course of the general presentation, the reader might have found it both distracting and confusing. At this point, we briefly present the results of analyses carried out within the mentally ill population.

(1) There are no differences between males or females, or between the young and older patients, on perception of the opportunity structure.

(2) There are no differences between males and females, or between the young and older patients, on any of the five stress scores, when the total populations are considered.

(3) Only one of the fourteen control group analyses yields a significant difference in stress scores between males and females, with the males showing higher scores. There are no significant differences between the young and older ill respondents in any control group comparison.

Summary of Stress Score Analyses

ON THE BASIS of material presented in this chapter, we conclude the following:

(1) The stress scores for the mentally ill population are higher than those obtained for individuals in the community population. This conclusion is based both on group and individual data and supports Hypothesis 1.

(2) The stress scores for the psychotics are higher than those for the neurotics (Hypothesis 1a).

(3) The stress scores for the high symptom group are lower than the scores for the low symptom group, but only when the hypothetical-son situation is considered (Hypothesis 1b).

(4) Those segments of the community population with a high yield of illness have higher stress scores than those segments of the community population with a low yield of illness.

(5) The mentally ill respondents perceive a more open social system than the community population respondents.

(6) Those subgroups of the community population with a high yield of mental illness see the social system as more open than those subgroups with a low yield of illness.

(7) The neurotics and the high symptom group do not appear to differ on the variables with which we have been concerned.

(8) A consideration of the stress scores in different content areas and for different reference individuals suggests that these scores are partly a function of common determinants that act upon the individual.

(9) Consistent with our expectations, the stress scores correlate with our mental health continuum when the nonlinear assumption is applied.

4

GOAL-STRIVING STRESS AND MENTAL DISORDER: COMPONENT ANALYSIS

In the previous chapter we presented detailed data relating mental disorder to respondents' perception of the social system and to their goal-striving stress scores. Our formulation of goal-striving stress incorporates the individual's achievement, level of aspiration, and his estimates of probability of success and valence of failure. This chapter will focus on these components of the stress scores; specifically, the analyses will relate the stress components both to one another and to mental disorder.

There are several reasons for making these analyses. First, they will indicate the degree to which a consistent and systematic relationship exists between each of the components and mental disorder. Second, these analyses will enable us to determine whether the observed relationship between stress scores and mental disorder is a function only of one or two components or of all the components acting together in a given stress score. Third, we shall be in a better position to evaluate whether relationships observed among the components are consistent with general assumptions of various motivation theories. Finally, we shall be able to relate the discrepancy between aspiration and achievement to mental disorder. The discrepancy concept is particularly central to the present study:

(1) This concept was the original focal point of our earlier work (which eventually culminated in this project).

(2) In addition, this discrepancy measure constitutes the "stressor" factor in the stress score formulation—that is, if the aspiration-achievement discrepancy in a given content area is zero, it is assumed that no goal-striving stress is operative.

The presentation of stress score analyses (Chapter 3) included data for each achievement or control group, in order to show the degree to which the observed relationships permeated all achievement levels of our population. Such detailed analyses will not be presented here. Control group analyses were made for each component, and the degree of consistency obtained was comparable to that observed for the stress scores.

The discussion of the discrepancy concept will include a review of relevant literature and an evaluation of the aspiration-achievement discrepancy measures in five different content areas. All of these discrepancy measures relate to the individual's achievement and aspirations for himself, and three of the five were involved in computing stress scores for the self. The discussion of probability and valence estimates will be limited to those measures used in computing the stress scores discussed in Chapter 3.

Finally, as was the case for the stress-score data, material on the components will be discussed in the context of three issues: (1) differences between the ill and community samples; (2) differences between high and low yield subgroups in the community population; and (3) the relationship of the components to the mental health continuum.

Goal-Striving Concepts and Psychopathology: Summary Review of the Literature

MOBILITY ORIENTATION AND MENTAL DISORDER

The empirical research in this area is primarily concerned with the discrepancy between level of aspiration and achievement, and its relation to mental disorder. There are many assertions in the literature, usually based on clinical observations, about the relationship between mobility orientation and mental disorder. Such well-known clinicians as Horney (1937: 162, ff; 172 ff) and Kardiner (1951: 315) have noted the emphasis our society places on status achievement as an important element of self-evaluation and self-esteem. Failure to achieve desired goals leads to feelings of worthlessness and, in some cases, to mental disorder. In his study of Negroes, Kardiner found achievement striving to be an important ideological factor in middle-, but not lower-class, psychopathology. Studies of mental illness in immigrant populations have also maintained that a discrepancy between expected (and also desired) and actual achievement frequently leads to mental disorder (Weinberg, 1953a; 1953b; 1955; Last, 1960).

Hollingshead, Ellis, and Kirby (1954) investigated this problem in New Haven. They found large discrepancies between occupational and educational aspirations and achievements among the lower- and middle-class mentally ill. The authors concluded that in both of these social classes vertical mobility, striving, and frustration were significant elements in the development of schizophrenia and neurosis, and that these factors merited more thorough investigation. Myers and Roberts (1959: 133–137) studied intensively a small sample of psychiatric patients and their families and found equally large discrepancies between the aspirations and achievements of individuals in Class III (middle) and Class V (lower). However, the authors felt that these discrepancies were psychologically significant only among Class III respondents. Class V patients appeared to be more reconciled to the low probability of achieving their desired goals, but patients in Class III spent a great deal of energy trying to narrow the gap between their achievements and aspirations. Most of those in Class III believed that working diligently toward a goal insured success; therefore, the failure of a middle-class individual to fulfill his aspirations caused a drop in his self-esteem and feelings of depression.

Other studies have reaffirmed the importance of differences in achievement striving in various psychiatric diagnostic groups. When social class was held constant, schizophrenic patients showed larger discrepancies relative to their siblings than did neurotic individuals (Myers and Roberts, 1959: 162). Becker (1960) compared the achievement-related characteristics of a small group of manic-depressive patients and the same number of "normal" individuals. The psychiatric patients placed significantly more emphasis on achievement values. Since manic-depressive psychosis is significantly associated with middle-class status, this study indirectly confirms the findings of Myers and Roberts. However, the patients did not score higher than the controls on "need for achievement," as measured by the Thematic Apperception Test. Becker concluded that in manic-depressive patients high achievement values and conformity in behavior seemed to aim toward gaining the approval of others, rather than satisfying internalized standards. Eysenck and Himmelweit (1946) compared the goal-striving behavior of two groups of psychiatric patients: those who manifested affective symptoms (i.e., introvert-dysthymic group) and hysterics. They found a marked tendency in the affective group to neglect the reality of past achievement and performance, and to be dominated instead by subjective factors. This group tended to depreciate their past performances and to overvalue (unrealistically) their future possibilities. In his intensive social–psychological study of the "schizophrenic type," Weinberg (1955; 1960) noted that the inability of such patients "to assess their own limitations and/or limitations of a given situation in which they participated was one direct contributing factor in their subsequent breakdowns." The author pointed out these patients' deep need for approval, leading to intense over-compensatory aspirations. Dunham (1959: 157–174) confirmed these conclusions in a study of catatonic schizophrenia.

Hinkle and Wolff (1957) studied a large sample of predominantly working-class persons. They found that those individuals who were most frustrated in their aspirations and disappointed in their accomplishments manifested a higher incidence of illness and showed more disturbances of mood, thought, and behavior than those who came nearer to reaching their aspirations. Sewell and Haller (1959) also reported a direct relationship between achieved frustration and psychiatric symptoms in a study of 1462 elementary school children. On the California Test of Personality, lower-class children scored as more maladjusted and also had significantly more concern over achievement than children in the middle class. In addition to showing a direct relationship between concern about achievement and symptoms of maladjustment, this study tended to question the frequently reported finding (e.g., Davis, 1947; Hyman, 1953b; Hollingshead and Redlich, 1958: 114–135) that socialization in lower socioeconomic groups results in a reduction of achievement striving and achievement anxiety. Parker, Kleiner, and Taylor (1960) found (both for Negro and white populations) that when occupational achievement was controlled, groups with higher educational achievement had relatively higher rates of schizophrenia than groups with less education. Assuming educational achievement to be an index of level of aspiration, it was inferred that those groups with high rates of schizophrenia were also characterized by large aspiration-achievement discrepancies. In two other papers by these authors (Kleiner, Parker, and Taylor, 1961; Kleiner and Parker, 1962), high rates of mental disorder (including all diagnostic categories) were found to be significantly correlated with large discrepancies between aspiration and achievement. In these studies the discrepancies were measured directly from data obtained in interviews.

All these studies suggest that mobility orientation is a significant factor in mental disorder. In addition, they indicate that larger discrepancies between aspiration and achievement may be more prevalent among individuals in the lower socioeconomic groups. However, Myers and Roberts (1959) showed that middle-class individuals were more psychologically involved in their aspirations than lower-class individuals. This disparity indicates a need for studies on the psychological effects of the individual's estimate of the probability of goal attainment (probability of success) and the importance of the goal area (valence) to him. These variables are suggested by the goal-striving theory of Lewin, Festinger, and their associates (1944).

SMALL GROUP STUDIES OF ACHIEVEMENT-RELATED BEHAVIOR
AND MENTAL DISORDER

The following studies are concerned mainly with small group research, using experimentally created tasks. Although some of these studies were carried out with medically diagnosed psychiatric cases, others employed different measures of maladjustment and anxiety.

There is a large body of research indicating that individuals with some evidence of maladjustment also tend to select experimentally created tasks with a very high or very low probability of successful completion. The discrepancies between their aspirations and their actual performances are either extremely high or low (but more often predominantly high) compared to more well-adjusted subjects (Atkinson, 1957). In a study of the achievement behavior of a group of college students, Atkinson, Bastian, Earl, and Litwin (1960) found that individuals characterized by a strong need to avoid failure (as determined by the T.A.T.) tended to avoid tasks with intermediate risks and to select those with high or low probabilities of success.

Cohen (1954), using a sample of fifty neurotic patients, attempted to determine the relationship between goal-setting behavior and feelings of self-rejection, as indicated by these subjects' responses on the Rorschach Test; both very high and very low goal settings were significantly related to a high degree of self-rejection. A low degree of self-rejection was related to medium-high and medium-low goal settings. Self-acceptance was found to be associated with low positive or low negative aspirations.

Atkinson (1954) showed that persons with high aspirations had large discrepancies between their actual and ideal self-images. Individuals in need of psychotherapy also had large discrepancies between their perceptions of what they were and what they would like to be (Butler and Haigh, 1954; Turner and Vanderlipp, 1958).

Pauline Sears (1941) found a definite relationship between various personality traits and achievement behavior on experimentally created tasks. It was somewhat anxiety provoking for students with negative discrepancies (i.e., goal levels lower than past performances) to admit that they were striving for more than they were able to achieve. These students had very low tolerance for failure. Even after one failure, they quickly dropped their levels of aspiration to points below their previous performances. Students with low positive discrepancies between their aspired goals and actual performances were relatively confident and secure. Those with high positive discrepancies also had considerable fear of failure, but they were able to admit failure without too much damage to their self-esteem.

Klugman (1948) investigated the relationship between aspiration on contrived tasks and emotional stability in a group of thirty native-born white subjects. His results indicated that the more stable subjects tended to have narrower discrepancy ranges between aspiration and level of attainment than the less stable subjects. The more emotionally stable individuals appeared to be flexible and capable of shifting their goals in response to their previous performances. However, those characterized as less stable were inclined either to maintain their aspirations rigidly, or to show extreme changes.

Mahone (1960) attempted to apply some of the findings reported above to a situation in which the respondent selected socially relevant goals instead of aspiration levels on contrived laboratory tasks. He administered vocational interest questionnaires and anxiety schedules to a sample of 135 college students. As predicted, he found that those students characterized by high "debilitating anxiety" set unrealistically high occupational aspirations. In addition, these individuals were the least accurate in placing themselves in rank order of achievement in their class. It was difficult for them to give realistic estimates of their own abilities.

Many laboratory experiments have demonstrated the occurrence of relatively high aspiration-achievement discrepancies in subjects manifesting definite psychopathology. Himmelweit (1947) compared psychoneurotic individuals with "normals" and found that the former had higher "D-scores" (i.e., discrepancy scores). Jost (1955) obtained the same difference in D-scores when he compared a schizophrenic and a nonpsychotic group. Children diagnosed as emotionally disturbed showed higher discrepancy scores than did their normal peers (Ferguson, 1958). High discrepancy scores between aspiration and achievement on laboratory tasks were also found in those with multiple psychosomatic symptoms

(Klugman, 1947), asthma (Little and Cohen, 1951), and peptic ulcers (Raifman, 1957).

The evidence cited above indicates that emotionally disturbed subjects either over- or under-aspire, compared to more well-adjusted subjects. Most of these studies, however, indicate that the maladjusted and pathological groups over-aspire. Two lines of reasoning have generally been advanced to explain this phenomenon. One approach argues that, compared to others, maladjusted subjects have high levels of anxiety and considerable fear of failure. They attempt to minimize this anxiety by selecting a task which is so easy that success is assured, or one which is so difficult that failure will be no cause for self-blame (Atkinson, 1957). The other explanation suggests that the high level of anxiety experienced by maladjusted subjects prevents them from accurately evaluating their own abilities relative to realistic difficulties encountered in reaching certain goals (Mahone, 1960).

Although most studies confirm the selection of very high or very low levels of aspiration by maladjusted subjects, not all research supports this finding. The selected level of aspiration may be a function of personality type. Chance (1960) selected a group of maladjusted (as determined by the M.M.P.I.) college students and divided them into "depressives" and "repressors." She hypothesized that the former group would tend to minimize their past achievements and under-aspire in the experimental situation, while the repressors, who generally denied their failures, would over-aspire. Both groups were subjected to an experimentally contrived failure situation; students of the depressive type lowered their aspirations considerably, but the repressors maintained their old goals or reduced them only slightly. Davids and White (1958) studied thirty normal children and a matched sample of thirty who were diagnosed as emotionally disturbed. Prior to the experience of experimental success or failure, the disturbed children showed larger discrepancies between aspiration and achievement on the tasks. After the experimentally produced success, the normal and the disturbed groups increased their aspirations; the increase for the normals was higher. After experimentally produced failure, the disturbed group decreased their aspirations significantly more than the normal children. In addition, the disturbed children showed much more heterogeneity in their responses after failure. These results indicate that the maladjusted group selected (relatively) extreme aspirations only after a failure situation.

The hypothesis has been advanced, with some supporting evidence, that schizophrenics are minimally responsive to external environmental stimuli in their achievement behavior, and that they tend to raise or lower their aspirations indiscriminately either after the experience of success or failure (Hausmann, 1933). Olson (1958) investigated this question in a sample of forty-five male schizophrenics between twenty and forty years of age, and in a comparable group of nonpsychotic subjects. This investigator was interested in the reactions of the two groups to three kinds of experimentally created situations. In one situation the investigator approved subjects' performances by telling them that they had done well, better than others, etc. In the second situation he told them that their performances had been poor. In the third, he expressed neither a positive nor a negative reaction. There was no way for the subjects in this situation to evaluate their performances realistically. After mild disapproval, the subsequent achievement of the normals improved, but that of the schizophrenics remained relatively the same. Members of the ill group showed the greatest subsequent improvement after their performances were approved by the investigator. This study lends little support to the idea that schizophrenics are unresponsive to external environmental stimuli. It also shows that praise, even in mild form, was a more effective enhancer for these ill individuals than disapproval. Thus, there is some evidence that disturbed subjects are hypersensitive to failure.

The research reviewed in this section shows that individuals who are considered emotionally disturbed do not manifest uniform kinds of goal-oriented behavior. There is considerable variation among personality types and diagnostic categories. Little is known at this point about the applicability of theory concerning achievement behavior to real life situations. Assuming that it is relevant, an interesting methodological problem arises. We have reviewed research concerned with the ideological pertinence of achievement-related behavior for mental illness. We have discussed, for example, whether the magnitude of the discrepancy between aspiration and achievement is related to mental illness. Some of the small group research suggests that the size of this discrepancy acts as a defense against emotional disturbance, rather than as one of its causes. Achievement-related behavior may be relevant both as an antecedent and a consequence of mental disorder. Therefore, it is crucial for any research in this area to determine carefully the temporal relationship between the onset of mental illness and changes in achievement-related behavior. Only in this way can the role of such behavior be delineated either as an antecedent or a consequence of mental disorder. It is to this last point that our discussion of the yield issue is directed in this and the following two chapters.

The Discrepancy Concept and Mental Disorder

WE MAKE TWO ASSUMPTIONS about the meaning of the discrepancy between level of aspiration and achievement:

(1) The greater the discrepancy between these two variables, the more stress is experienced by the individual.

(2) As the stress deriving from this discrepancy increases, the likelihood of mental disorder also increases.

On the basis of these assumptions and the summary of the literature presented, we predict a larger discrepancy score for the mentally ill than for the community population. Table 4.1 presents the findings for discrep-

Table 4.1—Mean Aspiration-Achievement Discrepancy for Ill and Community Populations

	TOTAL		MALES		FEMALES		YOUNG		OLD	
	Ill	Comm.	Ill	Comm.	Ill	Comm.	Ill	Comm.	Ill	Comm.
Occupation-Self	1.19	1.32[1]	1.23	1.35	1.15	1.30	1.26	1.38	.99	1.25[2]
Income Self-	2.15	3.23[3]	1.78	3.37[3]	2.42	3.12[3]	2.35	3.44[3]	1.59	2.97[3]
Striving Scale Self	4.15	2.50[3]	4.39	2.57[3]	3.99	2.45[3]	4.24	2.89[3]	3.93	2.04[3]
Striving Scale-Exp/Ach.[4]	2.80	1.60[3]	2.96	1.64[3]	2.67	1.54[3]	2.95	1.93[3]	2.44	1.18[3]
Education-Self[5]	4.30	4.20	4.84	4.35	3.92	4.06	3.78	3.51	5.58	4.97

(Pairs of means are significant by "t" test (one-tailed test), at the level indicated by the footnote notation.)

1. P=<.05 (For occupation-self, two-tailed test)
2. P=<.01 (For occupation-self, two-tailed test)
3. P=<.001 (For income-self, two-tailed test)
4. This D-score represents the discrepancy between expected striving scale step and achieved striving scale step.
5. This D-Score represents the discrepancy between aspired educational level when in school and achieved educational level.

ancy scores in five content areas. The prediction is not confirmed in the area of occupational striving for self—the discrepancy for the ill population is smaller than that of the community population. The direction of this difference holds not only for the total ill–total community comparison, but for similar comparisons controlling for sex and age. Two of the five comparisons made in this content area are significant (between the total populations and between the older respondents). In the area of income-self (see Table 4.1) the average discrepancy for the community population is larger than for the patients, for comparisons of total samples and those involving sex and age controls. The differences between the populations are significant in every case. The general prediction is not confirmed for the occupation and income discrepancy.

A consideration of the striving scale discrepancy reveals a very different pattern. The discrepancy between aspiration and achievement in this area is significantly larger for the ill population in each of the five comparisons (see Table 4.1), clearly supporting our initial expectation.

There is more than one possible explanation for the inconsistent findings with respect to these three discrepancies. At this point, however, the data do not allow any definitive statement about which of these is correct.

(1) The first explanation does not account for the inconsistency in results; it merely reiterates the fact of a contradiction. It is possible that the occupational and income aspirations of the patients are, in fact, not far different from their achievement levels in these areas. The community respondents perceive much larger discrepancies between their aspirations and achievements, although on a generalized striving scale measure this tendency is reversed.

(2) The second possibility also assumes that the responses given in these three content areas are direct measures of how the ill and community respondents actually feel about the given issues. Since the patients evidence small occupation and income discrepancies, these may be areas of peripheral importance to the mentally ill, but relatively more important to the community population. In order to give a response on our striving scale measure, a person must determine goal-striving areas important to himself and then evaluate his position relative to these areas. The striving scale discrepancy score may reflect areas of striving which are of greater importance or relevance to the individual than the income and occupational areas. If this supposition is valid, it suggests that investigators in the field who assume that occupational and income striving are invariably important to their respondents are laboring under a misconception. This explanation further implies that, before beginning a goal-striving study, investigators must find out what striving areas are essential to the individuals with whom they are concerned. Since goal-striving areas of particular personal importance undoubtedly vary according to a person's race, national origin, social status, sex, age, etc., the specification of major striving areas without prior knowledge of the population being studied may be very misleading. It is also possible that some of the contradictions noted in the field concerning occupational and income aspirations of different groups grow out of the naiveté of existing assumptions about striving areas.

(3) The third explanation considers the individual's responses as "coping" or "defensive" reactions to the interview situation or to the generalized social situation in which he finds himself. More specifically, this approach implies that in the occupational and income areas the patients lower their aspirations, and, consequently, their discrepancies, to a greater degree than the community respondents. This is motivated by a wish to avoid being publicly exposed as a failure and thereby subject to ridicule. One's occupational achievement is obvious to those around him. If he publicly states aspirations much above this level, he is admitting to his own failure. Since both his aspiration and achievement levels on the self-anchored striving scale are privately determined (i.e., an observer cannot really ascertain the basis on which the individual evaluates his achievements), this situation is more ambiguous than in the case of occupation and income. If we assume that the individual's responses to the striving scale questions are direct reflections of his own striving, rather than defensive reactions to situations seen as potentially "threatening," then the larger discrepancy scores in this area among the patients may be more directly associated with psychopathology.

(4) Our fourth possible interpretation of the discrepancy score data assumes, as in the previous explanation, that the patients tend to lower their occupation and income scores to lessen the threats of public exposure of their failures. In this context we suggest that a high striving scale discrepancy emerges because the individual is anxious to emphasize publicly that he really does have high personal goals, despite his low aspirations in such specific areas as occupation and income.

We have arbitrarily created four possible explanations of the apparent contradictions in the discrepancy score data. One of these interpretations is a restatement of the findings. In reality, different individuals may reflect various combinations of these interpretations. For example, those who lower their occupation and income discrepancy scores to avoid public knowledge of their failures may maintain large discrepancy scores on the striving scale measure in order to indicate their high aspirations in goal-striving areas that are important to them. If the lower discrepancy scores among the patients actually reflect "coping" or "defensive" reactions, then our analysis of community groups differing in yield of mental illness may be a more adequate indicator of the antecedents of psychopathology than the ill-community comparisons. Since those in the subgroups for which the yield is determined are not themselves mentally ill, the influence of possible defensive reactions of mentally ill individuals is thereby minimized.

Two additional discrepancy scores which were computed are also summarized in Table 4.1. The first of these is the discrepancy between the step on the striving scale that one *expects* to reach (Appendix B, Question 182) and his stated achievement level (Appendix B, Question 180). The striving scale discrepancy previously discussed considered the "like" rather than the "expect" level. One's expected achievement is presumably more influenced by day-to-day experiences encountered in real life situations. For the total populations, as well as for comparisons using sex and age controls, the discrepancy between the expected and achieved striving scale level is greater for the ill than for the community population (see Table 4.1). Regardless of whether we consider "like" or "expect" responses, then, the patients evidence larger striving scale discrepancies than respondents in the community population.

The final discrepancy to be considered involves a score derived from the individual's responses to questions about his educational aspirations while still attending school (Appendix B, Question 20) and his actual subsequent educational achievement (Appendix B, Question 17). The use of this discrepancy is problematic insofar as the aspiration component is based on the respondent's recall of a relatively distant event. Remembering an aspiration held in the past not only involves difficulty in accurate recall, but also provides the respondent with an opportunity to give the interviewer a stereotypic response designed to obtain social approval. The score was computed and analyzed in spite of these problems. The average discrepancy scores for the total ill and total community populations are not significantly different (see Table 4.1). An examination of the actual distributions of the discrepancies, however, reveals an over-representation of the mentally ill population at the high and low ends of the scale, and an over-representation of the community population in the intermediate discrepancy range. When the data are analyzed with sex and age controls, different patterns emerge. Ill males have a larger average discrepancy than community males, but the reverse is true for females. Both the young and older respondents in the ill sample are characterized by higher average discrepancy scores than the corresponding age groups in the community population, but these differences are not significant.

In summary, regardless of age or sex, aspiration-achievement discrepancies in the areas of occupation and income striving are greater for community than for ill respondents. The discrepancies between aspiration and achievement, and between expectation and achievement, in the striving scale area are larger for the ill than for the community population, regardless of sex or age. With respect to the difference between one's educational aspiration when in school and his subsequent educational attainment, the mentally ill are more discrepant than the community individuals in both age subgroups and among the males; however, the converse holds for females.

Two of our attempts to explain the contradictory findings for the occupation, income, and striving scale discrepancies involve the possibility that the patients' responses are "coping" or "defensive" reactions to the particular situation. We have suggested a procedure for circumventing the influence of illness on questionnaire responses. This procedure involves comparing two community groups differing in yield or rates of mental disorder. As mentioned earlier, since high and low yield community groups are not mentally ill according to our criteria, the effects of illness are thus reduced or minimized. We predict that a community subgroup with a high yield of illness will manifest more of the characteristics believed to be correlated with mental disorder than will its low yield community counterpart.

In Chapter 3 it was noted that community-sample males had a higher yield of mental disorder than females. On this basis, we expect larger discrepancy scores for males than for females. This expectation is confirmed in the occupational and income areas, but the difference is significant only for the income discrepancy (see Table 4.2). The two

Table 4.2—Mean Aspiration Achievement Discrepancy Scores for High-

and Low—Yield Community Sub-Populations

	Males	Females	Young	Old
Occupation-Self	1.35	1.30	1.38	1.25[1]
Income-Self	3.37	3.12[1]	3.44	2.97[3]
Striving-Scale-Self	2.56	2.45	2.89	2.04[3]
Striving Scale-Exp/Ach[4]	1.64	1.54	1.93	1.18[3]
Education-Self[5]	4.34	4.06	3.50	4.96[3]

(Pairs of means are significant by the "t" test (one-tailed test), at the level indicated by the footnote notation.)

1. $P = < .05$
2. $P = < .01$
3. $P = < .001$ (Education-Self, Young vs Old, by two-tailed test)
4. This D-score represents the discrepancy between expected striving scale step and achieved striving scale step.
5. This D-score represents the discrepancy between aspired educational level when in school and achieved educational level.

discrepancies based on the striving scale (i.e., one involving the "like" and one the "expect" level) are also larger for males than for females, but in neither case is the difference significant. There is no significant difference between the community males and females with respect to the educational discrepancy. All five discrepancies discussed go in the predicted direction, and one is significant. These findings support our prediction, although not as strongly as data obtained for the age subgroups.

Since the young are over-represented among the patients, we predict that in the community population this age subgroup will show larger average discrepancies between aspirations and achievements than the older subgroup. Four of the five discrepancy scores are significantly larger for the young than for the older respondents (see Table 4.2). The discrepancy between one's educational aspiration when in school and his subsequent educational achievement is significant in the opposite direction: the older community respondents manifest a larger mean discrepancy than those classified as "young." This finding may be attributed partly to the fact that older members of the community have achieved lower educational levels than younger members. If we assume that completing high school or attaining some college education was as desirable a goal when the older subjects were in school as it is for those in school today, the larger discrepancy for these older individuals is not surprising, given their lower educational achievements.

Nine of the ten analyses carried out on the yield issue using sex and age breakdowns in the community population are in the expected directions (by sign test, $P = < .02$), and five of these nine are statistically significant. Apparently our suggested procedure for circumventing the effect of illness on responses strongly supports our prediction of larger discrepancies between aspirations and achievements, as well as between expectations and achievements, in high yield community subgroups.

THE SCALE PROBLEM

The data presented up to this point have dealt with differences between the total mentally ill and community populations and have not discussed material related to the achievement levels of these two populations. Since the ill and community populations differ significantly with respect to their achievement levels, the reader may wonder whether the population with the higher achievement level has, by necessity, smaller average discrepancy scores than the group below them in attainment. If, for instance, group A reaches level 4 on an arbitrary achievement scale, and group B reaches level 6, the former group has six points on the scale in which to evidence a discrepancy score, while group B has only four. The narrower potential range for aspiration setting in group B may prevent these individuals from manifesting larger discrepancy scores than group A. Such a situation is commonly referred to as "the scale problem."

A consideration of this issue implies that differences in discrepancies may not necessarily be a function of the particular phenomenon under investigation. Nonetheless there are several reasons why this scale problem cannot account for our findings. First of all, we have already indicated that the differences observed between the ill and community populations apply at almost all achievement or control group levels. Second, the community respondents report higher achievement on the income scale than the patients, and at the same time manifest significantly larger discrepancy scores. If the scale problem applied, we would expect larger discrepancies for the mentally ill because of their lower achievement levels. Third, aspirations do not cluster around the highest points on the achievement scales, as we would anticipate if scale limitations explained our findings. Occupational aspirations usually fall between positions 3 and 5 on a seven-step achievement scale; the absolute income aspiration levels are concentrated between steps 9 and 12 on a sixteen-step scale; striving scale aspiration levels cluster around position 9 on a ten-step scale. Most of the striving scale expectation responses fall around level 8.5, also on a ten-step scale. Responses dealing with educational aspirations when in school fall within the 11-to-13 step range on a seventeen-step scale. It is difficult to explain these findings in terms of scale limitations.

DISCREPANCY SCORES AND THE
MENTAL HEALTH CONTINUUM

Earlier in this chapter we offered various explanations of why the ill and community populations differ in one direction for the occupation and income discrepancies, and in the opposite direction for the striving scale discrepancy. One possibility suggested that in the areas of occupation and income the fact of being mentally ill influences patients to lower their aspirations, both as a defense against public ridicule and a means of minimizing their own failures. If illness does have this effect we can expect the occupation and income discrepancies to decrease as we move along our mental health continuum from the low symptom group in the community to the psychotics in the ill population. Since the two discrepancies involving the striving scale are significantly larger for the patients than for the community subjects, we predict that both of these discrepancies will increase as we move from the low symptom group to the psychotics.

The size of the occupation discrepancy increases from the low symptom to the high symptom group, and then, as expected, it decreases from the high symptom group to the psychotics. The pattern for the income discrepancy and the two striving scale discrepancies conforms to our expectations. Of the four discrepancies analyzed, three show a clear relationship to the mental health continuum. The analysis described was not carried out for the education aspiration-achievement discrepancy, in view of the limited consistency obtained when sex and age controls were applied.

DISCREPANCY SCORES AND VARIANCE

In Chapter 3 we observed an increase in variance for each of the five stress scores as we moved from the low symptom group to the psychotics. One explanation proposed at that time attributed the variance to the discrepancy score component. According to Lewin et al. (1944), Atkinson (1957), Atkinson and Litwin (1960), Atkinson et al. (1960), and Mahone (1960), individuals with low self-esteem may select very high goals which are impossible to attain; by this means they do not have to attribute failure to any lack of personal ability. These respondents may also select very low or easily obtained goals in order to guarantee success and in this way avoid threats to self-esteem.

We investigated differences in the variance of the discrepancy scores for the four mental health groupings in order to evaluate this explanation. Assuming that self-esteem decreases from the low symptom group to the psychotics, we predict that the number of individuals who set either very high or very low goals will increase along the mental health continuum. The variance of the high symptom group is significantly greater than that of the low symptom group for only one of the five discrepancies, however. When we compare the neurotics with the high symptom group, we find no significant differences in variance for any of the five discrepancy scores. The difference in variance between the psychotics and the neurotics is significant for only one of the five discrepancies. Only three of the eighteen tests of difference in variance are significant, but these three do indicate an increase in variance with increasing severity of illness along our mental health continuum.

There are several implications to these findings. First, the increasing variability of the stress scores along the mental health continuum cannot be explained in terms of the variance of discrepancy scores. Second, if self-esteem does increase in the order assumed (and data presented in Chapter 7 suggests that this is the case), then the assumptions of Lewin and Atkinson about the influence of self-esteem on the choice of very high or very low goals become highly tenuous. When we compare nonadjacent groupings on the illness continuum, however, we do find a number of significant differences in variance. For instance, all five discrepancy scores are associated with significantly higher variance among the psychotics than among the low symptom individuals. This indicates a possible relationship between self-esteem and the variability of discrepancy scores only when the groupings being compared differ markedly in severity of illness, but the variability is by no means closely tied to self-esteem. It is also apparent that the variability of stress scores must be a function of probability or valence, or must be a joint function of both variables.

INTERCORRELATIONS BETWEEN DISCREPANCY SCORES AND PSYCHOPATHOLOGY

The analysis of discrepancy scores and illness status presented up to this point has been based on group data. We have compared groups with respect to the significance of differences between means (or averages) and distributions of scores. We have not considered the relationship between the discrepancy scores and the illness status of a *given individual*. If we ignore illness status and rank our entire population from the smallest to the largest discrepancy score, and then order the same individuals from the healthiest to the sickest on the illness variable, will both rankings be congruent? In other words, to what extent are the discrepancy scores and illness status interdependent? In essence, we are asking the same question about the interdependence of discrepancy scores and psychopathology as we asked about the intercorrelation between the goal-striving stress scores and psychopathology. The analyses carried out to answer this question employed correlation techniques based on the linear and nonlinear assumptions (this was also done for the stress scores; both assumptions were explained in Chapter 3).

These analyses involved a total population of 1995 respondents (see Chapter 3). Correlations were computed for a two-step illness continuum (i.e., the diagnosed mentally ill vs. the community population), and for our four-step mental health continuum.

In the first series of analyses, four aspiration-achievement discrepancies were correlated with the two-step illness continuum. Discrepancies in the content areas of occupation for self and hypothetical son, income, and the striving scale were analyzed. The correlation coefficients representing the interdependency of each discrepancy score with the two-step illness continuum are presented in the first column of Table 4.3; these correlations are based on the linear assumption. There are significant

Table 4.3—Correlations between Discrepancy Scores and Illness Status

	Illness-Community Dichotomy (Linear Assumption		Four-Step Illness Continuum (Linear Assumption)		Four-Step Illness Continuum (Non Linear Assumption)	
	r	P	r	P	r	P
ccupation-Self	−.07	<.05	−.07	<.05	−.06	N.S.
acome-Self	−.12	<.01	−.12	<.01	−.02	N.S.
*riving Scale-Self	.34	<.01	.35	<.01	.36	<.01
ccupation-Hyp. Son	−.07	<.05	−.08	<.05	−.05	N.S.

negative correlations between three of these four discrepancy scores and illness status (the striving scale discrepancy score is the exception). In the areas of occupation for self, occupation for a hypothetical son, and income the likelihood of being mentally ill increases as the discrepancy scores decrease. This finding is consistent with earlier analyses of discrepancy scores using the group, rather than the individual, as the basic unit of analysis. As the striving scale discrepancy scores increase, the likelihood of being diagnosed as mentally ill also increases (see Table 4.3). Again, this is consistent with the analyses based on group data.

The second column of Table 4.3 presents the correlation coefficients (based on the linear assumption) indicating the interdependence of the four discrepancy scores with the four-step mental health continuum. The magnitude and the signs of these correlations are almost identical to those presented in the first column of the table. Apparently, subdividing the two-step illness continuum into four steps makes no difference in the magnitude of the correlations obtained.

The third column of Table 4.3 lists the correlations coefficients relating the discrepancy scores to the four-step illness continuum, but making the nonlinear assumption. In the areas of occupation for self, occupation for a hypothetical son, and income the correlations are negative and insignificant. The correlation between the striving scale and the four-step continuum is the same as in columns 1 and 2 of Table 4.3, and it is significant. These findings suggest that the distribution of the discrepancy scores against the illness continuum fits a linear regression more accurately than a nonlinear regression.

It was noted in Chapter 3 that the correlation of stress scores with scores on the psychosomatic symptom inventory yielded almost no significant results. Correlations computed between discrepancy scores and psychosomatic symptom scores also yield nonsignificant coefficients, except in the striving scale area. Although the correlations between psychosomatic symptom scores and the two- and four-step continua are .48 and .51, respectively, there are relatively few significant correlations between the symptom scores and either stress scores or discrepancy scores. These results provide further support for our decision to omit consideration of the symptom inventory from analyses of the stress scores and their components.

We conclude that the aspiration-achievement discrepancies in various content areas are significantly related to mental illness. We cannot say, however, that the direction of the relationship between the two variables is always the same. We note in addition that none of the discrepancy scores is related in a nonlinear fashion to the two- or four-step illness continuum.

In analyzing the components of the stress scores, we must also determine the correlation between the size of a particular discrepancy and the stress score in which it is used. The magnitude of such a correlation indicates the degree to which the D-score determines that particular stress score. A correlation of 1.00 between these two variables means that the stress score is totally a function of the discrepancy component; a zero correlation indicates that the discrepancy score contributes nothing to its stress score. Correlations between discrepancy and stress scores were obtained in the content areas of occupation for self and hypothetical son, income, and the striving scale. The correlation coefficients for occupation for self (.16), for hypothetical son (.29), and for income (.25) are all significant at less than the .01 level of confidence. The correlation for the striving scale is not significant. This indicates that the striving scale discrepancy score does not contribute significantly to the variability of the striving scale stress score, although this discrepancy score does discriminate significantly between the various ill groups, both on the two- and four-step continua.

The intercorrelations between the discrepancy scores and stress scores were computed within each of the four mental health groupings in order to determine the degree to which the correlations applied regardless of illness status. In the low symptom group, all four correlations are positive and significant. In the high symptom group two of the correlations are significant. In the neurotic and the psychotic groupings, six of the eight correlations are significant. These correlations necessitate a revision of our previous general statement about the relationship between the striving scale discrepancy score and the corresponding stress score. Although the correlation between these two variables is significant in the low symptom group, it does not reach significance in the other three mental health groupings. We must conclude that an interdependence between this discrepancy score and its stress score exists only in the low symptom, or "healthy," grouping. This conclusion suggests that the probability and/or valence element in the striving scale stress score must account for the variability of this score in those mental health groupings manifesting at least some degree of emotional disturbance.

In conclusion, fifteen of the sixteen correlations between discrepancy scores and stress scores are positive, and twelve of the fifteen are significant. The one negative correlation is not significant. The variation in magnitude of the correlations from one mental health grouping to another supports the possibility that the relationship between a given discrepancy score and its corresponding stress score changes with the illness status of a particular individual. It should be remembered that when these correlations are significant, the factors in the stress score determining the tension level (i.e., probability and valence) increase in their relative importance for a given individual.

INTERDEPENDENCE OF DISCREPANCY SCORES

The final issue to be considered involves the degree to which the discrepancy scores intercorrelate or are interdependent with one another—to what extent is a given individual characterized by a high or low discrepancy score in all content areas analyzed? Assuming linearity, three of the six possible correlations are significant. Only one of the six correlations is significant when the nonlinear assumption is made, but this correlation is significantly smaller than the same correlation computed on the basis of a linear assumption. Although a given respondent tends to have discrepancy scores of similar magnitude, there is evidence that he reacts to the particular content area in which the discrepancy is being measured.

The discrepancy scores were also intercorrelated within each of the four mental health groupings. Only seven of the twenty-four correlations reach significance. This provides further support for the observation that the size of the discrepancy score is not independent of content area. The differences in these correlations indicate that the linear assumption fits the data more accurately than the nonlinear assumption.

Perceived Probability of Success

THE DATA PRESENTED up to this point on stress scores and discrepancy scores in various content areas have been discussed with reference to three specific issues: (1) differences between the total ill and community populations; (2) a consideration of subgroups within the community population differing in rates or yield of mental illness; and (3) the changes in a given variable as a function of the four-step mental health continuum. We shall continue to consider these issues in our discussion of probability-of-success estimates attached to the discrepancy scores in the areas of occupation, income, and the striving scale (i.e., the self-related striving areas). As was the case for the discrepancy score presentation, no control group analyses will be discussed for these probability estimates. We should reiterate, however, that such analyses were carried out and that they yielded the same consistency of results observed both for goal-striving stress scores and discrepancy scores.

Table 4.4—Mean Values of Perceived Probability and Valence Estimates

for Ill and Community Populations

	TOTAL		MALES		FEMALES		YOUNG		OLD	
	Ill	Comm.	Ill	Comm.	Ill	Comm.	Ill	Comm.	Ill	Comm.
Probability										
Occupation	6.60	6.36[1]	6.59	6.53	6.60	6.24[1]	6.59	6.52[2]	6.61	6.18[1]
Income	6.79	6.24[3]	7.02	6.65[1]	6.62	6.02[3]	6.84	6.56[2]	6.65	5.85[2]
Striving Scale	4.63	4.71[3]	4.67	4.48[3]	4.60	4.89[1]	4.69	4.97[3]	4.49	4.42[3]
Valence										
Occupation	2.58	2.53[2]	2.63	2.52[3]	2.54	2.53[2]	2.57	2.41[3]	2.60	2.69
Income	2.64	2.46[3]	2.60	2.33[3]	2.67	2.55[1]	2.60	2.32[3]	2.75	2.63
Striving Scale	2.05	1.90[3]	2.19	1.86[3]	1.96	1.92	1.97	1.80[3]	2.25	2.01[2]

(Distributions underlying pairs of means are significant, at the level indicated by the footnote notation. Any significant differences between nonadjacent groupings are reported in the text. The "t" test was not used because the distributions of these components did not satisfy the assumptions necessary for this procedure.)

1. By chi-square test $P = <.05$
2. By chi-square test $P = <.01$
3. By chi-square test $P = <.001$

Table 4.4 presents the data on perceived probability of success for each of the three content areas related to the self; no estimates for a hypothetical son are given. In the areas of occupation and income the ill give higher probability estimates than the community subjects, for the comparison of the total samples and when sex and age controls are applied. Nine of the ten comparisons carried out in these two content areas are significant. If the probability estimate is considered as a separate factor unrelated to the other components of the stress score, these findings suggest that the mentally ill have higher expectations of success than the community individuals. Discrepancy score analyses in these two content areas indicate higher aspiration-achievement discrepancies among the community subjects than among the mentally ill. The mentally ill thus have low aspirations relative to their achievements and high estimates of success attached to these low goals; those in the community population have high aspirations relative to their achievement levels and relatively low estimates of success. Both patterns appear to be logical: a greater likelihood of success is, in fact, attached to low, rather than to high, aspirations.

The probability estimates for the striving scale are not as clear and consistent as those reported for occupation and income. The total community population has significantly higher probability-of-success estimates than the total ill population in this area (see Table 4.4), a finding inconsistent with the probability estimates obtained in the areas of occupation and income. Analyses carried out for the striving scale within each of the sex and age subgroups (although statistically significant) do not generally show the same direction of difference as occupation and income. Probability estimates are higher for ill than community males, and for the older patients than for the older community subjects. The probability estimates for the community female subpopulation are significantly higher than the corresponding estimates given by the ill females. Similarly, the young community subjects give higher probability estimates than the young ill respondents. Therefore, in the area of the striving scale we cannot infer differences between the two populations that will apply regardless of sex or age. Since the aspiration-achievement discrepancy in the striving scale area is consistently larger for the mentally ill than for the community population, the variability of probability-of-success estimates observed here suggests that this component acts independent of the discrepancy score. This independence is apparently more characteristic of the striving scale area than the areas of occupation and income.

It has already been noted that males in the community population showed larger discrepancy scores than females in all three goal-striving areas related to the self, although there were not as many significant differences between the sex subgroups as between the two age subgroups. Since males did have higher rates of mental illness than females, however, the direction of the difference for the discrepancy score averages was as predicted. On the basis of the logical relationship between high and low discrepancy scores and the associated probability estimates—an inverse relationship between these two components—we expect community population males, characterized by large discrepancy scores, to manifest lower probability estimates than females. These expectations are not supported in the occupational or income areas (these contradictory findings are significant for the income probability estimates). Only in the area of the striving scale does the expected inverse relationship between discrepancy score and probability estimate occur: probability estimates in this content area are lower for males than for females.

In two of the three goal-striving areas analyzed, males (with the higher rate of mental illness) show larger discrepancies and probability estimates than females. Although sex differences in the community population are less consistent than those observed for the two age subgroups, more males than females do seem to be characterized by high goals accompanied by high expectations of success. Such a combination may set the scene for mental illness.

It has also been noted that in the three self-related content areas, the younger community group (with a high yield of mental illness) manifested higher aspiration-achievement discrepancies than the older group (with a relatively lower yield of mental disorder). This observation was consistent with our expectations and predictions. Bearing in mind that high goals seem logically related to low probability-of-success estimates, we expect lower probability estimates for the young than for the older subjects in the community. The data reveal *higher* probability estimates for the young than for the older respondents in all three content areas, however. These findings are significant for occupation and income. Young respondents in the community population manifest high discrepancy and high probability scores in all three striving areas. The size of these two components may explain the larger stress scores obtained for this age group. This suggests that the combination of high discrepancy scores and high probability estimates are antecedent conditions to mental illness.

How does the probability-of-success estimate vary along the mental health continuum? Table 4.5 presents the average probability estimates for the four mental health groupings. As one moves from the psychotics (Table 4.5, column 1) to the higher symptom group (Table 4.5, column 3), a decrease in occupational probability-of-success estimates occurs.

Table 4.5—Mean Values of Perceived Probability and

Valence Estimates, by Illness Status

| | ILL | | COMMUNITY | |
	Psychotics	Neurotics	High Symp.	Low Symp.
Probability				
Occupation-Self	6.67	6.38	5.99	6.41
Income-Self	6.82	6.71	6.26	6.24
Striving Scale-Self	4.60	4.71	4.98	4.68[1]
Valence				
Occupation-Self	2.65	2.36[3]	2.59	2.53
Income-Self	2.71	2.45[3]	2.52	2.45
Striving Scale-Self	2.09	1.94[1]	2.00	1.89

(Distributions underlying pairs of means are significant, by chi-square, at the level indicated by the footnote notation. Any significant differences between nonadjacent groupings are reported in text. The "t" test was not used because the distributions of these components did not satisfy the assumptions necessary for this procedure.)

1. $P = <.05$
2. $P = <.01$
3. $P = <.001$

However, the probability estimates increase in the low symptom group (Table 4.5, column 4). The nature of this curve suggests a nonlinear relationship between the four-step illness continuum and the probability estimates. These data also indicate that in the occupational area the neurotics and the high symptom subjects, who manifest symptoms of emotional disturbance, have higher anticipations of failure (i.e., lower probability-of-success estimates) than the psychotics. The psychotics have lower expectations of failure than the low symptom group. In the discussion of goal-striving stress scores we demonstrated the existence of a nonlinear relationship between the illness continuum and scores in the occupational area. Earlier in this chapter, we observed a linear relationship between aspiration-achievement discrepancy scores and the mental health continuum. Since probability estimates suggest a nonlinear relationship in the occupational area, the nonlinear relationship observed for the corresponding stress scores may perhaps be explained in terms of the probability-of-success component.

In the area of the striving scale, the probability of success again increases from the psychotics to the high symptom group, but then decreases in the low symptom group (see Table 4.5). This pattern indicates, as for occupation, that the nonlinear relationship between the striving scale stress scores and the mental health continuum may be explained in terms of the probability component. When each of the mental health groupings is compared to each of the others, the psychotics give lower, and the neurotics higher, probability-of-success estimates than the low symptom group. As noted for occupation, the neurotics and the high symptom group do not differ in their probability estimates in the area of the striving scale. These findings provide additional support for our earlier suggestion that these two mental health groupings cannot really be clearly distinguished from each other.

The probability estimates for income decrease consistently as one moves along the continuum from the psychotics to the low symptom group. This decrease is consistent with the previously mentioned inverse relationship between size of discrepancy and probability estimate. It has already been noted that the income discrepancy scores increased along the mental health continuum from the psychotics to the low symptom group. Earlier data revealed a linear relationship between the continuum and both the discrepancy and the stress scores. Findings presented here also suggest a linear relationship between probability estimates and the mental health continuum.

The relationships between the probability estimates and the illness continuum in the three self-related content areas are identical to those noted between the corresponding stress scores and the illness continuum.

INTERCORRELATIONS OF PROBABILITY-OF-SUCCESS ESTIMATES

In this section correlations based on individual, rather than on group, data will be considered. The probability estimates will be correlated with the two- and four-step illness continua, and correlations of the probability estimates with stress and discrepancy scores will also be presented.

Correlations between the probability estimates and the two-step illness continuum are significant in two of the three content areas. The correlation for the striving scale is negative ($-.12$, $P = < .01$); the correlation for income is .07 ($P = < .05$); the correlation for occupation is not significant. As one becomes ill, then, his probability estimates decrease in the area of the striving scale, but increase for income. Significant correlations, of like sign and magnitude, are obtained in the same two content areas when we consider the four-step illness continuum. Changing the dependent variable from a two- to a four-step continuum apparently does not affect the correlations. It is interesing that those content areas which yield significant correlations are not the same areas in which significant stress score differences were reported between the different illness groupings. These data indicate that the probability estimates are not necessarily the major determinant of the stress scores and cannot account entirely for the differences obtained in these scores.

At this point we ask whether the probability estimates given in different content areas intercorrelate significantly with one another. In other words, is there a generalized tendency to give the same type of probability responses in all areas, regardless of content? The correlation between occupation and striving scale is .25 ($P = < .01$); the correlation between occupation and income is .24 ($P = < .01$); and the correlation between income and striving scale is .22 ($P = < .01$). If we consider all individuals in the combined samples, the intercorrelations of probability estimates on the three questions are significant and of the same magnitude. As a further test of this issue, we computed the correlations between these three probability estimates within each of the four mental health groupings on the continuum, in effect providing us with twelve additional correlations. All intercorrelations are significant ($P = < .01$), regardless of the respondent's illness status. We conclude that a generalized tendency to give the same probability estimates, regardless of content area, permeates our entire population.

Earlier we discussed the possibility of an inverse relationship between the discrepancy score and the probability-of-success estimate. We noted that sex and age subgroups in the community population with high yields of mental disorder were characterized by high discrepancy scores *and* high probability estimates. The present analysis enables us to determine whether this pattern is reflected in a given individual, or is merely a function of group distribution. The correlation between discrepancy and probability scores for occupation is —.34; for the striving scale —.39; and for income —.09. All three correlations are significant ($P = < .01$). The negative coefficients indicate an inverse relationship between the two sets of scores at the individual level of analysis: when a respondent has a high discrepancy score he is also likely to give a low probability estimate, and conversely. To test the extent to which this relationship permeated our population we computed these same three correlations in each of our four mental health groupings. Eleven of the twelve correlations are negative and nine of the twelve are significant. The data present a relatively strong argument that, regardless of illness status, an inverse relationship exists between discrepancy scores and probability estimates.

This finding poses an interesting problem. When the two populations are compared, the mentally ill show low discrepancy scores and high probability estimates in occupation and income, while the community respondents show high discrepancy scores and low probability estimates in these areas. We might expect the interaction effect of the two variables to balance each other out, resulting in similar scores for the ill and community populations. In fact, however, the stress scores are higher for the ill than for the community sample. How can we reconcile these apparently contradictory facts? We suggest that the patient may lower his goals in order to avoid failure and consequent threats to his self-esteem. In lowering his goals, his perceived probability of success increases, but in his eagerness to prove himself he overstates the likelihood of success. A patient with high goals may lower his probability estimates, but perhaps does not lower them until they are appropriate to the reality of the discrepancy situation. Again, the individual maintains his high expectations of success in order to prove his worth.

We have already discussed the interrelationship of probability estimates with mental illness, with discrepancy scores, and with one another. Now we shall investigate the relationship of these probability estimates to the goal-striving stress scores. The correlation coefficients between probability-of-success estimates and the corresponding stress scores in the three self-related content areas (occupation, income, and striving scale) are .37, .24, and .47, respectively. All three coefficients are significant ($P = < .01$) and positive, indicating that the probability-of-success component contributes significantly to the total stress score.

We also computed the correlations between these probability estimates and stress scores within each of the four mental health groupings. All of the twelve correlations are positive and significant ($P = < .01$). Significant correlations are obtained between the stress scores and the probability estimates, regardless of a person's illness status. As one moves from the low symptom group to the psychotics, these correlations tend to increase in magnitude. Apparently the contribution of the probability-of-success estimates to the stress scores increases the size of the coefficients, at least in the occupational and striving scale areas. This increasing interdependence may reflect the ill person's increasing eagerness or need to prove himself by overstating his likelihood of success.

The correlations between stress scores and discrepancy scores are lower than those involving stress scores and probability estimates. This suggests that the probability estimate constitutes a more important determinant of the total stress score than does the discrepancy size. This is true for occupation and the striving scale, but not for income.

We make the following points in summary: First, there are significant correlations between probability estimates in the income and striving scale areas, for the two- and four-step illness continua. Second, the probability estimates intercorrelate with one another, showing a generalized approach to all content areas, which permeates all the groupings along our mental health continuum. Third, there is an inverse relationship between probability of success and the discrepancy score, which also permeates all the mental health groupings. Finally, there are significant positive correlations between each of the probability-of-success estimates and the corresponding stress scores. This indicates that the probability-of-success estimate is an important determinant of the total stress score.

Measures of Valence of Success

LIKE THE EVALUATION of probability-of-success estimates, the analysis of valence estimates was limited to the three goal-striving areas related to the self (occupation, income, and the striving scale). Also, as was the case for discrepancy scores and probability estimates, the valence discussion will involve three major issues: (1) differences between the mentally ill and community populations; (2) differences between subgroups within the community population differing in yield of mental illness; and (3) changes in valence as a function of position on the mental health continuum.

In previous analyses comparing the mentally ill and community populations, it was noted (1) that the stress scores for the mentally ill were greater than those for the community population; (2) that the magnitude of the aspiration-achievement discrepancy was smaller for the mentally ill in the areas of occupation and income, but larger in the striving scale area; and (3) that the ill set higher probability estimates than the community respondents in the areas of occupation and income but were characterized by lower estimates for the striving scale.

In all three self-related content areas the total ill population is characterized by higher valence estimates than the community population (see Table 4.4). This pattern also holds when analyses are carried out with sex and age controls. All fifteen possible comparisons show the same direction of difference (by sign test $P = < .01$), and eleven of the fifteen comparisons are significant. The direction of difference for valence, then, is the same as was noted for probability estimates, but opposite in direction to results obtained for two of the three discrepancy scores. In discussing the interrelationships between discrepancy scores and probability estimates in the occupational and income areas, we have suggested that the patients, to a greater degree than community respondents, lower their aspirations to avoid public failure and loss of self-esteem. At the same time, their intense desire to succeed at these adjusted levels influences them to raise their expectations of success to disproportionately high levels. In the striving scale situation, the mentally ill impose on themselves larger discrepancies and lower probability estimates than those characteristic of community subjects. Their intense desire to avoid a private sense of failure or compromise prevents them from lowering these probability estimates sufficiently. The rationale proposed to explain the findings for occupation and income on one hand, and the striving scale on the other, assumes a very strong desire to succeed in each case. The three valence measures may be taken as indices of this desire. The data clearly support these assumptions.

Our analysis of valence differences among subgroups in the community is again based on the view that a subgroup with a high yield of mental disorder will manifest more of the characteristics predicted for the mentally ill than will a subgroup with a low rate of disorder. In this way we minimize the problem of the effect of illness on responses. In addition, by comparing the differences among these community subgroups with the differences obtained between the total mentally ill and community populations, we are provided with some insight into how the presence of illness affects our data.

It has already been noted that community subgroups with a high yield of mental disorder (i.e., the males, and the young subjects) have larger stress scores, larger discrepancy scores, and higher estimates of the probability of success than low yield subgroups. Contrary to prediction, the females manifest higher valence scores than the males in all three self-related content areas, but only one of the three comparisons reaches significance (income area). Again contrary to prediction, the older respondents have significantly larger valence scores than the young in all three striving areas. All six comparisons show lower, not higher, valence scores for the high yield subgroups: the direction of the differences between the subgroups is opposite to that observed for total ill-community sample comparisons.

If differences between high and low yield subgroups in the community *do,* as we assume, reflect differences in antecedent conditions to mental disorder, several effects of illness are revealed by the data, especially with respect to occupation and income. The higher stress scores in the high yield community subgroups are a function of the large aspiration-achievement discrepancies (our stressor factor) and high expectations of success. Individuals in this group tend to show lower valence-of-success scores, compared to low yield community respondents. When an individual becomes mentally ill, he tends to lower his aspirations and to raise his expectations of success to even higher levels. His desire for goal attainment also increases, although it is now attached to a lower goal. The increase in goal-striving stress scores among the ill, therefore, seems to be a function of the increasing probability estimates and, to a greater degree, of the more marked increase in the valence of success.

The effect of illness is somewhat different in the area of the striving scale. The high rate community group again shows high striving scale stress scores, large discrepancies, high probability estimates, and low valence scores. Illness influences valence in this striving area as it does in the areas of occupation and income (i.e., a sharp increase in valence), but it causes an increase in the striving scale discrepancy and a decrease in the occupation and income discrepancies.

Findings on changes in valence as a function of position on the mental health continuum require some modification of our previous statements about the effects of illness. Valence increases from the low symptom to the high symptom group and decreases among the neurotics in all three content areas (see Table 4.5), but there are no significant differences between any of these groupings. The psychotics have significantly higher valence scores than the neurotics and the low symptom groups in all three areas, and significantly higher valence scores than the high symptom group on two of the three measures. Therefore, the relationship between high valence scores and illness discussed earlier must be limited to the effect of psychosis on valence.

We have mentioned that both the stress scores and probability estimates show nonlinear relationships with the mental health continuum, whereas the discrepancy scores show a linear relationship. It has been suggested that the nonlinear character of the stress scores is a function of probability *and* valence. The fact that the valence scores do not change from the low symptom, to the high symptom group, to the neurotics, but then increase significantly among the psychotics suggests that valence scores fit a nonlinear, rather than a linear regression line. In addition, we have noted that the neurotics and the high symptom individuals do not differ on stress scores, probability, or valence estimates, but that they do differ in the size of the occupation and striving scale discrepancies. The question of whether there are any real qualitative differences between the neurotics and the high symptom group remains unresolved. In terms of our variables, differences between these groupings may, in fact, be indistinguishable.

INTERCORRELATIONS INVOLVING VALENCE

In accordance with the analyses carried out with probability-of-success estimates, we correlated the valence scores with the two- and four-step mental health continua, the stress scores, the discrepancy and probability components of the total stress scores, and with one another. Again, these analyses were limited to the individual's own striving in the areas of occupation, income, and the generalized striving scale.

The correlations between the three valence scores and the two- and four-step continua range from .01 to .10. With the two-step continuum, significant correlations are obtained for income ($P = < .01$) and the striving scale ($P = < .01$). Significant coefficients in these two striving areas are also obtained with the four-step continuum ($P = < .01$ and $< .05$, respectively). Clearly, it makes little difference whether we use the two- or four-step continuum.

In order to determine their relative contribution to the total scores, the valence estimates were correlated with the three corresponding stress scores. The correlation between valence and goal-striving stress is .26 for occupation, .29 for income, and .45 for the striving scale (all significant at $P = < .01$). Although valence contributes significantly to the total stress score in all three content areas, its relative contribution varies with the particular goal-striving area. For example, in the area of occupation, the probability score correlates most highly with the overall stress score (.37), valence shows the next highest correlation (.26), and the discrepancy score yields the lowest correlation (.16). The correlations between the income stress score and its three components show a different pattern: the correlations between each component and the stress score are .25, .24, and .29, respectively. None of these coefficients differs significantly from the others. In the income area each component apparently contributes equally to the total stress score. The correlations computed within each of the four mental health groupings indicate the generalized influence of valence on the respective stress scores. Eleven of the twelve correlations are significant (all at $P = < .01$).

The correlations of the three sets of valence estimates with the comparable discrepancy scores vary from .08 to .24; all are significant. The magnitude of these coefficients indicates a relationship between aspiration-achievement discrepancy and valence of success. Level-of-aspiration formulations (especially the Resultant Weighted Valence Theory) assume that a high aspiration level implies a correspondingly high valence of success. The more inaccessible the goal, the more ego-central it becomes. These correlations, although not very high, provide some support for these assumptions.

The correlations between each of the three valence scores and its associated probability estimate vary from $-.32$ to $-.44$ (all are significant at $P = < .01$). The original Resultant Weighted Valence formulation states a rough inverse relationship between the probability and valence variables; as the probability of success increases, the valence tends to decrease; conversely, as the probability of success decreases, the valence tends to increase. There is no implication of a one-to-one relationship. In his revision of this formulation, Atkinson assumed (and presented some data from laboratory experiments in support of his assumption) an almost perfect inverse relationship between these two variables. On the basis of these experiments, Atkinson felt that his "incentive" factor could be derived from probability estimates. The absolute values of our correlation coefficients, however, are considerably below the almost perfect correlations he obtained in the laboratory. This leads us to question the generality of his experimental findings, and to propose instead that his high correlations may have been a function of that particular experimental situation.

The three valence measures were also intercorrelated with one another to determine whether there was any generalized tendency to give similar valence scores independent of specific content striving areas. When the illness status of the individual is disregarded, the coefficients vary from .24 to .28 (all significant at $P = < .01$). Similar correlations were computed for each of the four mental health groupings. All of the twelve correlations are positive in sign, and ten are significant (all at $P = < .01$). The weight of these data supports the assumption of a generalized tendency to give the same valence score in all goal-striving areas.

Characteristics of Subgroups in the Mentally Ill Population

Analyses of all three components of the goal-striving stress scores were carried out within sex and age subgroups in the ill sample.

Three of the five discrepancy scores reveal no significant differences between ill males and females. The two other discrepancy scores are significant but each indicates an opposite trend. The probability estimates show no significant differences between the sex subgroups. Finally, for valence, two of the three male-female comparisons are insignificant, and there is no consistency of direction of difference among the three.

Four of the five discrepancy analyses for the age subgroups yield higher average scores for young than for older patients. Three of these four are significant. The one discrepancy that goes in the opposite direction on the age comparison (i.e., the education discrepancy for the self) is also significant. The differences observed in the ill sample between the age subgroups, then, reflect the same differences obtained within the community population. The probability estimates show no consistent direction of difference in the three content areas, when age comparisons are made. One of the three comparisons is significant. With respect to valence, all three comparisons yield higher scores for the older respondents, and one of the three comparisons is significant.

Since we do not offer specific predictions about subgroups within the ill population, and since the findings are not characterized by a high degree of consistency, we shall not discuss these data further in this context.

Summary of Findings for the Three
Goal-Striving Stress Score Components

THE MAJOR FINDINGS for each goal-striving stress score component, in each of the three content areas related to self-striving, are enumerated below.

ILL-COMMUNITY SAMPLE COMPARISONS

The mentally ill show significantly larger aspiration-achievement discrepancies than the community respondents in the striving scale content area. The opposite pattern emerges (i.e., the community individuals manifest larger discrepancies than the patients) in the occupational and income striving areas. These trends are consistent, even when sex and age are held constant.

The ill individuals give significantly higher probability-of-success estimates than the community individuals in the occupational and income areas. This pattern is maintained when sex and age are controlled. In the striving scale area, probability estimates given by the ill are again higher than those given by the community respondents, but this direction of difference does not hold up consistently when sex and age controls are applied.

When the valence component is analyzed, the patients manifest higher estimates in all three content areas, both for the total sample comparison and for comparisons involving sex and age controls.

HIGH YIELD (MALES AND OLDER SUBJECTS) VS LOW YIELD (FEMALES AND YOUNG RESPONDENTS) COMMUNITY SUBGROUPS

The community sample males show larger discrepancies than females in all three self-striving content areas. This difference is significant for the occupation and income discrepancy. The young community respondents are characterized by significantly larger discrepancies than the older respondents in all three content areas.

Within the community sample, males give larger probability-of-success estimates than females for occupational and income aspirations (significant for income). The opposite trend is observed in the striving scale area: females give higher probability estimates than males, although this difference is not significant.

The high yield age subgroup conforms to expectations; the young subjects give higher probability estimates than the older subjects in all three content areas (this difference is significant for the occupational and income estimates).

The pattern of valence scores within the community population is opposite to prediction. The females are characterized by higher valence-of-success scores than the males in all three content areas (this difference is significant for income), and the older respondents have higher scores than the young (significant for all content areas).

RELATIONSHIP OF COMPONENTS TO THE FOUR-STEP MENTAL HEALTH CONTINUUM

None of the components shows either a consistent increase or decrease with changes in illness status. The relationship between the direction of change in any one component and the illness continuum sometimes varies directly, inversely, or even in a nonlinear fashion. Since the relationship between each component and illness status seems to depend on the content area in which it is being investigated, no generalizations are possible.

CORRELATION OF COMPONENTS WITH THE TWO- AND FOUR-STEP ILLNESS CONTINUA

Regardless of content area, and whether we consider discrepancy, probability, or valence measures, there is no difference between using the two- (ill-community dichotomy) or the four-step (our mental health groupings) illness continuum.

CONTRIBUTION OF COMPONENTS TO OVERALL GOAL-STRIVING STRESS SCORE

The occupation and income discrepancies apparently do contribute significantly to the final stress scores, but the relationship between a particular D-score and its corresponding stress score changes with the respondent's illness status. The striving scale discrepancy does not seem to contribute significantly to the striving scale stress score. There is some indication that the respondent reacts to the particular content area of the D-score.

The probability-of-success estimate is a significant factor in the final stress score, and the contribution of this component does not vary with the content area in which stress is measured.

The valence score does affect the total stress score significantly, but its relative contribution varies with the specific content area in which the goal striving is measured.

FINDINGS RELATIVE TO GENERAL THEORETICAL CONCEPTIONS

In the occupational and income areas, both the probability and valence estimates increase as the aspiration levels relative to respondents' achievements decrease. Both sets of findings support the assumptions underlying the Resultant Weighted Valence formulation.

Supplementary Confirming Data

WE HAVE PRESENTED considerable data supporting our stated predictions about the relationship between the goal-striving stress scores and mental disorder, and our less formal expectations about the stress score components and illness. From this material we conclude that the patients are more oriented toward goal striving and are under greater stress than the community respondents. In view of the intercorrelations among the stress scores and among the components of these scores, we seem to be dealing with a generalized orientation toward goal striving which may be independent of content area and which may permeate the questionnaire items analyzed. We still must consider whether the patients, to a greater degree than the community subjects, give stereotyped responses which they think are expected of them.

American society emphasizes ambition and striving as desirable values. Mentally ill individuals, who are particularly vulnerable to stigma and criticism and who are conscious of being hospitalized or treated for an emotional disorder, may be strongly motivated to impress an interviewer favorably. There are certain factors that preclude attribution of our findings to stereotypy of responses.

(1) The stress scores were derived from questionnaire items in different content areas. Since the questions in these various areas were separated by intervening items, it is unlikely that respondents could keep track of their answers. In addition, they had no way of knowing how their responses were going to be used.

(2) Analyses of high and low yield subgroups within the community population were designed to circumvent any possible effects of illness on questionnaire responses.

(3) In analyzing the discrepancy scores, we found that the patients expressed low aspirations in the areas of occupation and income. If they had been concerned about impressing the interviewer, they would have verbalized more socially accepted stereotyped aspirations. Apparently these individuals were oriented more toward reality than toward "making a good impression."

Additional questionnaire data are also relevant to this issue. A number of interview items were designed to provide further support for the reliability analyses carried out on stress scores, discrepancy scores, and probability estimates. One such question asked whether the individual had ever returned to school after withdrawing during his teens or early adult years (Appendix B, Question 18). The ill and community samples were compared, for totals and with sex and age controls. In all comparisons a significantly larger proportion of ill than community respondents report a return to school sometime after their first withdrawal $(P = < .005)$.

A similar questionnaire item asked whether the respondent planned to continue his education in the future (Appendix B, Question 24). Again, the total patient and community populations were compared, with and without sex and age controls. In all five comparisons, significantly more patients than community individuals express intentions to continue their education $(P = < .005)$. We have no information on whether these individuals did, in fact, return to school, nor can we determine whether they will do so at any time in the future. The latter would necessitate a longitudinal study, beyond the scope of the present project.

The findings on both of these questions show that the mentally ill are strongly oriented toward educational mobility, specifically, and toward goal striving in a more general way. It should be noted that these data do not establish educational orientation as an antecedent condition, but only as a correlate, of illness. There is still the possibility of some response stereotypy among the ill; disturbed individuals may have felt more obligated than community subjects to give "approved" responses.

In order to circumvent the effect of illness in this area, we must again consider the yield issue and compare community sample subgroups differing in rates of mental disorder. The responses to Question 18 ("Have you returned to school?") were based partly on fact and were not necessarily an indication of respondents' striving. In some instances, answers to this item might have been fictional, reflecting a need to impress the interviewer or an actual wish on the part of the respondent in the past.

For these reasons, this questionnaire item will not be analyzed further here.

When we analyze Question 24, we see that, as predicted, significantly more males than females plan to continue their education in the future $(P = < .03)$. Similarly, significantly more young than older respondents intend to return to school $(P = < .005)$. Logically, we expect a greater proportion of young individuals to be in a position to continue their education; although this does not preclude the possibility that the greater desire for additional education has psychological effects on these individuals. Findings obtained for the high yield community subgroups indicate that responses in the area of educational goal striving may reflect an antecedent condition to illness, rather than stereotyped responses among the patients.

Finally, we investigated the relationship between answers to this educational question and the four mental health groupings comprising our illness continuum. As one moves along the continuum from the psychotics to the high symptom group, the proportion of those planning to continue their education decreases. The neurotics differ significantly from the high symptom group $(P = < .005)$. However, the number of those intending to resume school increases in the low symptom group. This apparent nonlinear relationship between the distribution of responses and the four-step mental health continuum parallels the non-linear pattern of educational stress scores for a hypothetical son observed in these same mental health groupings.

FATE OF ONE'S AMBITIONS

We noted a decrease in the size of the occupation and income discrepancy scores as one moves from the low symptom group in the community to the psychotics in the ill population. We concluded that illness results in a lowered level of aspiration, relative to one's achievement. Our questionnaire instrument included a number of items concerning one's perception of changes in his ambitions. We assumed a direct relationship between the height of one's ambitions and the height of his level of aspiration.

The first of these questions asked the respondent how his ambitions had changed in the course of time (Appendix B, Question 196). Again, the total ill and community samples were compared, and similar comparisons were made controlling for sex and age. In all five analyses significantly more ill than community subjects report lowering their ambitions ($P = < .005$). The community subjects do not raise their ambitions, but merely maintain them over time. These analyses imply that the patients have actually lowered their ambitions as a function of their experiences. This implication supports one of the interpretations suggested earlier in this chapter to explain the lower occupation and income discrepancy scores among the patients.

When we analyze this question with respect to the yield issue, we predict that those in the high yield community subgroups will manifest more of the characteristics of the patients than will members of the low yield subgroups. Thus, we expect high yield individuals to have lowered their ambitions to a greater degree than low yield individuals. A significantly larger number of males than females do show this tendency ($P = < .03$), and significantly more young than older subjects also report lower ambitions ($P = < .005$). Our assumed correlation between ambitions and level of aspiration must also be taken into account, however. We have noted that the high yield subgroups evidence larger aspiration-achievement discrepancies than their low yield counterparts. If our assumption about ambitions is valid, those with a high yield of mental illness should maintain higher ambitions than those with a low yield of illness. This is in fact the case: community subgroups with a high rate of illness, who have already lowered their ambitions in accordance with our expectation based on the yield issue, *still* maintain relatively higher ambitions than those subgroups with a low rate of mental disorder.

Up to this point, the data on "ambitions" have compared only the total ill and community samples, and the high and low yield subgroups within the community population. We may now investigate the relationship between the lowering of ambitions and the four-step illness continuum. As one moves from the low symptom group to the psychotics, the percentages of those whose present ambitions are "About the same" are 56, 51, 41, and 40 per cent, respectively. The number of those who have lowered their present ambitions increases along the mental health continuum (5, 12, 16, and 21 per cent, respectively). Both of these sequences are significant ($P = < .001$). An earlier discussion indicated a direct linear relationship between the discrepancy scores and the mental health continuum. The percentages of those reporting their "Present ambitions lower" show a similar pattern. The data on this "ambitions" response apparently correlate with findings obtained for the discrepancy scores.

The second question relating to one's ambitions asked the *degree* to which the subject's ambitions have changed (Appendix B, Question 197). Of those who report raising their ambitions, a significantly larger proportion of ill than community subjects answer "Very much" ($P = < .005$). On the other hand, significantly more community than ill respondents reply "Somewhat" and "Very little." This pattern continues to emerge when sex and age controls are applied (all at $P = < .005$). Of those who have lowered their ambitions, a greater proportion of ill than community individuals answer "Very little," while more community than ill persons reply "Somewhat." This pattern approaches significance ($P = < .10 > .05$). The data clearly show that of those individuals who report raising their ambitions, the patients raise them to a greater degree than community respondents.

There is also evidence that the ill are more resistant than the community subjects to lowering their ambitions. In Chapter 3 we noted that the young and older patients differed very little in goal-striving stress. We attributed this finding to the ill person's resistance to reducing his goal striving over time—that is, to his adherence to his early goal-striving orientation. In the present context, the greater resistance to the lowering of ambitions among the patient population seems to reflect this same inflexibility.

Ill-community differences on this questionnaire item may also be correlated with differences between the two samples observed for the striving scale discrepancy. The reader may recall that in this area the patients were characterized by significantly larger D-scores than their community counterparts. One interpretation advanced at that time suggested that aspirations on this subjectively anchored striving scale reflected striving in general areas of particular personal relevance to the individual. The same psychological processes may be involved in the ill individual's greater resistance to lowering his ambitions, and in his setting such high aspirations in the striving scale area.

CHANGES IN GOAL EXPECTANCIES

We have been discussing the general orientation of our populations toward educational striving and achievement, and toward the status of their ambitions. We may now consider a number of questionnaire items concerned with respondents' expectations. The first such item asked the subject whether he expected to have a better job in the future than he had at present (Appendix B, Question 46). This question is not associated with any particular level of aspiration, but represents a generalized estimate of the respondent's expectations. The ill and community samples were compared on this item, with and without sex and age controls—a total of five comparisons were made. In four of these five analyses more ill than community respondents say they expect to hold better positions at some time in the future ($P = < .005$). The comparison between young subjects in the two samples does not reach significance, but the direction of difference is consistent with the other analyses.

Earlier in this chapter we pointed out that the patients were characterized by higher probability-of-success estimates than the community subjects. The data on the "expectancy" question under discussion seem to correlate with these probability estimate results. In the earlier discussion of probability estimates, we also noted higher scores for the high yield than for the low yield subgroups within the community sample. In analyzing this question, also, significantly more males than females expect better jobs ($P = < .005$). (The reader should bear in mind that females who answered this question were all full-time members of the working force; housewives who remained at home were not included.) Similarly, a significantly larger proportion of young than older respondents give affirmative responses to this question ($P = < .005$). Logically, we can expect that younger subjects will be more likely than older subjects to expect improvement in their vocational situation. When responses on this item are correlated with the four-step illness continuum, we find no differences between the psychotics and neurotics, or between the high and low symptom groups in the community. Again, these findings, like the other data gathered on this question, correlate almost perfectly with patterns obtained for analyses of the probability-of-success estimates.

The questionnaire item just discussed dealt with respondents' future expectations. Another item was designed to investigate changes in expectations from some point in the past to the present. This question asked whether the individual had lowered his expectations, in comparison to what they had been in the past (Appendix B, Question 48). Since data reported earlier indicated that the community subjects were characterized by lower probability-of-success estimates than the patients, we predict in this instance that more community than ill individuals will have lowered their expectations over time: this is, in fact, the case. All five ill-community comparisons, with and without sex and age controls, are significant (three at $P = < .005$, and two at $P = < .05$). We also anticipate that within the community population a greater proportion of low yield subgroups (i.e., the females and the older subjects) will have lowered their expectations. The data reveal no differences between males and females or between young and older individuals in the community. These findings do not confirm our predictions and apparently do not parallel the differences observed on ill-community comparisons for this question.

We also look for a decreasing proportion of respondents with lowered expectations as we move from the low symptom group in the community to the psychotics in the ill population. Neither the high and the low symptom groups, nor the psychotics and neurotics, differ. This lack of differences is similar to that observed for Question 46. However, more individuals with lowered expectations appear in the low symptom group than among the neurotics or the psychotics (both comparisons are significant at $P = < .005$). Similarly, the high symptom group contains significantly more subjects with lowered expectations than the neurotics ($P = < .03$) or the psychotics ($P = < .01$). These findings present an opposite pattern to that observed for the "expect to be in a better job" question. The mentally ill clearly have higher expectations of mobility than the community respondents. Also, more of those in the community sample have lowered their expectations. These data are not surprising—we assume that Question 46 correlates with probability of success and that Question 48 is an index of probability of failure, and we anticipate an inverse relationship between these two variables.

A final item to be considered deals with the *degree* to which one has lowered his expectations (Appendix B, Question 49). This question was asked only of those who reported lower present than past expectations (Question 48). Of these respondents, a significantly larger proportion of ill individuals say that their expectations have been lowered "Very much," while more community subjects reply "Very little" ($P = < .01$). The direction of the difference does not change when sex and age are controlled, but only one of the analyses with controls (comparing young subjects in each sample) is significant ($P = < .03$). The limited significance obtained when analyses are carried out with sex and age controls suggests that the patients tend to resist lowering their goals in much the same way they resisted lowering their ambitions, but that they give up their expectations more easily than their ambitions.

Further evidence that the mentally ill resist lowering their expectations is found in the analysis of this question with respect to the four mental health groupings. There are no differences in the degree of lowering among individuals in the low symptom group, the high symptom group, or the neurotics. The psychotics do differ significantly from two of the three other mental health groupings in the number of respondents who have lowered their expectations "Very much." Thus, not until we consider the psychotics (i.e., the "illest" grouping) do we observe this increase in proportion.

We should emphasize that those patients who lowered their ambitions lowered them relatively little, whereas ill individuals who lowered their expectations lowered them considerably. Earlier in this volume, we suggested that the level of aspiration is more resistant than expectation to the realities of day-to-day experience. If our assumption of a direct relationship between height of ambition and level of aspiration is valid, we can conclude that level of aspiration is more resistant to change.

5

PERCEPTION OF THE NATURE OF THE OPPORTUNITY STRUCTURE

In the two preceding chapters we have discussed the perception of the social system, the goal-striving stress scores, and the components of these stress scores. In the present chapter we shall analyze respondents' evaluations of the "best" and "worst possible way of life," and their perception of barriers to goal achievement. These analyses will indicate the degree to which the ill and community samples, as well as subgroups within these populations, differ in their perception of the societal opportunity structure. If differences in their views emerge, these analyses will help in defining the nature of mental illness. If, on the other hand, ill and community sample individuals have similar concepts of "best" and "worst possible way of life" and see the same obstacles to goal achievement, we must conclude that they cannot differ in their perception of the problems to be overcome. In that case, differences in their perception of the social system (i.e., their view of the possibilities of meeting these obstacles) and their reactions to this perception (i.e., their goal-striving stress scores) will assume roles of more central importance, especially since these factors are based on a specific theoretical framework.

The "Best" and "Worst" Possible
Way of Life

SUBJECTIVE ESTIMATES OF "BEST" AND "WORST" CRITERIA

We have already described the self-anchored striving scale on which each respondent was asked to specify the conditions representing the "best" and "worst possible way of life" (Appendix B, Questions 178 and 179). In this section we shall analyze the content of these open-ended questions and show how these data parallel findings already presented.

It has been noted that each respondent could, if he wished, give more than one response to each of these striving-scale questions. Community respondents tended to give two codable responses much more frequently than ill respondents. It was necessary to correct the resulting inequality of the response yield and to make the two populations more comparable. After *all* responses were coded, we determined the frequency of occurrence of each response category, for the first and second responses. The coding categories were listed in order of frequency of occurrence for each of the response classifications. The two listings of percentages were correlated by means of the rank order correlation technique to determine the degree to which those categories selected most frequently as a first response were also chosen most often as a second response. This procedure was followed for the "best" and "worst way of life" questions, both in the ill and community populations. In view of the high correlation coefficients obtained between first and second response choices on the two questions (higher than .85 in all cases; $P = < .01$), we felt that little would be lost by analyzing only the first response given on either of the questions by an ill or community respondent.

The rankings of the coding categories for the "best" and "worst" questions were correlated within the ill and community populations. In the ill population the correlation between the two sets of rankings is .74 ($P = < .05$), and in the community population .91 ($P = < .01$). These correlations indicate that, regardless of his illness status, an individual tends to use the same criteria for the "best" and "worst way of life." If, for example, he applies economic considerations to his determination of the "best possible way of life," he will also use this criterion in evaluating the "worst possible way of life." When computing and interpreting rank order correlations, we considered only the order of listing, and were not concerned with any actual differences in frequency of occurrence for a given response.

Table 5.1—Criteria of "Best" and "Worst Possible Way of Life."

	ILL	COMMUNITY
		Per Cent
"Best Way of Life"		
Good Health	6	8
Economic Security and Mobility	57	47
Positive Interpersonal Relationships–Family	12	13
Positive Interpersonal Relationships–Other	4	4
"Good" or "Moral" Life	10	18
Improvement of Personality Traits	3	4
Race and Social Betterment	2	2
Education and Training	2	2
Other	4	2
	100	100
"Worst Way of Life"		
Poor Health	19	14
Economic Insecurity	40	40
Poor Interpersonal Relationships–Family	8	9
Poor Interpersonal Relationships–Other	6	4
Immoral or Sinful Life	8	16
Negative Personality Characteristics	14	10
Poor Race Relations and Continued Inferior Position	1	2
Little or No Education and Training	–	2
Other	4	3
	100	100

Table 5.1 presents the percentages of responses in each category, for the "best" and "worst way of life" questions. In both the ill and community samples "Economic security and mobility" is mentioned as a factor in the "best way of life" significantly more often than "Economic insecurity" is given as a determinant of the "worst way of life." "Poor health" and "Negative personality traits" are noted as components of the "worst way of life" significantly more often than the corresponding categories are cited as factors in the "best way of life." These data reaffirm the similar responses to the two questions by both populations.

The rank order of "best way of life" responses in the ill population correlates significantly with the ranking of the responses in the community population (.86, $P = < .01$). "Worst way of life" responses also correlate significantly (.93, $P = < .01$). The magnitude of these two correlations indicates no difference between the two samples in the criteria selected or in the order of their importance.

The second stage of this analysis involved percentage differences between the two populations in different response categories. The distribution of responses for the "best way of life" differs significantly in the ill and community populations ($P = < .05$). The significance of the chi-square is determined almost exclusively by differences in the "Economic security and mobility" and "Good or moral life" categories. Fifty-eight per cent of the ill, and 47 per cent of the community respondents mention the former category (see Table 5.1). We have already reported significant ill-community differences in stress scores in the occupational and income areas; the difference obtained here between the two populations for the "Economic security and mobility" response confirms the fact that striving in the economic area is of greater importance to members of the ill population.

Eighteen per cent of the community, and 10 per cent of the ill respondents mention "Good or moral life" as a factor in the "best way of life." This difference implies that, relatively speaking, a greater number of community individuals value nonmaterial sources of satisfaction, compared with material items (which may be more difficult for a Negro population to obtain).

The data with respect to "worst way of life" yield no significant differences between the ill and community populations, although a greater percentage of the ill mention "Poor health" and a greater percentage of the community cite "Immoral or sinful life" as the major criterion of the "worst way of life."

We showed in Chapter 3 that, within the community population, the males (with a high yield of mental illness) had higher occupation and income stress scores than the females (with a low yield of mental disorder). In this context, we expect males to show greater concern than females over economic factors—that is, to manifest more of the characteristics of the ill population. Fifty-one per cent of the males and 44 per cent of the females select responses in the "Economic security and mobility" category $(P = < .01)$ for the "best way of life" question. Forty-three per cent of the males and 39 per cent of the females give responses in the "Economic insecurity" category for the "worst way of life" item. This difference is not significant.

Similarly, since the high yield young respondents have higher occupation and income stress scores than the low yield older respondents, we predict for them the same pattern of differences observed between the two sex subgroups. With respect to the "best way of life" question, 50 per cent of the young and 43 per cent of the older individuals select "Economic security and mobility" responses $(P = < .01)$. With respect to the "worst way of life" question, 44 per cent of the young and 35 per cent of the older subgroup give responses in the "Economic and insecurity" category $(P = < .01)$.

We conclude that more ill than community respondents are concerned with problems of economic insecurity and mobility. This is consistent with the differences in occupation and income stress scores cited in an earlier chapter. In addition, the two high yield community sub-groups (i.e., the males and the young respondents) also show greater concern for economic factors than low yield subgroups (i.e., the females and the older respondents). This suggests that the greater concern of the ill population with economic matters may be considered an antecedent, rather than a result, of their illness.

Barriers to Goal Achievement

THE DATA PRESENTED EARLIER on the open nature of the opportunity structure provided some information about the perceptual cognitive world of our respondents. These data did not provide specific information on the perceived barriers or obstacles to goal achievement, however. Respondents in both populations were asked a series of questions dealing with the perceived barriers to goal achievement in different goal-striving areas, as well as for three different reference persons. For example, in the area of occupational striving, the respondent was asked what barriers might hinder his own occupational advancement (Appendix B, Question 44), and the mobility of a "hypothetical son" (Appendix B, Question 81). If the respondent was not himself the head of a household, he was asked what factors might prevent the head of his household from realizing his occupational aspirations (Appendix B, Question 62).

Although all the questions involving barriers to advancement permitted the respondent to state more than one obstacle, not all individuals did so. As was the case in analyzing criteria for the "best" and "worst way of life," considerably more community than ill subjects mentioned two barriers. In order to determine whether we would reach erroneous conclusions by considering only the first barrier given by each respondent, we followed the same procedure used to insure comparability of the population in analyzing the "best" and "worst way of life" items. In each population, the rank order correlations between the first and second responses were greater than .90 and significant ($P = < .01$); consequently, we felt justified in limiting our analyses to a consideration of first responses only.

PERCEIVED BARRIERS TO ONE'S OWN
OCCUPATIONAL ACHIEVEMENT

The responses of the two populations on this item fell into nine general categories. The first step in analyzing ill-community differences was to correlate the rank order of these categories in each population. The correlation is .76, significant at $P = < .01$. This coefficient suggests that the two samples assign a similar order of importance to their responses. As noted earlier, this does not imply that the percentages in each category are the same for both populations.

The second step in the analysis of this questionnaire item involved the comparison of the actual percentage differences between each of the response categories for the two populations.

Table 5.2 shows the percentage distribution of the expected barriers

Table 5.2—Perceived Barriers to Occupational Aspirations in Percentages

	TOTAL		MALES		FEMALES		YOUNG		OLD				High Symp. (13)	Low Symp. (14)
	Ill (1)	Comm. (2)	Ill (3)	Comm. (4)	Ill (5)	Comm. (6)	Ill (7)	Comm. (8)	Ill (9)	Comm. (10)	Psy. (11)	Neur. (12)		
No Barriers	16	24	20	25	13	23	15	24	18	24	15	18	20	25
Family Responsibilities	5	3	2	2	7	5	6	4	3	2	4	6	6	3
Financial Reasons	9	15	7	15	10	14	9	14	8	15	8	11	14	15
Lack of Education and Training	24	27	23	23	25	29	28	31	16	21	23	27	28	26
Illness	19	9	14	7	23	10	16	6	26	11	20	16	14	8
Negative Personality Traits	11	5	13	6	8	5	12	6	8	4	11	9	2	5
Age	3	8	3	8	3	7	2	2	8	14	4	3	7	7
Race	2	3	3	5	1	1	2	4	1	2	2	2	2	3
Limited Availability	6	5	9	6	4	5	6	6	6	4	6	6	6	5
Other	5	2	5	3	5	1	4	2	5	2	6	1	1	2
Total N	1145	1177	532	575	613	602	821	616	324	559	847	271	122	1055

to one's own occupational achievement. The most frequently mentioned category in both populations refers to "Lack of education and training" necessary for occupational advancement. The two populations do not differ in the importance they attach to this category. It is particularly surprising that only 2 per cent of the ill and 3 per cent of the community respondents spontaneously specify "Race" as a primary barrier to occupational advancement. One might expect greater proportions of these populations to regard their racial membership as a major barrier. A third response category which does not differentiate between the two populations is "Limited availability." Such responses as "Inability to take advantage of the opportunity because of illness, etc." or "Unwilling to give up security already obtained in order to take advantage of the opportunity," fall into this general category.

Certain response categories do differentiate significantly between the two populations (see Table 5.2). Sixteen per cent of the ill and 24 per cent of the community respondents believe that there are "No barriers" to their own occupational advancement ($P = < .05$). At the same time, it is not surprising that 19 per cent of the ill and 9 per cent of the community individuals specify "Illness" as a first barrier to mobility ($P = < .05$). It is conceivable that a person diagnosed as mentally ill may be concerned that his illness will interfere with the realization of his goals. If the "Illness" and "No barriers" categories are combined, the differences between the ill and community populations disappear.

It should also be noted that "Illness" is the second most frequently mentioned response for the ill population, whereas it is ranked fourth in importance by those in the community. This difference provides a major source of error in the rank order correlation between the two populations. The ill-community differences observed for these two response categories are obtained even with sex and age controls.

The two populations also differ significantly on "Financial reasons" ($P = < .005$). A greater percentage of community than ill individuals perceive barriers in this area. Significantly more patients mention "Negative personality traits" ($P = < .005$) as a barrier to occupational achievement. This difference may reflect the ill individual's preoccupation with his own inadequacies—that is, it may reflect his low self-esteem (this concept will be discussed in Chapter 6).

A final category that yields significant differences between the two populations is "Age." More community than ill individuals see this factor 'as an occupational barrier ($P = < .005$). This difference is not surprising, since the average age of the community population (thirty-nine years) is greater than the average for the ill population (thirty-four years). Seventy-three per cent of the ill, compared to only 56 per cent of the community respondents, are between twenty and forty years of age. When the differences between the two populations are reexamined using sex and age controls, only the response categories "Negative personality characteristics" and "Age" continue to discriminate between ill and community respondents.

We reiterate that although the perceived barriers to occupational goal achievement tend to exist in the same sequence of importance for both samples, the two populations differ in the frequency with which they choose each of the categories. Both populations agree that "Lack of education and training" is the most important obstacle. After this response, the community individuals mention such objective factors as "Financial reasons" and "Age," whereas the patients cite "Negative personality characteristics" and "Illness" as the obstacles next in importance to them. The observed differences and similarities between the two populations with respect to the "Illness" and "Negative personality characteristics" categories continue to appear when analyses are carried out in each of the sex and age control groups. This fact indicates that these differences and similarities represent general characteristics of the two populations.

Within the community sample the rankings of categories in the male subgroup were compared with the rankings for females, and similarly, the rankings of the young were compared to those of the older subjects. The correlation for the male-female comparison is .91 $(P = < .01)$, and for the age comparison, .75 $(P = < .05)$. The differences between the sex subgroups with respect to each of the categories are minimal. The lower correlation between rankings for the age subgroups suggests greater response variability between young and older respondents. The two age subgroups do differ on three categories. Thirty-one per cent of the young and 21 per cent of the older community respondents mention "Lack of education and training" as a major obstacle $(P = < .005)$, but a greater proportion of the older individuals cite "Illness" and "Age" $(P = < .005)$ as barriers. These findings reflect the influence of age, and the anxiety about illness associated with it. We conclude that there are relatively few differences between subgroups in the community population. It has been emphasized that, regardless of differences obtained with respect to the "Lack of education and training" category, this is still the first or second most important barrier cited by all subgroups in the community population.

Finally, we determine whether there is some systematic relationship between our four mental health groupings and barriers to occupational goal achievement. Three response categories show a systematic relationship among these groupings. The percentage of those estimating that "No barriers" to their occupational achievement exist, increases from 15 to 25 per cent as one moves from the psychotics to the low symptom group $(P = < .005)$. At the same time, the proportion of those mentioning "Illness" as a barrier decreases on the continuum from the psychotics to the low symptom group (20, 16, 14, and 8 per cent, respectively). Apparently there is an inverse relationship between these two response categories, a fact already noted in the discussion of ill-community population comparisons.

These findings provide additional evidence that those individuals in need of treatment, or diagnosed as ill are aware of their illness and its incapacitating potential. The response category "Financial reasons" also shows a significant relationship with our mental health continuum. The proportion of respondents choosing this area as a barrier to achievement increases significantly from the psychotics to the low symptom group (8, 11, 14, and 15 per cent, respectively; $P = < .005$). The data continue to disclose identifiable systematic relationships among the four mental health groupings and the variables under consideration. It is interesting that the neurotics and the high symptom group do not differ from each other on any of these three barrier categories. This reaffirms our earlier suggestion that these two mental health groupings are not different.

PERCEIVED BARRIERS TO THE OCCUPATIONAL ACHIEVEMENT
OF A HYPOTHETICAL SON

Respondents in both populations were asked to designate the barriers that might hinder a hypothetical son in the realization of his occupational aspirations (Appendix B, Question 81). The procedure reported in previous sections to determine whether it was necessary to consider a second or third barrier cited by any given individual was also employed in analyzing this question. For the same reasons mentioned earlier, on this question only the first barrier perceived by respondents was considered.

Table 5.3 presents the percentages of responses falling into each

Table 5.3—Perceived Barriers to Occupational Aspirations for Hypothetical Son

in Percentages

	TOTAL		MALES		FEMALES		YOUNG		OLD					
	Ill (1)	Comm. (2)	Ill (3)	Comm. (4)	Ill (5)	Comm. (6)	Ill (7)	Comm. (8)	Ill (9)	Comm. (10)	Psy. (11)	Neur. (12)	High Symp. (13)	Low Symp. (14)
No Barriers	14	11	15	11	13	11	13	11	16	12	15	8	11	11
Financial Reasons	23	26	21	20	25	39	24	27	22	24	21	28	35	25
Lack of Motivation or interest	35	40	35	47	35	35	36	39	33	40	34	37	29	41
Negative Influence of Friends	2	2	1	1	3	2	2	2	2	2	2	2	4	1
Race	3	3	4	4	2	2	3	3	3	2	3	3	5	2
Lack of Education and Training	10	11	10	10	10	12	10	11	10	11	10	11	10	11
Illness	9	5	9	5	9	5	8	5	11	5	10	8	4	5
Other	4	2	4	2	4	3	4	2	4	3	4	3	1	3
	100	100	99	100	101	99	100	100	101	99	99	100	99	99
Total N	1385	1422	557	574	828	848	982	759	403	660	1033	352	164	1258

category for the two populations. The two sets of percentages were ranked and then correlated using the same statistical procedure noted in the previous sections. The correlation between the two sets of rankings is .96 $(P = < .01)$. This almost-perfect correlation again indicates that both populations see the same barriers to goal achievement, and in the same order of importance—in this case for a hypothetical son. Significant correlations of comparable magnitude are obtained when the ill and the community samples are compared using sex and age controls. As one might expect, a significantly larger proportion of the ill than the community population mentions "Illness" as a barrier ($P = < .005$). There are no other differences between the two populations.

Within the community population, the rankings for males and females and for both age subgroups yield significant correlations (.91 and .92, respectively; $P = < .01$ for both). The percentage distributions of males and females differ in two categories: 47 per cent of the males and 35 per cent of the females mention "Lack of motivation or interest" ($P = < .005$), and 20 per cent of the males and 30 per cent of the females mention "Financial reasons" ($P = < .005$). The higher incidence of "Lack of motivation or interest" responses among the males suggests that they are more sensitive to, and acutely aware of, the problem of motivation. This possibility lends some support to the previously reported finding of higher stress scores for males than for females. Data analyses for the two age subgroups in the community yield no significant differences. We may point out, finally, that there is no systematic relationship between any response category on this questionnaire item and the four mental health groupings on our illness continuum.

Clearly, then, both the ill and community population see the same barriers to occupational achievement for a hypothetical son, and in the same order of importance. These similarities tend to be maintained even when analyses are carried out with sex and age controls.

PERCEIVED BARRIERS TO THE OCCUPATIONAL ACHIEVEMENT
OF THE HEAD OF HOUSEHOLD

Each ill and community respondent who was not himself the head of a household was asked to specify the obstacles that might interfere with the aspirational strivings of the head of his particular household (Appendix B, Question 62). For the same reasons discussed in the previous sections, only the first response given to this question was analyzed. A comparison of the rankings of the response categories for the ill and community respondents yields a correlation of .85 ($P = < .01$). There are no differences between the two populations in the percentages of responses in any category other than "Illness." As was the case for self and hypothetical son, significantly more ill than community individuals give responses that fall into this category.

Within the community population, the correlations of rankings for the sex and age subgroups are both .88 (significant at $P = < .01$). Males tend to give fewer responses than females in the "Negative personality characteristics" category ($P = < .03$). At the same time, more males perceive "No barriers" to goal achievement ($P = < .05$). There are no significant differences between the percentage distributions of the two age groups. Finally, we may note that, except for the "Illness" category, there is no systematic relationship between the four mental health groupings and any of the other response categories.

In summary, the barriers perceived by respondents for head of household are the same in the ill and community populations, and are seen in the same order of importance. In addition, within the community population, there are almost no differences among the response categories when sex and age are controlled.

ADDITIONAL BARRIER QUESTIONS

We have already discussed in considerable detail data obtained for questions concerned with barriers to the individual's occupational mobility. Ill respondents were also asked to discuss the barriers that might prevent them from realizing their own income aspirations. (Appendix B, Question 90). The rankings of the ten categories for the ill population on this question were correlated with the comparable rankings obtained from the question on obstacles to one's own occupational attainment. This correlation was computed because the same reference individual was involved in both questions, although the content area differed. The correlation between the two sets of rankings is .81, and significant ($P = < .01$).

The patients were also asked to specify the barriers they anticipated in the educational strivings of a hypothetical son (Appendix B, Question 27). The rankings of the various response categories for this question were correlated with the rankings associated with the question on barriers to occupational achievement of a hypothetical son. This correlation was computed because the reference individual in both questions was the same (hypothetical son), although again the content areas were dissimilar. The correlation is .93 ($P = < .01$).

These correlations show that the barriers seen by the ill population, with respect to the self, tend to be consistent, regardless of the striving area. Similarly, the patients perceive the same obstacles to goal attainment of a hypothetical son, regardless of content area. These two correlations may also be interpreted as measures of the internal reliability of the responses given by the ill population. It should be emphasized that the responses of the patients change somewhat when the question deals with another reference individual, but that varying the content area with respect to the same reference individual has little appreciable effect on the responses.

GENERAL SUMMARY OF ANALYSES ON
BARRIER QUESTION

A number of generalizations can be inferred on the basis of these data. First, all correlations between rankings are significant, indicating that ill and community respondents perceive the same barriers to goal achievement in the same order of importance (1) in each of the content areas tested; and (2) for each of the three different reference individuals. Second, there are relatively few significant differences between the ill and community populations for any given category. Third, the significant correlations among the responses to barrier questions within the ill population suggest that the ill are consistent and reliable in their perception of the obstacles to goal achievement. Fourth, the patients are apparently aware of their incapacity and, to a certain extent, are able to articulate the potency of their illness as an obstacle to goal achievement and mobility. Fifth, there seems to be a tendency for a greater percentage of males than females to perceive "No barriers" to goal achievement. Finally, there is some tendency for a greater percentage of young than older respondents to cite "Negative personality characteristics"and "Lack of education and training" as barriers to goal achievement.

When analyses are carried out within the ill population controlling for sex and age, almost no differences emerge. This holds for the questions on "best" and "worst possible way of life," and for all the barrier questions.

These findings allow us to draw some general conclusions:

(1) The fact that the patients show almost no differences when divided by sex or age controls suggests a relatively homogeneous population.

(2) Both ill and community respondents tend to see the same barriers to goal achievement, in the same sequence of importance (a similarity that holds up even in subgroups within the community population). This generalization implies that the mentally ill and community populations differ not in their perception of obstacles to be overcome, but rather in their evaluation of the *possibility* of overcoming these prob-

lems, and their reactions to the evaluation (e.g., high or low stress scores).

(3) It is interesting that the older patients never mention age as a barrier to goal achievement. This fact relates to our earlier discussion about the rigidity of the ill individual. The reader may recall that the older patients tend to maintain their high goal-striving stress. This failure or inability to lower their goal-striving stress suggests a denial of how age must necessarily modify hopes and ambitions. The fact that age is not mentioned as a major barrier to goal achievement clearly supports this "denial" interpretation.

(4) The greater concern of the young individuals over "Lack of education and training" in the ill and community populations shows the strong emphasis placed on goal striving by the younger respondents.

6

REFERENCE GROUP BEHAVIOR
AND MENTAL
DISORDER

The goal-striving patterns of the community and mentally ill respondents have been considered in some detail. We are now prepared to examine the reference group behavior of these populations. It is assumed here that one's perception of his goal-striving experiences and the psychological impact of this perception will be partly determined by the standards by which he evaluates his performance. Further, that these standards and norms of comparison are derived from the significant groups (or individuals) he desires to emulate. In this chapter we shall investigate the ways and the extent to which community and ill subjects differ in their reference group behavior, and we shall discuss the possible consequences of such differences for mental health.

At the outset we must clarify the "reference group" concept as it will be used in this study. Although there is some overlapping in the research literature in the application of this concept, some important differences are present. These differences contribute to the ambiguity of generalizations emerging from such empirical studies. Shibutani (1955) delineated three separate usages of the term "reference group:"

(1) It may refer to that group which serves as the individual's criterion in making *comparisons*, particularly evaluations concerning his own status or self-image.

(2) It may designate that group from which the individual wishes to *gain or maintain acceptance*.

(3) The term may also refer to that group whose perspectives and norms provide the individual with an orienting framework for *structuring his own perceptual field*.

Although Shibutani's distinctions are conceptually clear and important to bear in mind when designing relevant research, these three different usages seem to be logically related and are probably empirically linked in actual ongoing social behavior. If an individual employs a reference group as a basis for self-evaluation, doesn't this group also structure his perceptual field? Similarly, if a reference group serves as a basis for self-evaluation and provides the individual with a normative structure, it seems logical that he also (if only in fantasy) wishes to gain admittance to this group.

In this study, the reference group concept designates the group (or individual) which serves as a reference point or means of evaluating oneself. This was the major emphasis placed on the concept in Hyman's pioneering study (1942). It seems that the use of a reference group as an anchor point enabling the individual to make judgments concerning his own achievements and self-image is most relevant to his sense of self-esteem and ultimately to his state of mental health. Given two persons of identical objectively defined status, the individual who evaluates himself by the standards of a relatively higher status reference group may be less satisfied with his own status and thus more prone to various manifestations of maladjustment and psychopathology.

This chain of reasoning has appeared frequently in the research literature (Hyman, 1942; Merton, 1957: 225–280; Myers and Roberts, 1959: 142, ff; Zander and Quinn, 1962). It is often assumed that people choose reference groups or reference individuals occupying a status relatively close to their own. Hyman (1942) attributed this tendency to "proximity to him [the individual] in life situations, or as the result of objective facts which facilitate such comparisons." Festinger, et al. (1950: 4) regarded similar or proximal status choices as a result of "the pressure toward uniformity which may exist in a group." In the context of this study we assume that, because of their objectively circumscribed range of social interaction with others of similar status, and because of the need to maintain feelings of competence, most people do tend to select reference points at, or close to, their own positions.

When an individual is below his reference group on a scale of status positions, we say he is characterized by a "negative discrepancy." If his own position is above that of his reference group, he is said to have a "positive discrepancy." Up to this point the discussion suggests that if we compare people of equal status, those with relatively high reference groups (i.e., negative discrepancies) will be more prone to self-devaluation and mental illness. The hypotheses presented in this chapter incorporate this idea of a direct relationship between degree of negative discrepancy from reference group and severity of mental illness (i.e., the more negatively discrepant, the greater the severity of illness).

Hypothesis 2.   *The degree of negative discrepancy from a reference group will vary directly with the severity of mental illness.*

Hypothesis 2a.   *Within the mentally ill population, negative discrepancy from a reference group will be higher for the psychotics than for the neurotics.*

Hypothesis 2b.   *Within the community population, negative discrepancy from a reference group will be larger for a high symptom group than for a low symptom group.*

We have specified no formal predictions about positive discrepancies from reference group. Such predictions would involve the very problematic issue of using reference groups for psychologically defensive purposes, or alternatively, as a means to enable the individual to cope with his felt anxieties. In agreement with Festinger and Hyman, we assume that pressures toward uniformity are such that most people select a reference group close to their own status position. It has also been noted in the literature, however, that individuals experiencing threats to their interpersonal relations are likely to choose reference groups considerably above *and* below their own position—there can be wishfully high and low choices.

Hyman (1942) distinguished between "realistic" and "autistic" reference group choices. As the term implies, an autistic choice is determined by felt pressures to minimize threats, and, to varying degrees, it ignores elements of the realistic situation. Realistic choices, on the other hand, do not "stand in major contradiction with reality." Hyman cited examples of people who, in order to be reassured of their own superiority, evaluated themselves by comparisons with individuals who were considered inferior. Other individuals used reference points considerably above their own positions in order to reassure themselves that they could and would reach higher levels. Similar examples demonstrating both defensive types of reference group choices were reported by Frenkel-

Brunswick (1951). Based on carefully conducted clinical interviews she concluded:

It would appear that we do not always see ourselves as we are but instead perceive the environment in terms of our own needs. Self-perception and perception of the environment actually merge in the service of these needs. Thus, the perceptual distortions of ourselves and the environment fulfil an important function in our own psychological household.

A bimodal defensive pattern of reference group behavior in psychiatric patients was further evidenced in a large scale study conducted in New Haven (Myers and Roberts, 1959: 147).

Although the hypotheses stated above constitute our only formal predictions, in view of these kinds of findings in the literature, we anticipate greater negative discrepancies from reference groups, and, to a lesser extent larger positive discrepancies, for the patients than for the community subjects.

In this chapter we shall principally be concerned with Hypotheses 2, 2a, and 2b, but we shall also see whether high yield community subgroups (i.e., the males and the younger subjects) are more discrepant from their reference groups than their low yield counterparts (i.e., the females and the older respondents).

In order to operationalize our measures of discrepancy from reference group and test the relevant hypotheses, certain assumptions and choices between alternative procedures were made. First, it was necessary that the respondent choose the criteria sufficiently salient *for him* to be used as the basis by which he compared himself to his reference group. Obviously, there were different criteria serving such functions. Second, we felt that the choice of reference group should be limited to those with which the respondent had face-to-face relations, rather than groups more psychologically remote. Previous research had indicated that such face-to-face groups were likely to provide more potent bases for self-judgments. Finally, within the range of face-to-face reference groups, we felt it was important to select a given reference point for all respondents that would maximize the comparability of responses. Hyman's study (1942) indicated that one's friends and acquaintances constituted the most common reference group to which he compared his own achievements. Therefore, we decided to make our self-anchored striving scale measure a basis for deriving data on the degree of discrepancy from reference group.

The self-anchored striving scale has already been described: each respondent was presented with a diagrammatic representation of a flight of ten steps, the bottom one labelled the "worst possible way of life" and the top, the "best possible way of life." After specifying the content of these two anchor points, the respondent selected the step that represented his own current position (Appendix B, Question 180). At a later point in the questionnaire he was asked to choose the step-position of his "close friends" (Appendix B, Question 189) and to specify "the things you had in mind when you compared the position of your close friends to yourself" (Appendix B, Question 190). By determining the size and the direction of the difference between the respondent's own step-position on the striving scale and that of his "close friends," we were provided with a measure of his discrepancy from his reference group.

Brief mention should be made of the criteria specified by community and ill respondents by which they compared themselves to their close friends. The first and second criteria given in response to this question were tabulated separately in each population. Since correlations between first and second choices are extremely high (.94 and .92 respectively, $P = < .01$) for both populations, this discussion will be limited only to first choices. The distributions of responses for the two populations correlate significantly (.84, $P = <.01$; see Table 6.1). There are ap-

Table 6.1—Criteria for Comparing

Self with Close Friends [1]

	COMMUNITY	ILL
	Per Cent	
Health	3	5
Economic Factors	54	53
(financial and occupational)		
Relations with Friends	4	3
Family Relations	9	10
Morality ("Good Life")	14	6
Personality Characteristics	10	12
Education and Training	3	7
Miscellaneous	3	4
	100	100
Total N	1446	1390

1. The rank order correlation between response distributions. of the community and ill populations is .84 ($P=<.01$)

parently no significant differences in the choices of criteria by which the two populations compare themselves to their respective reference groups. By far the most common criterion of comparision between self and friends used by patients and community respondents is "Economic factors." (Over 50 per cent of each population use this criterion.) The large percentage of responses falling into this category is consistent with reports from other relevant research (Hyman 1942). The only response category for which there is a sizable percentage difference between the two samples is "Morality" (see Table 6.1).

The average discrepancy between one's own perceived position and that of his "close friends" for both populations and subgroups within these populations is a negative one—that is, the step chosen for self is usually lower than that chosen for reference group. This finding is consistent with other research (Hyman, 1942). As predicted in Hypothesis 2, the mentally ill place themselves further below their reference group than do those in the community ($P = < .001$; see Table 6.2). It should

Table 6.2—Mean Negative Reference Group Discrepancy by Illness

Status, Sex, and Age

(1)	(2)	Mean (1)	Mean (2)	N1	N2	P (By "t" test)
Total Ill	vs Total Comm.	1.63	.44	1390	1446	<.001
Ill Males	vs Comm. Males	1.67	.40	565	585	<.001
Ill Females	vs Comm. Females	1.60	.46	825	861	<.001
Ill Young	vs Comm. Young	1.63	.48	983	772	<.001
Ill Old	vs Comm. Old	1.62	.39	407	671	<.001
Psychotics	vs Neurotics	1.81	1.10	1036	354	<.001
High Symp.	vs Low Symp.	.95	.38	165	1281	<.001
Psychotics	vs Low Symp.	1.81	.38	1036	1281	<.001
Neurotics	vs Low Symp.	1.10	.38	354	1281	<.001
Comm. Males	vs Comm. Females	.40	.46	585	861	N.S.
Comm. Young	vs Comm. Old	.48	.39	772	671	N.S.

be remembered that respondents were free to use any criteria of comparison, and to place themselves and their reference group at any position on the ten-step scale. The mean discrepancy for the patients is significantly larger than the corresponding discrepancy for the community subjects.

These significant differences between the two populations persist when sex and age controls are applied. Not only is the average negative discrepancy consistently considerably larger for the mentally ill, but the variance of the mentally ill sample (9.49) is also significantly greater than that of the community sample (3.06). This tendency among the patients to manifest more dispersion on the discrepancy continuum is related to the previous discussion about the use of reference group comparisons as a psychological coping mechanism. The relative propensity for extreme discrepancies at both ends of the continuum will be explored more fully in subsequent analyses of the data.

The data in Table 6.2 confirm all three hypotheses involving reference group discrepancy. In support of Hypothesis 2, there is a direct relationship between negative reference group discrepancy and severity of illness. The psychotics are significantly ($P = < .001$) more negatively discrepant than the neurotics (Hypothesis 2a). The high symptom group is characterized by a significantly ($P = < .001$) larger mean negative discrepancy than the low symptom group (Hypothesis 2b).

At this point we should restate the assumption that the low symptom group, the high symptom group, the neurotics, and the psychotics constitute a continuum of increasing severity of mental illness. This sequence will be implied whenever subsequent reference is made to these four mental health groupings.

The mean negative discrepancy increases along our mental health continuum, as expected, and all comparisons of adjacent groupings are significant except for the high symptom-neurotics comparison. In Chapter 3 we reported little difference between these two mental health groupings on goal-striving stress scores. In the present context, not only does the mean reference group discrepancy become increasingly negative with severity of mental illness, but the variances around the respective means for mental health groupings also increase with illness (2.79, 4.93, 7.02, and 10.24, respectively)—there is a greater spread of discrepancies above and below the mean position of the group as severity of illness increases. This general pattern of variability was also manifested in the goal-striving stress scores of the mental health groupings.

With respect to the yield issue, there are no significant differences between sex or age subgroups within the community population (see Table 6.2). Contrary to expectation, females have slightly higher negative discrepancies than males, but the difference is not statistically significant. The mean negative discrepancy of the young is higher than that of the older subjects. Although this latter difference goes in the expected direction, it does not reach significance. In general, our expectations based on the relative yield of mental disorder are not supported by data on the reference group discrepancy.

Although the findings just reported strongly confirm our major hypotheses about the relationship between mental illness and reference group behavior, they also raise questions necessitating further investigation. The mean negative discrepancy from reference group becomes progressively larger with an increase in severity of illness, but this indicates little about the distributions of actual discrepancies within these groupings. Similar means may result from very dissimilar distributions. This problem relates to the possible defensive function of reference group behavior—that is, its function as a means of coping with threats to the self. We have speculated that such defenses may be characterized by a tendency to choose reference groups above and below one's own perceived position.

Table 6.3—Distribution of Reference Group Discrepancies,

by Illness Status in Percentages

| | TOTAL | | | | | | CONTROL GROUP 1-3 | | 4-6 | | 7-1 | |
	Ill	Comm.	Low Symp.	High Symp.	Neur.	Psych.	Ill	Comm.	Ill	Comm.	Ill	C
Relationship to Reference Group												
Above	17	18	18	19	21	17	4	5	16	13	30	
At	25	47	49	37	30	23	11	29	23	36	37	
Below	57	35	33	44	50	61	85	66	61	50	33	
	99	100	100	100	101	101	100	100	100	99	100	
Total N	1390	1446	1281	165	354	1036	330	79	536	473	461	

Table 6.3 presents the distributions of negative, positive, and zero reference group discrepancies within various population subgroups, with and without striving scale achievement controls. Twenty-two per cent more ill than community respondents place themselves below their reference group. There are almost no differences between the two populations in the proportions who place themselves above their reference group. Consequently, many more community than ill respondents place themselves at the same position as their reference group. This pattern of differences is also found in each of the sex and age subgroups and is significant in each instance $(P = < .001)$. Apparently, the "defensive" response of placing oneself above his reference group does not occur.

Within the community population no significant sex differences in reference group discrepancy are noted. The distributions of responses in the three reference group placement categories are fairly similar for males and females. Similarly, there is no significant difference in reference group discrepancy between the young and older community subjects, although the younger respondents manifest a more frequent tendency to be below their reference group. Since these differences do not reach statistical significance, they lend no support to our predictions based on the relative yields of mental disorder.

Some of the reference group discrepancy differences between the ill and community samples may be a function of the positions selected and the limitations imposed by the use of the ten-step scale. For example, although the patients tend to select lower positions on the scale than the community respondents, their potential discrepancy from reference group may be greater merely because there are more positions above them on the scale at which to place their reference group. An individual who places himself at step 9 can only be one step below his reference group, whereas an individual who selects step 3 as his position has a much larger potential negative discrepancy. This scale problem (which has been discussed in Chapter 4) can be eliminated by controlling, or holding constant, the respondent's perceived position on the ten-step scale. As a further refinement of the reference group discrepancy analyses—we compared only those individuals who placed themselves at approximately the same position on the striving scale. This procedure was intended to determine whether the ill-community differences were maintained when striving scale achievement controls were used. In order to facilitate control group comparisons, we divided our populations into three achievement control categories: respondents who placed themselves at positions 1 through 3, 4 through 6, and 7 through 10. Table 6.3 presents the results of the total ill-community sample comparisons. We shall discuss in text the relevant trends for the four mental health groupings within these control groups.

Within each of the three control categories, more ill than community respondents place themselves below their reference group. Therefore, the differences already observed between the ill and community samples are not merely artifacts of respondents' selected striving-scale positions. In every control group, the percentage of individuals at the same position as their reference group is smaller among the patients than among the community respondents. However, differences among the three control groups *do* emerge when we consider respondents with positive discrepancies. Community and ill subjects in the lowest control category (self-step 1 through 3), show a negligible difference in positive discrepancy, but more patients than community individuals are characterized by a positive discrepancy in the next control category (self-step 4 through 6). This preference for a position above that of the reference group is significant only in the highest control group (self-step 7 through 10; $P = < .01$). The mentally ill in the two highest control groups are more likely to choose reference groups above *and* below their own position, but this tendency is particularly apparent and statistically significant in control group 7 through 10 (see Table 6.3). These findings suggest the occurrence of a larger proportion of defensively high and low reference group choices among the mentally ill in the high achievement groups. This is not meant to imply, however, that the majority of negative reference group discrepancies among the patients are of a psychologically defensive nature.

When reference group discrepancy is examined in the four mental health groupings without applying striving scale achievement controls, we find a progressive increase in the occurrence of negative discrepancies from the low symptom group to the psychotics (see Table 6.3). The differences between the high and low symptom groups, and between the neurotics and the psychotics, are both statistically significant ($P = < .02$ and $< .01$, respectively). There is no significant difference between the high symptom group and the neurotics. As was the case in comparing the total samples, there are no differences among the mental health groupings in the proportion of those who place themselves above their reference group. As a result, the number of individuals at the same position as their reference group becomes progressively smaller as severity of illness increases. The degree of difference in negative discrepancy, and its consistent relationship with illness, is a striking finding.

When control group analyses are carried out for the four mental health groupings, the trends noted earlier for ill-community differences within the achievement control categories are generally maintained. In the two lowest striving scale achievement control groups (self-step 1 through 3, and 4 through 6) the proportion of respondents who place themselves at the same position as their reference group decreases along the continuum from the low symptom group to the psychotics. At the same time, the number of those who are negatively discrepant increases with severity of illness. There is no relationship in either control group between the mental health continuum and subjects with positive reference group discrepancies.

The highest achievement control group (self-step 7 through 10) generally manifests the same trends. The number of respondents who place themselves at the same position as their reference group decreases from the low symptom group to the psychotics. The percentage of subjects with negative discrepancies increases along the continuum with increasing severity of illness. There is a concomitant increase in severity of illness and in the proportion of negatively discrepant individuals from the low symptom group to the neurotics; contrary to expectation, this proportion declines among the psychotics.

On the whole, the more detailed control group analyses support predictions made for the mental health grouping without controls and reveal some additional findings. At every striving scale control level more community and fewer ill respondents place themselves at the same position as their reference group. Furthermore, as severity of illness increases, there is a definite but not invariant tendency for fewer individuals to place themselves at their reference group position. In addition, at every achievement control level, fewer community and more ill respondents are negatively discrepant. The proportion of those who place themselves below their reference group tends to increase directly with severity of illness. Only among subjects who place themselves above their reference group does control group position make a difference. At the highest striving scale control position the number of respondents with positive discrepancies tends to increase directly with severity of illness. Among the patients at this control level, it is mainly the neurotics who account for the relatively higher percentages of those with positive discrepancies. The data thus indicate that the "defensive" positive reference group discrepancy occurs only under certain circumscribed conditions.

In the previous paragraphs we have compared the patients and community respondents using group statistics. Now we consider the interdependence of reference group discrepancy and illness within the individual himself, by means of correlation coefficients. Following the same procedure used in analyzing the goal-striving stress scores and their components, correlations were computed for the two- and four-step illness continua on the basis of the linear and nonlinear assumptions.

When the linear assumption is applied, the correlations between the reference group discrepancy and the two- and four-step illness continua are .21 and .22, respectively (both significant at $P = < .001$). When the nonlinear assumption is used, the coefficient is again significant (.22, $P = < .001$). These correlations indicate that as discrepancy from one's reference group increases, so does the likelihood of his being in the "sickest" mental health grouping. The almost-identical linear and nonlinear coefficients provide further evidence that the incidence of the "defensive" positive discrepancy is relatively infrequent.

In Chapter 3 we considered scores on the psychoneurotic symptom inventory as one of three measures of illness. In that context, the correlations obtained were generally low and not significant. When reference group discrepancy scores are correlated with symptom scores, however, a significant coefficient is obtained, (.16, $P = < .001$). The assumption of linearity or nonlinearity makes no difference in this coefficient. Thus, a respondent's psychoneurotic symptom score increases as negative discrepancy from reference increases.

VARIABILITY OF REFERENCE GROUP DISCREPANCY BY
ILLNESS STATUS

The variability (or variance) of reference group discrepancy scores increases progressively as one moves from the low symptom group to the psychotics on our four-step illness continuum. It is tempting to attribute this increased variability to "defensive" or "coping" responses, aroused by psychologically threatening situations. The problem of explanation, however, becomes complex and elusive when we try to define what is meant by "defensive." Nevertheless, it is instructive to consider a few of the many possible interpretations of this progressive change in variability of scores.

According to Festinger (1954), if an individual does not have *significant others or reference groups* by which to evaluate his own achievements and abilities, the estimation of his position relative to others will be unstable. If the mentally ill individual is socially isolated (according to Festinger's definition of social isolation) and lacks available social bases for evaluation, he will place himself further above or below some vague reference point than the individual in the community who is not characterized by such isolation. If we assume that the patients' reference group choices are random, we can expect as many ill individuals to perceive themselves above, as below, their reference group.

Related to this interpretation is the possibility that the defensive systems of the patients are breaking down and becoming inefficient. This would also account for the greater variability of reference group discrepancy scores among the patients. If this inference is valid, and since in this context there is no reason to expect the patients to place themselves either above or below their reference group in any systematic fashion, both positional tendencies should be manifested. Both of these "explanations" (social isolation and the breaking down of defensive systems) should lead to a greater tendency among the patients to place themselves above or below their reference group, with no necessary preference for one position or the other.

It is also possible that the mentally ill person places himself above his reference group to bolster his self-esteem, or selects a reference group above his own position in order to derive vicarious pleasure through identification with "high-class" individuals. Although there is no reason to expect one particular tendency to be more prevalent in the ill population, we do predict more variability in reference group estimates among patients than community subjects.

These "explanations" of the increased variability of scores are speculative and *ad hoc* hypotheses related to placing oneself above or below his reference group. The variability of scores may be a function of less tenuous, more definable factors, such as achievement level and perception of the opportunity structure. We predict that a person at a high achievement level will manifest a small discrepancy, placing himself at or slightly above his reference group. A person with low achievement can be expected to show a larger discrepancy and to place himself below his reference group. The individual who perceives a closed opportunity structure will not necessarily choose a reference group much above his own position. If he perceives an open opportunity structure, he will probably select a reference group that is anywhere from slightly to considerably above his own position.

Since our data did show variations in achievement and in the perception of the opportunity structure in the ill and community populations, we investigated the possibility that the variability of reference group discrepancy scores was a function of these factors. In these analyses, we compared the psychotics and the low symptom group because they represented the extremes on our illness continuum and evidenced the greatest difference in variability of scores. From each of these two extreme groupings, we selected those who were at occupation level 2 on the seven-step occupational scale, and who perceived a very open opportunity structure. The variance for each of these subsamples was computed, and the significance of the difference between them was evaluated. We reasoned that if the difference in variance between these two groupings disappeared as a result of this analysis, the variability in scores could be attributed to achievement level and perception of the opportunity structure. In that case, the "defensive" hypotheses mentioned earlier could be considered superfluous.

There is little difference between the psychotics and the low symptom group in the proportion who place themselves above their reference group (15 and 13 per cent, respectively). Eighteen per cent of the psychotics, and 64 per cent of the low symptom individuals perceive themselves at the level of their reference group, while 67 per cent of the psychotics and 23 per cent of the low symptom group place themselves below their reference group. Clearly, the "defensive" or "coping" interpretations suggesting that ill individuals place themselves unsystematically above and below their reference group are not confirmed. Although the view of *nonsystematic* assignment of reference group position among the patients is not supported, more ill than community subjects do place themselves below their reference group, a finding consistent with the theoretical issues discussed earlier in this chapter.

We must consider whether controlling for achievement (i.e., occupation level) and for perception of the social system in these two mental health groupings affects the variability of reference group discrepancy scores. The difference in variability is reduced, but it is still significantly different—thus, although "defensive" interpretations which emphasize placement above and below one's reference group are untenable in this context, "defensive" or "coping" mechanisms cannot be completely disregarded in accounting for the greater spread of patients' choices below their reference group.

The analysis just described has certain implications for general theoretical views. According to social comparison theory (Festinger, 1954) and cognitive dissonance theory (Festinger, 1957), the individual who perceives a (negative) discrepancy between himself and a reference group will attempt to reduce this discrepancy in order to maintain his self-esteem. He may accomplish this by redefining the situation in one of two ways: he may select new, lower reference groups, closer to his evaluation of his present position. Or he may choose new reference groups which are higher than the old ones, but which have the effect of psychologically raising him to this higher achievement level. In either case he places himself at the achievement level of his reference group and thereby maintains his self-esteem.

Although the community respondents in our study behave in a manner consistent with social comparison theory, the mentally ill do not. How can this difference in behavior be explained? One possibility stems from the significantly lower self-esteem among the patients than among the community subjects (see Chapter 7). When an individual in the community sample places himself at the level of a reference group, he is maintaining an already comparatively high self-esteem level. If the patient, who has relatively low self-esteem, were to select a new reference group closer to his own achievement level, he would be reinforcing or acting to maintain this low self-esteem level. There is little reason to expect even an ill individual to behave in such a manner.

Reference Group Behavior Determined by
Subjective Social Status Position

A SECOND MEASURE was used in addition to the self-anchored striving scale to investigate the general relationship between reference group behavior and mental illness: the individual's subjective status position. Subjective status refers to one's evaluation of his own social status position compared to that of some relevant reference group. Perception of one's own position depends upon the status attributed to the others with whom he compares himself. As an example, individuals in a middle income range will perceive their own income level as low if compared to a Rockefeller, and as high if compared to that of a Southern sharecropper.

On the basis of this assumption we asked each respondent, "What things do you think of when you decide what social class a person belongs to?" (Appendix B, Question 199). The respondent either selected factors from a precoded list of various criteria of social class, or else specified additional unlisted criteria. He was then asked: "Taking into account the things you just told me, which of these choices best describes where you are?" (Appendix B, Question 200). The precoded alternatives were "Much above average," "Somewhat above average," "Average," "Somewhat below average," and "Much below average." We reasoned that most people probably compare themselves on overall status position to others who occupy a fairly similar position on the status continuum, and therefore regard themselves as "Average." In a group of individuals occupying the same objectively defined status position, those regarding themselves as "Below average" are comparing themselves with a higher status reference group, and those placing themselves "Above average" are comparing themselves with a status group lower than their own. This reasoning provided us with a procedure for determining the relative discrepancy from reference group and its direction. In order to simplify the presentation of these analyses, we combined the five subjective status categories into three: "Average," "Below average," and "Above average," The findings reported below were also obtained when all five subjective status categories were considered, however.

Table 6.4—Distribution of Subjective Social Status,

by Illness Status in Percentages

	TOTAL						MULTI-STATUS 1		MULTI-STATUS 2		MULTI-STATUS 3		MULTI-STATUS 4	
	Ill	Comm.	Low Symp.	High Symp.	Neur.	Psych.	Ill	Comm.	Ill	Comm.	Ill	Comm.	Ill	Comm.
⌐ch or Somewhat Above Average	18	15	15	14	16	19	11	9	14	12	19	12	33	26
⌐erage ⌐ch or Somewhat Below Average	43 39	63 22	63 22	63 23	48 36	42 40	40 50	54 36	45 42	65 22	46 35	69 19	40 28	62 12
	100	100	100	100	100	101	101	99	101	99	100	100	101	100
Total N	1394	1457	1285	172	353	1041	332	340	349	348	430	379	273	373

mmary of significant chi-square analyses
Total Ill vs Total Comm., $P < .001$
Psychotics vs High Symptom, $P < .001$
Psychotics vs Low Symptom, $P < .001$
Neurotics vs High Symptom, $P < .005$
Neurotics ve Low Symptom, $P < .001$
Multi-Status: Ill vs Comm., $P < .01$
Multi-Status: Ill vs Comm., $P < .001$
Multi-Status: Ill vs Comm., $P < .001$
Multi-Status: Ill vs Comm., $P < .001$

Table 6.4 presents data on the subjective status item for the total community and ill samples, for the mental health continuum, and for each of four objectively determined multi-status positions[1] within each sample. Hypothesis 2, which predicts that the degree of negative discrepancy from a reference group will be higher in the ill than in the general community population, is confirmed. The proportion of those regarding themselves as "Below average" (i.e., negative discrepancy from reference group) is significantly greater ($P = < .001$) for the patients than the community subjects. More of the community respondents regard their status position as "Average," but slightly more ill than community subjects consider their status "Above average." These same trends are evident in each of the four objective multi-status control groups and are significant in each case. These differences between the ill and the community populations also hold for each of the different sex and age subgroups and again are significant in every instance.

A more detailed examination of these four multi-status control groups reveals some additional findings. In each status control group more than half the responses of community respondents indicate "Average" subjective status. Among the mentally ill, all the corresponding percentages for the "Average" response are less than 50. As objective multi-status position increases from level 1 to 4, the proportion of those considering themselves "Below average" decreases among community and ill respondents, but it remains consistently higher among the mentally ill. Both mental illness and objective multi-status position appear to be influential in determining subjective social status position. It is important to note that as objective multi-status level goes from 1 to 4, "Above average" response choices tend to increase more rapidly among ill than among community respondents. The percentage difference between the ill and community populations on this response increases from 1 to 7 per cent. Thus, although respondents' objective and subjective social status positions rise simultaneously as expected, the ill are increasingly more likely to consider themselves "Above average." This suggests that as objective status increases, the mentally ill become relatively more prone to compare themselves with a reference group at a position below their own. The same tendency emerges in the analyses of the self-anchored striving scale: in the highest striving scale achievement control group, more patients than community individuals chose reference groups below their own position. This type of reference group choice may serve to (defensively) inflate

1. Social class, or "multi-status position," refers to the composite index of education, income, and occupation that has been discussed in Chapter 2. See also Appendix D.

self-esteem, but even in the mentally ill population such defenses are exaggerations, rather than complete distortions, of reality.

Earlier it was predicted that the psychotics would place themselves further below their reference group than the neurotics (Hypothesis 2a), and similarly, that the high symptom group would be more negatively discrepant than the low symptom group (Hypothesis 2b). Although the data on the subjective status item go in the predicted direction, neither hypothesis is supported by significant findings. When the four mental health groupings subsumed under the two hypotheses are considered on an illness continuum, the percentages of "Below average" responses increase progressively from the low symptom group to the psychotics (see Table 6.4). This sequential increase is statistically significant ($P = < .001$).

In addition, the percentages for both ill diagnostic groupings are significantly higher than either of the community sample groupings. There are no significant differences among the four mental health groupings on the "Above average" choice of subjective status position, nor is the direction of these responses consistent. Although there is no difference between the high and low symptom groups in the proportion of "Average" responses (i.e., no discrepancy from reference group), this percentage decreases progressively from the high symptom group, to the neurotics, to the psychotics. This tendency supports the idea that positive states of mental health are associated with little or no discrepancy from reference group.

No sex or age differences exist within the community population to support our expectations based on relative yield of mental disorder.

Reference Group Behavior Determined by Blue/White-Collar Occupational Choices

OUR QUESTIONNAIRE INSTRUMENT presented every subject with three pairs of occupations, each having a specified salary attached. The respondent was asked to select his own job preference from each pair (Appendix B, Question 93). Each paired choice consisted of one white- and one blue-collar occupation. The salary associated with the latter choice was always somewhat higher than for its white-collar counterpart. We assumed that when two individuals at the same objective socio-economic multi-status position were presented with these alternative choices, the one selecting the white-collar occupation with its lower salary did so because his reference norms were associated with a higher status nonmanual "middle-class" orientation (people, values, style of life, etc.). Since such occupations are considered to be higher and more prestigious on the social status continuum in our society, we felt that an analysis of these occupational choices constituted one index of the relative height of the reference groups selected by our subjects.

In order to insure additional validity for this assumption, we associated the white-collar occupations with particularly low weekly salaries ($60 to $80 range). Under such conditions, only those with a strong middle-class orientation would probably select the nonmanual job alternative. Two qualifications should be noted:

(1) Since some of the choices listed (e.g., bricklayer) are considered to be male occupations, we present only the responses given by males in our sample population.

(2) All those at multi-status positions 1 and 2 already have blue-collar occupations of differing degrees of skill. Position 3 contains individuals with both blue- and white-collar occupations, while level 4 includes only respondents in white-collar positions. Therefore, our assumption that the white-collar choice reflects a higher reference point applies mainly to subjects at the two lowest multi-status levels. This assumption should be less applicable at status level 3, and not at all applicable at level 4.

The blue/white-collar occupations and their attached salaries are listed in Table 6.5. Consistent with Hypothesis 2, we predict that significantly more patients at each multi-status level will choose the white-collar

Table 6.5—Blue-Collar White-Collar Occupational Choice as an Indicator of Reference

Group (Males) in Percentages

	MULTI-STATUS 1		MULTI-STATUS 2		MULTI-STATUS 3		MULTI-STATUS	
	I_{II}	Comm.	I_{II}	Comm.	I_{II}	Comm.	I_{II}	Comm.
Choice 1								
Blue-Collar: Bricklayer–$120	47	68	37	58	37	42	31	30
White-Collar: Teacher–$90	53	32	63	42	63	58	69	70
Total N	110	104	126	128	197	165	140	193
Choice 2								
Blue-Collar: Machine-Operator–$100	54	71	42	69	42	56	46	52
White-Collar: Gov't. Clerk–$80	46	29	58	31	58	44	54	48
Total N	110	104	126	128	197	165	140	193
Choice 3								
Blue-Collar: Factory Worker–$80	66	77	39	79	60	68	63	53
White-Collar: Sales Person (Department Store)–$60	34	23	61	21	40	32	37	47
Total N	110	104	126	127	197	163	140	187

Summary of significant chi-square analyses
Choice 1: Multi-Status-1, I_{II} vs Comm., $P = <.005$
Choice 1: Multi-Status-2, I_{II} vs Comm., $P = <.005$
Choice 2: Multi-Status-1, I_{II} vs Comm., $P = <.01$
Choice 2: Multi-Status-2, I_{II} vs Comm., $P = <.001$
Choice 2: Multi-Status-3, I_{II} vs Comm., $P = <.001$
Choice 3: Multi-Status-2, I_{II} vs Comm., $P = <.001$

occupations, despite the lower weekly salaries. With regard to the first pair of choices, more patients at multi-status levels 1, 2, and 3 select the white-collar position, although it offers a salary $30 below that of the blue-collar job. At levels 1 and 2, there is a 21 per cent difference between the ill and community respondents in number of white-collar choices ($P = < .005$). At level 3, the mentally ill are also more prone to choose the white-collar position, but the difference between the two populations is not significant. At the highest multi-status position there is virtually no difference between the two populations in occupational choices. As mentioned previously, since many level 3, and all level 4 individuals already occupy white-collar positions, the choice of this alternative (with its associated lower remuneration) does not tap any existing desire for upward social mobility.

With respect to the second paired set of jobs, at every multi-status position except the highest, significantly ($P = < .01$) more ill choose the white-collar job, despite its wage penalty of $20 and a fairly low absolute weekly salary ($80). Even at level 4, the percentage of white-collar choices is higher among the ill (although not significantly). As expected, the largest difference between the two populations in these choices occurs at levels 1 and 2 (17 and 27 per cent, respectively) and then decreases progressively at levels 3 and 4 (14 and 6 per cent, respectively).

The difference in salary between the third set of paired blue/white-collar positions is also $20, but the absolute weekly salary of the white-collar job is only $60. In addition, the status of a department store sales person is not as high as for the other white-collar alternatives. A relatively unattractive white-collar position was intentionally selected in order to see whether the expected pattern would continue to emerge. More mentally ill than community respondents at the first three status levels again choose the white-collar occupation (see Table 6.5). The differences between the ill and community populations are significant only at multi-status positions 1 and 2 ($P = < .05$). This trend is reversed at level 4, where the community respondents are more prone to choose the white-collar occupation.

Since the blue/white-collar analyses consider only responses given by males, we cannot discuss sex differences with respect to the yield issue. However, analyses were carried out to uncover age differences among males in the community sample. For the first paired blue/white-collar choice, 61 per cent of the young and 48 per cent of the older subjects choose the white-collar alternative ($P = < .01$). Similarly, for the second paired choice more young than older individuals (48 and 33 per cent, respectively) select the nonmanual occupation ($P = < .01$). Finally, for the third paired choice, 10 per cent more of the young respondents prefer the white-collar job ($P = < .05$). According to expectation, the young, who show a higher yield of mental disorder, manifest more frequent white-collar occupational aspirations for all three paired job choices.

In summary, ten of the twelve comparisons indicate that the patients are more prone than the community respondents to choose the low-salary white-collar occupations. Seven of these ten analyses are statistically significant (by sign test, $P = < .01$). This ill-community difference is pronounced at the lowest multi-status position, becomes even more apparent at level 2, and then decreases considerably at level 3. At the highest multi-status position, differences between the ill and community respondents are inconsistent in magnitude and direction. The results for the two highest levels are not unexpected, but the relative increase in the difference between the two populations in white-collar choices from status level 1 to level 2 is puzzling. The possibility of white-collar occupational achievement may be so remote to a Negro at level 1 that it does not evoke strong achievement striving. At level 2 such a possibility is not as distant, and striving for white-collar jobs is more salient. It is at this position that differences between the community and ill populations becomes most pronounced.

In this connection it is also interesting that within the community, the percentage of respondents selecting the white-collar alternative increases directly with multi-status position: the higher the level, the higher the proportion of white-collar choices. Only one of twelve relevant comparisons shows the opposite trend. In the mentally ill population this percentage increases sharply from level 1 to level 2, and at the two higher levels becomes erratic and inconsistent. One interpretation of these findings suggests that the reference group choices of community respondents are determined to a considerable extent by the objective reality of their achievement.

Findings reported earlier in this chapter clearly indicate that community respondents tend to place themselves at the position of their reference group more frequently than the patients (who deviate in both directions, but are predominantly below their reference group). The data relevant to the community respondents conform to what would be expected on the basis of Festinger's (1954) "social comparison theory." Festinger and his co-workers found that individuals in group situations tended to modify their opinions and aspirations so that they conformed to those of the other group members. Although the situation we are considering does not involve common membership in a formal group, most individuals will probably tend to adjust their opinions, attitudes, and aspirations to those of individuals with whom they commonly interact. This may account for the tendency of most community respondents to place themselves at, or close to, their reference group level. On the other hand, the mentally ill seem much less constrained by their objective status position and the pressures generated by their status peers. Their selections of goals may conform more to Hyman's designation of "autistic" choices.

Responses given by females to the three sets of paired occupational choices were also analyzed. Among females there are fewer white-collar choices, and no significant differences between the community and ill populations. The ability of the blue/white-collar questions to discriminate in the male population, and its failure to do so among females, suggests that males are more inclined to prove their adequacy and maintain their self-esteem in the vocational area. It is not surprising, then, that the occupational reference group should be higher for males than for females, and that it should constitute a more sensitive correlation of mental health among males.

Racial Identification of the Negro as an Indicator of Reference Group

THE TWO QUESTIONNAIRE ITEMS analyzed in this section involve the degree to which respondents use other Negroes as a reference group. Almost every clinical study of psychopathology among Negroes indicates that the Negro who is not indentified with other members of his group, or who aspires to "be white," is relatively more prone to manifest various forms of mental ill health. Sometimes this phenomenon is referred to as "self-hate" or "color denial." Its importance for mental health is extensively documented. Because this phenomenon cannot be conceptualized in terms of a quantitative scale, we shall use these data to explore the manifestation of this behavior in our various population subgroups rather than for the rigorous testing of our hypotheses.

One of the questions to be analyzed in this connection deals with the issue of "passing"—that is, a Negro's attempt to deny his racial membership and to "pass" as white. We felt that a Negro's attitude toward this issue was a good index of the strength of his identification with other Negroes, or the degree to which he used other Negroes as a reference group. It was assumed that if a Negro subject either condoned or showed no concern over the passing issue (i.e., had no affective reaction to it), he did not use other Negroes as a salient reference group. The individual who strongly condemned such behavior was assumed to be more prone to use other Negroes as a reference group. We asked each respondent for his reactions to a hypothetical friend who said that he wanted to pass "because of the advantages that it would give him" (Appendix B, Question 166). The responses to this open-ended question were subsequently categorized as follows:

(1) Condones passing (feels that it is a good decision, would like to do it himself, etc.).

(2) Not involved in the issue (does not care, or feels unconcerned about the matter).

(3) Ambivalent about the decision to pass (expresses both positive and negative affect toward the decision or toward the hypothetical friend).

(4) Condemns passing ("He is a traitor to his race;" "He is letting the rest of us down;" "I would have no use for him," etc.).

For purposes of analysis categories (1) and (2) were combined, with the assumption that individuals expressing either type of reaction were minimally inclined to use other Negroes as a reference group. We expected the mentally ill to show a greater inclination than the community individuals to condone or to feel uninvolved in the passing decision. At this point it is difficult to predict or speculate about the meaning of response categories (3) and (4); we shall merely examine the data and suggest possible interpretations.

Table 6.6 presents the percentage distributions of responses to passing. The difference between the total ill and community sample is statistically significant ($P = < .001$). More ill than community respondents either condone or feel uninvolved in this issue, suggesting, as predicted, that the mentally ill are less inclined to use other Negroes as a salient reference group. It should be reemphasized that this interpretation rests on the assumption of a positive correlation between group identification and its use as a reference group: the more strongly one identifies himself with a particular group, the more likely he is to use its norms and values in evaluating himself and events in his environment. Whatever its significance for understanding reference group behavior, the combination of response categories (1) and (2) is the modal one for individuals in both samples.

Table 6.6—Reaction to Hypothetical Friend's
Desire to Pass, in Percentages

| | TOTAL | | | | | |
	Ill	Comm.	Low Symp.	High Symp.	Neur.	Psych.
Condones passing or not involved in issue	48	39	41	35	43	49
Ambivalent	21	34	36	31	24	21
Condemns	30	22	22	29	32	29
Other	+	4	1	5	1	1
	100	99	100	100	100	100
Total N	1405	1479	1257	172	357	1048

Summary of significant chi-square analyses
Total Ill vs Total Comm., P=<.001
Psychotics vs High Symptom, P=<.001
Psychotics vs Low Symptom, P=<.001
Neurotics vs High Symptom, P=<.02
Neurotics vs Low Symptom, P=<.001
High Symptom vs Low Symptom, P=<.001
Comm. Males vs Comm. Females, P=<.02
Comm. Young vs Comm. Old, P=<.001

More patients than community subjects condemn the decision to pass (see Table 6.6). To be consistent with the interpretation offered in the above paragraph, we must maintain that, in this context, the patients are *more* prone than the community respondents to use Negroes as a salient reference group. It appears that the total ill population is characterized by the occurrence of both extreme responses, while the community population contains many more respondents who feel ambivalent about the passing decision. Community respondents apparently tend to consider both Negroes and whites as reference groups, while the patients are more absolute in choosing one or the other.

Within the community population, males (who have a higher yield of mental disorder than females) show a greater tendency to condone passing or to deny involvement in the issue ($P = < .02$). Our expectation of age difference based on the yield of mental disorder is not supported, however. There are no differences between the two age subgroups on this combined response category, although significantly more young than older subjects express ambivalence about passing ($P = < .001$).

These reactions to the passing question support some of the findings reported in clinical studies of mental illness among Negroes (Adams, 1950; Kardiner and Ovesey, 1951; Bernard, 1953), indicating that patients frequently use their Negro identity "as a defense against facing other problems . . . projecting all their difficulties onto the racial prejudice of the therapist or others . . . or denying the fact that being a Negro has any effect at all on their lives" (Shane, 1960). Therapists have often observed that Negro patients commonly accept many of the white negative stereotypes about Negroes, with a consequent rejection of self and other Negroes. This insight helps us to understand the rather high percentage of mentally ill in the present study who either condone passing or say that the issue does not concern them.

Assuming that the foregoing reasoning is valid, we expect an increase in both of these extreme reactions and a decrease in "Ambivalent" responses as severity of illness increases. As we move along the mental health continuum from the low symptom group to the psychotics, the proportion of extreme responses (i.e., "Condones," or "Not involved" responses, combined with "Condemns" responses) increase as predicted: 63, 64, 75, and 78 per cent, respectively. At the same time, the "Ambivalent" responses decrease progressively from 36 to 21 per cent through the four mental health groupings (see Table 6.6).

It is interesting that so many individuals in all mental health groupings select one of the extreme responses to passing, and also that the highest proportions of responses in all groupings fall into the "Condones-Not involved" category. Our data indicate that the community population is relatively inclined to use Negroes *and* whites as reference groups, whereas the patients apparently select one group or the other. The mentally ill may be less able to sustain the ambivalence and conflict implicit in the community responses and thus tend to give the more extreme responses. Although ambivalence in identification patterns has often been associated with psychopathology in the clinical literature, ambivalence in the present instance may very well be realistic and adaptive for the Negro. It is the polarization of racial identification or reference group behavior that is psychopathogenic. Our data show that the psychiatrically healthy Negro is an individual with conflicts about his racial identification. It is the mentally ill person who tends to remove this constant conflict from conscious awareness.

The problem concerning the use of other Negroes as a reference group warrants further investigation, both because the issue has been so frequently related to Negro mental health, and because our interpretation of the "passing" question is somewhat speculative. Each respondent was asked whether being a Negro "has prevented you from getting the things you wanted?" (Appendix B, Question 194). The four precoded response choices were "Yes, very much;" "Yes, to some degree;" "Yes, slightly;" and "No." We assumed that a Negro who did not use other Negroes as a reference group would be more inclined to answer "No" to this question—that is, since he did not use Negro norms and values to evaluate the social barriers to which he was exposed, he would deny that being a Negro was a barrier to his goal achievements. Implicit in this reasoning is the assumption that Negroes in our society have actually been handicapped considerably by their skin color, and that the Negro who completely denies this is also denying his own racial membership.

Table 6.7—"Being a Negro" as a Perceived Barrier to Achievement

in Percentages

| | TOTAL | | | | | |
	Iₙ	Comm.	Low Symp.	High Symp.	Neur.	Psych.
Very Much	11	8	8	7	11	11
Slightly or to Some Degree	32	57	58	52	40	29
Not at all	57	35	34	41	49	59
	100	100	100	100	100	99
Total N	1416	1473	1299	174	358	1058

Summary of significant chi-square analyses
Total Iₙ vs Total Comm., $P = <.001$
Psychotics vs Neurotics, $P = <.005$
Psychotics vs High Symptom, $P = <.001$
Psychotics vs Low Symptom, $P = <.001$
Neurotic vs Low Symptom, $P = <.001$

Table 6.7 presents the responses to this barrier question. Relatively few community and mentally ill respondents feel that being a Negro has been "Very much" of a barrier to their achievement, while a very high percentage of both samples say that it has not constituted any barrier. In this connection it should be noted that the modal response of the community and ill subjects to the "passing" question indicated either condonation or lack of concern about such behavior. The findings on both of these questionnaire items suggest a surprising lack of strong racial identification in these populations.[2] Significantly more mentally ill than community subjects ($P = <.001$) report that their racial membership has not been any barrier to achievement (see Table 6.7). This significant difference between the two samples is maintained for each of the sex and age control groups. If our assumptions about the meaning of this question are valid, we can conclude that considerably fewer ill than community respondents use Negroes as a salient reference group. Table 6.7 also shows that 57 per cent of the community respondents, compared to only 32 per cent of the patients, feel that being a Negro has constituted "Somewhat" of a barrier. Although more patients than community individuals see their racial membership as "Very much" of a barrier, the percentage difference between the two populations on this response is very small. As in the question on passing, the mentally ill are somewhat more inclined in this instance to select one or both of the extreme responses.

2. The data underlying this conclusion were gathered in 1960 and may not reflect the effects of current developments in the Negro civil rights movement.

When community sample males and females are compared, expectations based on the yield issue are not supported. Significantly more females than males in the community population feel that being a Negro does not constitute a barrier to achievement. Negro males apparently feel more disadvantaged than females by their racial identification. This probably reflects their greater actual involvement and frustration in vocational aspirations.

Since young respondents in our community sample have a higher-than-expected yield of mental disorder, we expect this age subgroup to be more inclined than the older respondents to answer "No" to this barrier question. This expectation is confirmed: 40 per cent of the young, and only 29 per cent of the older subgroup, give this response ($P = < .001$).

A consideration of the relationship between "No barriers" responses and the four mental health groupings reveals a direct increase in the expected direction. The number of subjects giving this response increases from the low symptom group to the psychotics (see Table 6.7). This progressive increase in denial suggests that, as illness becomes more severe, individuals are less inclined to use other Negroes as a reference group.

*Modes of Adjustment in Ethnic
Reference Group Behavior*

RESPONSE PATTERNS which emerge in the presentation and discussion of data on attitudes toward passing, and one's perception of his race as a barrier to goal achievement, raise some interesting problems. The community subjects are "Ambivalent" about passing and at the same time recognize that being Negro has been "Very much" or "Somewhat" of an obstacle to goal achievement. The patients are either "Angry" about a friend's passing, or else "Condone" and thus avoid emotional involvement in the issue. These patients also completely deny that being Negro has presented any obstacle to goal achievement.

The pattern that characterizes the community population seems logical and internally consistent: one who has been socialized to believe that the opportunity structure is open to all individuals, and who then discovers that Negroes are exceptions to this rule, will undoubtedly experience some ambivalence about his racial membership. Conversely, if a person is already ambivalent about being a Negro, any experiences emphasizing the handicaps imposed on him by his race will probably intensify his ambivalence.

The configuration of responses for the mentally ill shows two inconsistent patterns. On one hand, these individuals completely deny the importance of race as a personal barrier, and at the same time condone passing for the advantages it will provide. Apparently they actually perceive advantages to being white and therefore are admitting implicitly that race *is* a handicap to goal striving. On the other hand, some of the patients who deny the importance of race as a barrier concomitantly express anger toward a person who wants to pass. If they really consider race an unimportant issue, their annoyance is inappropriate. The inconsistencies in these patterns among the mentally ill suggest problems of racial identification and inefficient modes of adjustment to the fact of racial membership. However, subgroup analyses within the community population indicate possible modifications of this conclusion.

According to the yield issue, we predict that males (compared to females) and the young respondents (compared to the older subgroup) will manifest more of the characteristics of the mentally ill than of the community population. In the present context, neither of the high yield subgroups conforms fully to the response configurations of the ill population. Although males show significantly less ambivalence than females with respect to the passing issue, significantly more females than males deny that being a Negro has constituted any barrier to goal achievement. Unlike the ill population, the young show significantly more ambivalence about passing than do the older respondents, although, according to prediction, significantly more young than older subjects deny the role of racial membership.

When the responses to these two questionnaire items are analyzed across both samples with sex and age controls, different patterns of adjustment emerge. The response patterns characteristic of each total population are reflected in the ill and well male subgroups, but the female subgroups do not conform to these configurations. Community sample females manifest the predominant "Ambivalent" reaction to passing, but they also express a concomitant denial of race as a barrier in their lives. If race has never been a problem, why do these females have mixed feelings about a hypothetical friend who wants to pass? Mentally ill females show a decrease in the "Ambivalent" reaction to passing and an increase in denial. This decrease in ambivalence (i.e., resolution of conflict) is expressed in three responses: an approximately equal increase in subjects who would be "Angry," would "Condone," and would "Not get involved."

Like the female subgroup, the young respondents within the community population manifest ambivalence about passing, and, at the same time, deny the importance of race as a barrier to goal achievement. This pattern of responses again raises the question of why the young should show this ambivalence if being a Negro has never constituted a barrier. When we consider the young patients, the denial response becomes even more pronounced (as does the opposite extreme, "Very much" of a barrier), and the ambivalent reaction is replaced by an expression of anger toward the individual who wants to pass. The response pattern of the young patients is one of internal inconsistency. Although they deny the existence of racial barriers, the intensity of their emotional response (i.e., anger toward the individual who wants to pass) suggests that they do not really accept this. We must then ask why passing should be a matter of such concern to the ill individual. It is possible that he himself has thought about passing, and has either failed or experienced guilt at even considering it as a course of action.

The older community respondents are characterized by predominantly "Ambivalent" reactions toward passing, and they feel that being a Negro has been "Very much" or "Somewhat" of a barrier to achievement. This pattern appears to be internally consistent because a clear basis for the ambivalence exists. Again, as one moves into the mentally ill population, denial of race as a barrier becomes the predominant response (21 per cent in the community population and 51 per cent in the patient population), with a slight increase in respondents who consider race "Very much" of a barrier. As denial increases, the ambivalent reaction decreases, but the resolution of the conflict is again generally in one direction—the older ill subjects "Condone" this action. Clearly, the older respondents manifest a somewhat different mode of adjustment than the younger subgroup. Finally, it should be noted that the responses of the older patients create problems of internal consistency not encountered in the response pattern of their community counterparts. Race seemingly constitutes no barrier to the older patients, but they condone passing for its advantages, thereby implying that race *is* a problem.

In summary, the propensity of the mentally ill to select extreme reactions to passing is due to the young patients, who are "Angry" about it, and the older ill subjects, who "Condone" it. Also, the sex and age subgroups within the community population show different orientations toward their racial membership when compared with each other and with the corresponding patient subgroups. With respect to the passing issue, the patients manifest different resolutions of ambivalence than the community subgroups from which they come.

Summary

THE FINDINGS PRESENTED in this chapter offer striking support for the three hypotheses concerning reference group behavior. In spite of some deviations from the predictions, the data indicate that the mentally ill place themselves further below their reference group than do those in the community sample. Consistent with data on goal striving presented in previous chapters, findings on reference group behavior confirm that mental disorder is linked to relatively high social mobility strivings. Not only do the mentally ill experience high levels of stress associated with goal striving, but they also tend to compare themselves with reference groups considerably above them on various status criteria. Such a configuration might result in feelings of relative deprivation, personal failure, and loss of self-esteem. This issue will be investigated further in the following chapter. At this point we shall recapitulate some of the major findings on reference group behavior.

The major measure used to investigate this phenomenon was the discrepancy between the individual's perception of his own position and that which he attributed to his "close friends." The criteria involved in these evaluations were determined by the individual himself when he made these judgments. There is a high rank order correlation between the criterion choices of community and mentally ill respondents. Although the mean discrepancies in both populations are negative, the patients are significantly further below their reference group than the community subjects. This difference holds for comparisons using sex and age controls. Furthermore, when the position perceived for the self is controlled, the mentally ill continue to show significantly larger negative discrepancies than the community respondents at every control level. At the highest control level the mentally ill place themselves above their reference group more frequently than do community subjects.

There is a direct relationship between severity of illness and degree of negative discrepancy from reference group, thus confirming our predictions. We find significantly higher negative discrepancies among the psychotics than the neurotics, and among the high symptom group than the low symptom group.

Another measure of reference group behavior, although less direct than the reference group discrepancy, involved the concept of subjective status. When objective multi-status position is controlled, the mentally ill consistently regard their status as "Below average," to a much greater degree than those in the community population (i.e., the ill tend to be relatively more negatively discrepant from their reference group). This trend also emerges when sex and age controls are applied. The percentage of "Below average" responses increases directly with severity of illness as we move along the mental health continuum. Although this progression among the four groups taken together is statistically significant, the differences between the high and low symptom groups and between the psychotics and the neurotics are not significant.

A third measure of reference group discrepancy was determined by respondents' choices of blue- versus white-collar occupations. We predicted that at every objective social class level (in the male population) the patients would be more prone than the community respondents to select the lower salaried, white-collar positions. This prediction is supported in ten out of twelve relevant comparisons; seven of the ten are statistically significant. As expected, the exceptions to this prediction are confined to the highest multi-status positions, where individuals have already achieved white-collar positions. The findings do not support predictions based on relative yield of mental disorder within community sex and age subgroups. There are no consistent sex or age differences on any of these measures of reference group behavior.

Finally, two questions were utilized to learn more about the relationship between mental disorder and respondents' identification with other Negroes, taken as a group. The first of these questions dealt with attitudes towards passing. A greater number of the patients choose extreme responses (i.e., they either "Condone" or "Condemn" this behavior), while more community respondents feel "Ambivalent" about an individual who wants to pass. The proportion of those selecting these extreme responses increases along the mental health continuum, and the percentage of subjects who express ambivalence decreases progressively from the low symptom group to the psychotics. The second question dealing with racial identification involved the individual's perception of the degree to which being a Negro had constituted a barrier to his achievement. On this item, the most noticeable difference between the ill and community samples is that significantly more patients deny that being a Negro has constituted any barrier. The percentage of denial increases progressively with severity of illness along the mental health continuum. Both of these questions dealing with racial identification indicate that the ill subject is less inclined than his community counterpart to use other Negroes as a salient reference group, and also that this disinclination increases directly with severity of illness.

There has been no discussion up to this point of findings pertaining to sex and age differences within the mentally ill population. These data were not related to the specific questions we wished to explore, but brief mention will be made of these findings. In regard to the discrepancy between one's perceived position and that of his close friends, no significant differences emerge between males and females or between young and older subjects. Similar results are obtained when the subjective status question is analyzed. Neither sex nor age factors influence the perception of one's social status or class position. Attitudes towards passing in the patient population do not vary with sex, but do vary significantly when age is controlled—the younger respondents are "Angry" or "Ambivalent" toward a hypothetical friend who wishes to pass, whereas the older respondents are more inclined to "Condone" or "Not become involved" in this action. Both sex and age differences emerge in the question concerning perception of the degree to which being a Negro has been a barrier to achievement. Males are more inclined than females to see race as "Very much" or "Somewhat" of a barrier to achievement. Older individuals also tend to feel that being a Negro has been a significant barrier; the young are more prone to deny this.

7

SELF-ESTEEM AND MENTAL DISORDER

Some General Considerations of
Self-Esteem and Mental Disorder

In an earlier chapter we provided the rationale for including self-esteem as an important variable in the present study. The self, as defined here, involves "the individual person as the object of his own perception" (Murphy, 1947: 523). This definition includes both the content of what is known and one's evaluation of this content. If we accept the idea of the self-image as an historical resultant of social interaction with significant others, then low self-esteem must be closely linked with problems in interpersonal relationships. In accordance with many currently accepted psychiatric theories of mental disorder as a disturbance of such relationships (Sullivan, 1947), the etiological role of self-esteem assumes considerable importance. Low self-esteem has been found to characterize large numbers of Negro adults and children. Researchers who have studied psychopathology in this group have been particularly aware of the prevalence and depth of self-abasement in their subjects (Kardiner and Ovesey, 1951; Sclare, 1953). A person with low self-esteem tends to feel that others hold negative opinions of him. If we assume that one's self-evaluation can also be a means of preserving and enhancing the organism (in terms of what he considers important), then low self-evaluation indicates feelings of deprivation and threat by the social environment. We further assume that low self-evaluation is an important precondition for mental disorder.

Researchers in this area either have conceptualized self-esteem as contributing directly to illness, or have at least associated it with susceptibility to mental disorder. The weight of the evidence clearly establishes a direct correlation between negative evaluations of self and poor mental health (Rogers, 1951; Calvin and Holtzman, 1953; Cowen, 1954; Rogers and Dymond, 1954; Combs and Syngg, 1959: 267, ff.). However, studies in this area have employed different operational definitions of self-esteem and mental health. Self-esteem has been determined by such measures as responses to psychological tests, self-reports about satisfaction or dissatisfaction with "the self," trait check lists, and the discrepancy between actual and ideal self-image. The state of mental health related to one's self-esteem has also been determined by diverse methods and encompasses such phenomena as mild forms of maladjustment, physical symptoms assumed to reflect psychopathology, and severe psychotic disorders. These varying approaches not only reflect operational differences, but also raise substantive questions about the self-esteem concept itself (e.g., To what extent must the individual be aware of low self-esteem for it to have psychological consequences? What are the psychological effects of different types of adjustment on low self-esteem?). Despite these difficulties in conceptualization and operational definition, the consistency of the findings supports the generalization about the relationship between low self-esteem and mental disorder.

Carl Rogers and his associates (1954) have been among the most active contributors to the research in this field. Through a series of carefully conducted clinical studies they showed that the mentally ill had large discrepancies between their actual and ideal self-images. Furthermore, Butler and Haigh (1954) reported that psychotherapy judged successful by the use of various independent criteria was accompanied by significant reductions in these discrepancies.

There are studies suggesting that a simple and direct link between self-esteem and maladjustment does not always exist. Some investigators have reported a curvilinear relationship between these variables (i.e., groups regarded as maladjusted showed extremes of high and low self-esteem (Block and Thomas, 1955; Hatfield, 1958; Altrocchi, 1960)). It appears that self-evaluation, as measured by a self-ideal discrepancy, may be influenced by the specific personality configuration of the subject as it determines the means he uses to cope with threatening situations. Altrocchi (1960) and others (McGinnies and Adornetto, 1952; Friedman, 1955) found that some patients characteristically repressed perceptions that could result in lowered self-esteem. The individual with an inadequate self concept must be careful to prevent awareness of further threats to his self. This end may be accomplished by perceptual distortions, motivated by a strong need to enhance his self concept in his own and others' eyes (Cowen and Beir, 1950; Chodorkoff, 1954). However, in the face of prolonged or severe threats, such an individual may accept himself as defeated and incapable of dealing with life, and may readily acknowledge and even exaggerate his devalued self-image. Many psychotics show this kind of reaction (Combs and Syngg, 1959: 267).

In summary, the literature suggests that although mental illness appears to be associated predominantly with low self-esteem, a patient population will probably be characterized by greater extremes of self-esteem than a comparable randomly selected group from the community.

Hypotheses and Findings

HYPOTHESES 3, 3a, and 3b (Chapter 1) flow from our assumption of an inverse relationship between severity of illness and degree of self-esteem. These hypotheses predict that self-esteem will be lower in the ill than in the community population, lower among the psychotics than among the neurotics, and lower in the high psychiatric symptom group than in the low psychiatric symptom group. Although we make no specific predictions to this effect, we also entertain the possibility of lower self-esteem among the neurotics than among the high symptom group. If these expectations are confirmed, a progressive decrease in self-esteem from the low symptom group, to the high symptom group, to the neurotics, to the psychotics will be established.

In addition to testing these hypotheses, we shall determine whether self-esteem is lower in community subpopulations with high yields of mental disorder. It has already been reported (see Chapter 3) that males have a higher representation in the mentally ill sample than one would expect from their distribution in the community population, and similarly that the young age group (twenty to thirty-nine years) has a higher illness yield than the older group (forty to sixty years). Given these findings, we anticipate that within the community sample low self-esteem will be more characteristic of males than of females, and of young than of older respondents.

SELF-ESTEEM INDEX

Questionnaire items embodying different operational definitions of self-esteem were used to test these hypotheses and general expectations. We particularly emphasize the importance of the first measure to be reported here: the discrepancy between the actual and the ideal self-image, used as an index of self-esteem. The higher this discrepancy, the lower the self-esteem.

In order to derive a discrepancy score for each individual in the ill and community populations, each respondent was presented with two sets of seventeen statements (Appendix B, Questions 94–110 and 126–142). Each of the first set of statements was preceded by the phrase, "I am a person who . . ." (self-image), and the second set of statements by the phrase, "I would like to be a person who . . ." (ideal self-image). In order to negate any psychological set, questions in an unrelated content area (Appendix B, Questions 111–125) were interposed between the seventeen actual and ideal self-image statements. By this means we hoped to minimize the possibility that responses to the first set of statements would influence responses to the second. The specification of a wide variety of interpersonal situations in these statements was intended to elicit a stable and representative sample of each subject's behavior. For each of the actual and ideal self-image statements, the respondent selected one of four responses, ranging from "Almost never" to "Almost always." Each of these responses was previously assigned a numerical value. An average discrepancy score was derived for each individual by the following procedure:

(1) The numerical difference between the responses to each actual self-image statement and its ideal counterpart was determined.

(2) These differences were summed.

(3) This sum was divided by the number of paired statements actually answered.

Since the response categories for the two sets of statements were assigned numerical values from one to four, the size of the discrepancy between any pair of statements ranged from zero to three. An example may clarify this scoring procedure. Let us assume that to the statement, "I am a person who takes an active part in organizations," the respondent chose the alternative "Almost never," previously assigned a value of one. When presented with the corresponding statement, "I would like to be a person who takes an active part in organizations," he responded, "Almost always," with a predetermined value of four. Therefore, his discrepancy for this pair of statements was three. His average self-ideal discrepancy would be derived by adding the scores for all his discrepancies and dividing this sum by the total number of paired statements to which he actually responded. The self-ideal discrepancy for the total ill and community populations was obtained by taking the mean of all the average discrepancies for individuals within that group.

The seventeen pairs of statements used as a basis for our self-esteem index described behavior and participation in various types of activities and interpersonal situations (e.g., "I am a person who tries harder to win an argument with a white person than with a Negro." "I am a person who shares the responsibility of training my children."). Statements of this type were used instead of simple trait lists because we felt that a person's self-evaluations were linked to specific interpersonal situations rather than to "free floating" internalized traits. In evaluating himself, the individual considers his social performance, his own assessment of this performance, and the judgments of others, in specific situations. In addition, detached traits frequently reflect high-order abstractions in the mind of the investigator rather than within the subject himself. To force subjects, particularly those with low educational attainments, to evaluate such abstractions might well compound the difficulties in interpreting the results. We assumed that specifying behavior *in concrete situations* would reduce this potential source of misunderstanding and error. This method also allowed us to examine separately the perceived discrepancy within a few social roles or subidentities of the overall self-image. As noted previously, an individual may have markedly different self-evaluations in various areas of social role performance. There may be a considerable disparity, for example, between his perception of himself as a husband and as a father.

SELF-ESTEEM IN THE ILL AND COMMUNITY POPULATIONS

Table 7.1 summarizes the mean self-ideal discrepancies for the total ill and community samples and for various subgroups within these populations. The total ill sample is characterized by a significantly higher mean discrepancy (i.e., low self-esteem) than the total community

Table 7.1—Mean Self-Ideal Discrepancy and Illness Status,

by Sex and Age

(1)	(2)	Mean (1)	Mean (2)	N1	N2	P (by "t" test)
Total Ill vs Total Community		.74	.52	1423	1485	<.001
Ill Males vs Comm. Males		.74	.50	576	602	<.001
Ill Females vs Comm. Females		.75	.53	845	803	<.001
Ill Young vs Comm. Young		.76	.54	1007	795	<.001
Ill Old vs Comm. Old		.72	.50	414	687	<.001
Neurotics vs Psychotics		.74	.74	363	1060	<.001
High Symptom vs Neurotics		.63	.74	174	363	<.001
Low Symptom vs High Symptom		.50	.63	1311	174	<.001
Comm. Males vs Comm. Females		.50	.53	602	803	<.05
Comm. Young vs Comm. Old		.54	.50	795	687	<.02

sample. This difference is maintained even with sex and age controls. Hypothesis 3 is thus confirmed.

It should also be noted that the variance around the mean is significantly ($P = < .001$) higher in the ill sample, indicating more of a tendency among the patients to manifest greater extremes of self-esteem, or at least significantly larger deviations from the mean position. This finding is relevant to the previously mentioned possibility that ill respondents may use psychological defensive maneuvers in their self-evaluations. We assume that psychological defense involves a denial or distortion of threatening aspects of a situation, and that the number of such defenses increases with the severity of illness, a possibility to be explored further in subsequent data analyses.

Table 7.1 indicates that, contrary to Hypothesis 3a, the neurotics and psychotics do not differ in self-esteem. Although this lack of difference cannot be directly explained by these data, psychotic patients may be more prone to deny negative aspects of the self, as a defense against high levels of anxiety. Neurotics, on the other hand, may tend to depreciate themselves in order to rationalize their avoidance of striving and of potential threats to self-esteem.

As predicted by Hypothesis 3b, the high symptom group has lower self-esteem than the low symptom group. In support of our general assumption that self-esteem is inversely related to the severity of mental illness, it should be noted that the mean discrepancy for the neurotic population is significantly higher than that of the high symptom group. The mean discrepancy score for the high symptom group lies about midway between that of the low symptom group and the neurotics and is significantly different from both. As the severity of illness increases from the low symptom group to the neurotics, there is a progressive decrease in self-esteem. The psychotics do not conform to this expected pattern.

How are sex and age related to self-esteem? Based on the relative yield of mental disorder, we predict that in the community population, males will have lower self-esteem than females, and that the young will have lower self-esteem than the older subjects. Table 7.1 indicates that the young *are* more discrepant (lower self-esteem) than the older respondents, but that, contrary to expectation, females have higher self-ideal discrepancies than males. This latter finding is somewhat puzzling. A consideration of yield, as well as independent studies of self-esteem among Negroes (Ausbel, 1956), leads us to expect higher self-ideal discrepancies, or lower self-esteem, among males. It is possible that sex differences in socialization make females more prone to conceptualize their self-evaluation in terms of personality traits. Males may be more likely to use criteria related to achievement in socioeconomic areas of life. With this possibility in mind, we shall pay particular attention to sex differences on other measures of self-esteem considered in this chapter.

We now turn to a consideration of the correlations between self-esteem and the two- and four-step illness continua. These correlations are both significant ($-.34$, $P = < .001$). They indicate that as a person's self-esteem diminishes (i.e., as his self-ideal discrepancy increases), the likelihood of his falling into the psychotic grouping increases. The coefficient does not change, whether the linear or nonlinear assumption is made.

When self-ideal discrepancy scores are correlated with scores on the psychoneurotic symptom inventory, the same significant coefficient is obtained ($.35$, $P = < .001$) whether the liner or ninlinear assumption is applied. This coefficient indicates that an increase in the self-ideal discrepancy (i.e., a decrease in self-esteem) is associated with an increase in reported psychoneurotic symptoms.

VARIABILITY OF THE SELF-IDEAL DISCREPANCY AS A FUNCTION OF "DEFENSIVE" AND "COPING" REACTIONS

It has been noted that as one moves along the mental health continuum from the low symptom group to the psychotics, there is an increasing tendency to find both high and low self-ideal discrepancy scores (i.e., an increase in variance). This increasing variability may be a function of (1) the breaking down or collapsing of the individual's defensive systems; (2) differences in the use of "defensive" responses; (3) the erratic or "irrational" behavior of the disturbed person; or (4) the effect of the interaction between one's perception of the opportunity structure and his occupational achievement.

We have already shown that high self-esteem among the psychotics is associated with the perception of a relatively closed opportunity structure and comparatively high achievement levels. Conversely, low self-esteem in this mental health grouping is associated with the perception of an open opportunity structure and lower achievement levels. Each pattern seems logical and internally consistent. If such patterns are observed among the psychotics, we expect a similar logical consistency to characterize the low symptom group.

We have also noted more of a tendency for greater variability in the perception of the opportunity structure, and lower achievement levels, among the psychotics than among the low symptom respondents. Before suggesting that "defensive" or "coping" reactions account for the increasing variability of self-esteem scores among the "sicker" mental health groupings, we must consider whether this variability is a function of the interaction between perception of the opportunity structure and achievement level. If the psychotics and low symptom individuals are compared, controlling for perception of the opportunity structure and achievement level, and if the differences in variability between the two groupings are then reduced to insignificance, we can conclude that it is the interaction between perception of the opportunity structure and achievement level which accounts for the increasing variance of self-esteem scores.

All psychotic and low symptom individuals who perceived a very open opportunity structure and who were at occupation level 2 on our seven-step occupational scale were selected for this analysis. The variance of self-esteem scores for each of these mental health groupings was computed and compared. When perception of the opportunity structure and occupation level are controlled, the variability of scores in these two mental health groupings is almost the same. (When the analysis of variance procedure is used, the F value is reduced from a significant (1.33) to a nonsignificant (1.15) level.) Clearly, the variability differences between the two extreme groupings on the illness continuum are a function of perception of the opportunity structure and achievement level. "Defensive" and "coping" explanations seem superfluous in this context.

VARIABILITY OF ASPIRATION-ACHIEVEMENT DISCREPANCY SCORES

Those who study goal-setting behavior often assume that individuals with low self-esteem will select either very high or very low goals. Individuals characterized by low self-esteem may set goals that are easily accessible in order to guarantee success and avoid failure; or they may choose goals clearly impossible to attain so that failure can be attributed to the task rather than to personal shortcomings. Persons with moderate or high self-esteem select goals with about equal probabilities of success and failure (e.g., Lewin et al., 1944; Escalona, 1948; Atkinson, 1957; Atkinson and Litwin, 1960; Mahone, 1960). On the basis of these assumptions, we expect those subjects in our study with low self-esteem to show greater variability, or variance, in aspiration-achievement discrepancy scores than those respondents with higher self-esteem. The analyses carried out to test this expectation were limited to the three discrepancy scores involving the individual's own goals and achievements (e.g., occupation, income, and the striving scale). These discrepancy scores were examined in the four groupings which constitute our mental health continuum.

Since the psychotics and neurotics do not differ significantly in self-esteem, these groupings will not be compared with respect to variability of discrepancy scores. The psychotics are characterized by significantly lower self-esteem than the high symptom group, and so we predict that they will also manifest greater variability in discrepancy scores. No significant differences in variability are obtained for any of the three discrepancies. The neurotics (low self-esteem) do not differ significantly from the high symptom group (higher self-esteem) on any of the three tests. The high symptom group (low self-esteem) yield significantly more variability than the low symptom group (higher self-esteem) on any of the three tests. The high symptom group (low self-esteem) yield significantly more variability than the low symptom group (higher self-esteem) on two of the three discrepancies. Similarly, the neurotics (low self-esteem) manifest significantly larger variances than the low symptom group (higher self-esteem) in two of the three analyses. Finally, the psychotics (low self-esteem), when compared with the low symptom group (higher self-esteem), show significant differences in variance in two of the three content areas.

In summary, nine of the fifteen analyses in the three self-striving content areas do not yield significant differences in variance between mental health groupings differing in self-esteem. Six analyses show significant differences in the expected direction. Although there is some association between self-esteem and variance of discrepancy scores, our data do not support the close interdependency suggested in the literature.

The Subidentities of the Self

THE FINDINGS on self-esteem were derived from self-ideal discrepancies in diverse areas of social participation. These discrepancies were combined to obtain an average figure. Since the overall low self-esteem found among the mentally ill might not have been applicable to self-evaluations in discrete subidentities or roles, we analyzed separately those questions relevant to particular subidentities. Four such subidentities were examined: racial, spouse, parental, and generalized social-self. The particular sets of statements used to define the actual and the ideal self-image for the four subidentities are presented below. (It will be recalled that these statements were each preceded by "I am a person who . . ." and "I would like to be a person who . . .").

A. RACIAL SUBIDENTITY

". . . tries harder to win an argument with a white person than with a Negro;"
". . . keeps my anger to myself when a white person gets me angry;"
". . . expresses my opinion freely with white persons;"
". . . feels sensitive or 'touchy' about being a Negro."

B. SPOUSE SUBIDENTITY

". . . makes the decisions on money and other important family matters;"
". . . shares the responsibility of financially supporting the household with my wife (husband);"
". . . talks to my wife (husband) about things that bother me."

C. PARENTAL SUBIDENTITY

". . . shares the responsibility of training my children."

D. SOCIAL-SELF SUBIDENTITY

". . . takes an active part in organizations;"
". . . likes to be with a group of people."

We used the same procedure and method of analysis for the four subidentities as for the total self-ideal discrepancy. The discrepancies for each pair of items comprising a particular subidentity, ranging from zero to three, were averaged and are presented in Tables 7.2, 7.3, 7.4, and 7.5.

Racial subidentity relates to the individual's evaluations of his functioning as a Negro. It is logical to assume that in this population, feelings about being a Negro comprise a salient factor in self-image and self-evaluation. This role pervades a wide area of social participation. Table 7.2 indicates significantly lower self-ideal discrepancies for the

Table 7.2—"Racial" Self-Ideal Discrepancy and Illness Status,

by Sex and Age in Percentages

	TOTAL		MALES		FEMALES		YOUNG		OLD		Low Symp.	High Symp.	Neur.	Psy
	Ill	Comm.	Ill	Comm.	Ill	Comm.	Ill	Comm.	Ill	Comm.				
"Racial" Discrepancy														
Low	60	64	57	64	61	64	59	64	60	64	64	62	58	
Medium	21	23	23	24	20	23	22	23	21	23	23	23	23	
High	19	13	20	12	18	13	18	13	19	13	13	15	20	
	100	100	100	100	99	100	99	100	100	100	100	100	101	1
Total N	5638	5876	2282	2384	3371	3492	3991	3145	1647	2727	5186	690	1426	42

Summary of significant chi-square analyses
Total Community vs Total Ill, $P=<.001$
Low Symptom vs Neurotics, $P=<.001$
Low Symptom vs Psychotics, $P=<.001$

total community than for the total ill sample, providing additional support for Hypothesis 3. There is no significant difference between the neurotics and the psychotics. The latter actually have somewhat lower discrepancies than the neurotics. Similarly, although the low symptom subjects have smaller discrepancies (or higher self-esteem) than the high symptom subjects, this difference is not significant.

With regard to the mental health groupings, discrepancies become progressively larger as severity of illness increases from the low symptom, to the high symptom group, to the neurotics. The psychotics do not conform to this pattern. Although the community sample as a whole has a significantly smaller mean discrepancy than the ill sample, there is no significant difference between the high symptom group and the neurotics. It is the relatively low discrepancy of the low symptom group that is responsible for the significant difference between the total samples. The expectation of a difference in self-esteem between the sexes in the community sample is not supported by the data. Similarly, no difference is apparent between the young and older community sample respondents. With respect to the racial subidentity of our populations, except for the psychotics, the self-ideal discrepancy increases slightly with the severity of psychiatric illness.

The spouse subidentity of the self may be very relevant to mental disorder in our population. There is evidence of considerable disorganization and deviant role performance in Negro family life, particularly in the husband-wife relationship (Frazier, 1939; Dai, 1950). As in the previous analyses, the ill show significantly higher self-ideal discrepancies than the community subjects. Although there is no significant difference between the psychotics and the neurotics, as is the case for racial subidentity, we find somewhat lower discrepancies among the psychotics. As

Table 7.3— "Spouse" Self-Ideal Discrepancy and Illness Status,

by Sex and Age in Percentages

	TOTAL		MALES		FEMALES		YOUNG		OLD		Low Symp.	High Symp.	Neur.	Psych.
	Ill	Comm.	Ill	Comm.	Ill	Comm.	Ill	Comm.	Ill	Comm.				
"Spouse" Discrepancy														
Low	52	69	57	75	49	66	51	65	53	74	70	61	49	53
Medium	23	20	23	18	23	22	23	22	21	18	20	24	25	22
High	26	11	21	8	29	13	25	13	25	8	10	15	26	25
	101	100	101	101	101	101	99	100	99	100	100	100	100	100
Total N	2424	3180	869	1360	1555	1820	1666	1627	758	1550	2851	329	695	1729

Summary of significant chi-square analyses
Total Community vs Total Ill, P=<.001
Low Symptom vs High Symptom, P =<.001
Low Symptom vs Neurotics, P=<.001
Low Symptom vs Psychotics, P=<.001
High Symptom vs Neurotics, P=<.001
High Symptom vs Psychotics, P=<.001
Community Males vs Community Females, P=<.001
Community Young vs Community Old, P =<.001

predicted, the low symptom group has significantly smaller discrepancies than the high. An examination of the first three mental health groupings (the low symptom group, the high symptom group, and the neurotics) reveals a progressive increase in the self-ideal discrepancy. In addition, each of these groups differs significantly from the others. Again, the psychotics do not conform to this expected pattern. This strengthens the previous suggestion that some individuals in this diagnostic group attempt to defend themselves by being selectively inattentive to aspects of their social performance.

Contrary to the prediction based on the yield of mental disorder, community population females have higher discrepancies than males. Apparently, among Negroes problems in the husband-wife relationship are more likely to affect the self-image of females in a negative way. One may speculate that, due to value differences, males are not as likely as females to perceive role failures in this area. It is also possible that the salience of this role failure is greater for Negro females because they so frequently bear the major burden of family disorganization. Findings concerning age differences support the prediction based on the yield of mental disorder. The young, who have a higher yield of mental disorder, also show a significantly higher average self-ideal discrepancy. It is reasonable to expect that older people, who are more likely to be married for longer periods, have achieved more of a mutually satisfactory role accommodation in the spouse relationship.

With respect to parental subidentity, the total ill population has a significantly higher mean self-ideal discrepancy than the community sample. Comparisons of the various subgroups indicate no significant differences either between the neurotics and the psychotics or between the

Table 7.4— "Parental" Self-Ideal Discrepancy and Illness Status
by Sex and Age in Percentages

"Parental" Discrepancy	TOTAL Ill	TOTAL Comm.	MALES Ill	MALES Comm.	FEMALES Ill	FEMALES Comm.	YOUNG Ill	YOUNG Comm.	OLD Ill	OLD Comm.	Low Symp.	High Symp.	Neur.	Psy.
Low	69	87	67	87	69	87	69	85	67	89	87	83	72	6
Medium	18	11	20	10	16	11	18	12	18	9	10	15	17	
High	14	3	13	3	15	2	13	2	15	2	3	2	11	
	101	101	100	100	100	100	100	99	100	100	100	100	100	1
Total N	752	942	272	402	480	540	524	496	228	446	848	94	218	53

Summary of significant chi-square analyses
Total Community vs Total Ill, $P = < .001$
Low Symptom vs Neurotics, $P = < .001$
Low Symptom vs Psychotics, $P = < .001$
High Symptom vs Neurotics, $P = < .05$
High Symptom vs Psychotics, $P = < .005$

high and low symptom groups. It is interesting, however, that increasing severity of illness along the mental health continuum is associated with progressively larger mean discrepancies (i.e., decreasing self-esteem). In the community population, predictions based on sex and age differences are not supported by the findings. There are no significant differences between males and females, or between young and older respondents.

The mentally ill have significantly higher discrepancies for social subidentity than the community group. There is no difference between the neurotics and the psychotics, but the high symptom group has a significantly larger average discrepancy than the low symptom group. A consideration of the four mental health groupings once again shows a progressive increase in discrepancy from the low symptom group, to the high symptom group, to the neurotics. The psychotics are slightly less discrepant than the neurotics. There are no significant differences between sex and age groups within the community population.

It will be helpful at this point to summarize the findings on self-

Table 7.5— "Social Self" Self-Ideal Discrepancy and Illness Status
by Sex and Age in Percentages

"Social Self" Discrepancy	TOTAL Ill	TOTAL Comm.	MALES Ill	MALES Comm.	FEMALES Ill	FEMALES Comm.	YOUNG Ill	YOUNG Comm.	OLD Ill	OLD Comm.	Low Symp.	High Symp.	Neur.	Psy.
Low	45	55	44	57	46	54	45	54	46	57	56	47	44	
Medium	30	32	31	32	30	32	31	33	30	30	32	30	31	
High	24	13	25	12	24	15	24	13	24	14	12	23	24	
	99	100	100	101	100	101	100	100	100	101	100	100	99	1
Total N	2820	3032	1135	1195	1685	1737	1999	1569	821	1361	2587	345	711	21

Summary of significant chi-square analyses
Total Community vs Total Ill, $P = < .001$
Low Symptom vs High Symptom, $P = < .001$
Low Symptom vs Neurotics, $P = < .001$
Low Symptom vs Psychotics, $P = < .001$

esteem with respect to the various hypotheses being tested. In support of Hypothesis 3 (higher discrepancies, or lower self-esteem, in the ill population), the total ill sample has significantly higher discrepancies for the total self-ideal battery, as well as for each subidentity of self. The differences between the community and the mentally ill populations are maintained even when separate analyses are carried out in sex and age subgroups. These findings also confirm expectations based on research findings previously reported in the literature.

With regard to Hypothesis 3a (lower self-esteem for psychotics than for neurotics), there are no significant differences between the psychotics and the neurotics on any of the five self-ideal discrepancy comparisons. There are even indications that the psychotics have slightly lower discrepancies than the neurotics. We have suggested that the lack of support for this hypothesis may be a function of the psychological defenses used by psychotics.

The weight of the evidence supports Hypothesis 3b, which predicts that within the community sample those with a high level of psychiatric symptoms will have lower self-esteem than a low symptom group. This expectation is confirmed, but differences between the two symptom groups are significant only for the overall self-ideal discrepancy and for the spouse and social-self subidentities. The data only partially support the general assumption of an inverse relationship between severity of illness and self-esteem. For each of the five comparisons, there is a progressive increase in self-ideal discrepancy (i.e., decrease in self-esteem) from the low symptom group, to the high symptom group, to the neurotics. The psychotics do not conform to this pattern.

The expectation of higher self-ideal discrepancies for males than for females in the community population, based on the relative yields of mental disorder in the various subpopulations, is not supported by the findings. In fact, in four of the five self-ideal comparisons, females have higher discrepancies than males, and two of these differences are statistically significant. The yield issue also causes us to predict higher discrepancies for the young age group in the community sample. In four of the five comparisons the young do show higher discrepancies than the older subjects. The differences reach statistical significance in three of these comparisons.

It is interesting that of the four subidentities of the self-image, the highest self-ideal discrepancies are found in the spouse subidentity in the mentally ill sample. It is for this subidentity that we also find the most significant difference between the community and the ill samples. The spouse role is evidently one of the major determinants of low self-esteem among the mentally ill. This is not surprising in view of our knowledge of prevalent family disorganization among Negroes. On this subidentity of the self, females in the community sample are significantly more discrepant than males, and the young are more discrepant than the older respondents.

Other Measures of Self-Esteem

THE SELF-IDEAL DISCREPANCY is only one way to obtain information about self-esteem. We employed various methods to explore more fully the nature of self-esteem in our population subgroups. Each respondent specified the degree to which he wanted a hypothetical son (or daughter) to "be like" him (see Appendix B, Question 143) by selecting one of these precoded responses: "Exactly like me," "Pretty much like me," "Slightly like me," or "Not like me at all." It was assumed that a respondent who selected either of the last two categories evaluated salient aspects of himself negatively, and that the converse was true for a respondent who chose either of the first two alternatives.

Table 7.6 presents responses to this question for various subgroups in the community and ill populations. The mentally ill and community

Table 7.6—One's Desire for Hypothetical Child to "Be Like" Him and Illness Status,

by Sex and Age in Percentages

	TOTAL		MALES		FEMALES		YOUNG		OLD		Low Symp.	High Symp.	Neur.	Ps.
	Ill	Comm.	Ill	Comm.	Ill	Comm.	Ill	Comm.	Ill	Comm.				
"Exactly" or "Pretty much like me"	47	53	48	53	46	52	43	48	55	57	52	54	47	
"Slightly" or "Not at all like me"	53	47	52	47	54	48	57	52	45	43	48	46	53	
	100	100	100	100	100	100	100	100	100	100	100	100	100	1
Total N	1392	1463	557	595	873	868	981	785	411	675	1294	169	351	1

Summary of significant chi-square analyses
Total Community vs Total Ill, P=<.001
Community Young vs Community Old, P=<.001

samples differ significantly in their responses to this question—only 47 per cent of the community sample do not want their children to be like them, compared to 53 per cent of the ill population who select this response. On this measure also, the mentally ill appear to have lower self-esteem than those in the community. There are no differences for the various mental health groupings in the two larger samples. The psychotics do not differ significantly from the neurotics, nor the low symptom group from the high symptom group. Contrary to expectation, there is no difference between males and females in the community population. The younger age group has significantly lower self-esteem than the older group, however. Except for differences between the total community and ill populations, and between the two age groups, analysis of this questionnaire item does not support the predictions relevant to subgroups in our populations.

Up to this point we have said little about criteria used by individuals to derive self-evaluations. After subjects reported on the *extent* to which they wanted a hypothetical child to be similar to them, they were asked in what specific ways (if any) they wanted a child to be like and unlike them (Appendix B, Questions 144 and 145). These were open-ended questions for which no precoded responses were given. The respondent selected any characteristics that he considered important. We analyzed only the first response given to each of these questions, because:

(1) Although a large number of community sample individuals gave more than one response to each of these questions, the mentally ill tended to mention only one characteristic.

(2) When the responses of the ill and community samples were categorized and correlated, rank order correlations in both populations between the first and second response were significant at less than the .01 level of probability. Therefore, the presentation of both sets of responses would have been redundant.

Table 7.7 indicates that the ill and community subjects differ significantly in the ways they want their hypothetical children to be like them. Significantly fewer ill than community subjects choose the response categories "Other personality characteristics" and "Health and physical appearance," but significantly more patients select "Values related to status or status striving." The ill apparently perceive their own shortcomings in the first two response areas. With respect to the difference obtained for the third category, evidence already presented suggests that the ill perceive themselves as relatively ambitious and striving for desired goals. Because they place positive value on being ambitious, we expect the ill to be more anxious than the community subjects for their children to emulate them in this respect.

Responses concerning the ways in which subjects would like their children to be *unlike* them present some interesting contrasts. In this area, also, the distributions of responses for the two total populations differ significantly, but the most frequent response given by ill and com-

Table 7.7—Ways in Which Respondents Desire Their Children to Be

"Like" Them or "Unlike" Them and Illness Status in Percentages

	"LIKE ME"		"UNLIKE ME"	
	Ill	Comm.	Ill	Comm.
1. In no way	11	7	10	9
2. Moral and ethical characteristics	13	10	6	1
3. Ability to get along with people	17	12	6	2
4. Values related to status or status striving.	14	7	35	62
5. Other Personality characteristics	33	62	27	23
6. Health and physical appearance	12	2	16	3
	100	100	100	100
Total N	1325	1418	1334	1429

Summary of significant chi-square analyses — "Like me"
  Total Ill vs Total Community, $P=<.001$
  For Response 4, Ill vs Community, $P=<.005$
  For Response 5, Ill vs Community, $P=<.001$
  For Response 6, Ill vs Community, $P=<.001$

Summary of significant chi-square analyses — "Unlike me"
  Total Ill vs Total Community, $P=<.001$
  For Response 4, Ill vs Community, $P=<.001$
  For Response 5, Ill vs Community, $P=<.01$
  For Response 6, Ill vs Community, $P=<.001$

munity individuals revolves around status achievement and status striving. Contrary to some popular stereotypes, Negroes *are* concerned about personal shortcomings in this area and want their children to be unlike them in this respect. The response categories "Values related to status or status striving," "Other personality characteristics," and "Health and physical appearance" differ significantly in the ill and community populations (see Table 7.7), but the direction of these differences is opposite to that indicated by the analysis of ways subjects want their children to be like them (see Table 7.6). More of the mentally ill, apparently aware of their illness, want their children to have "Health and personality characteristics" unlike their own. In the previous discussion we assumed that ill individuals were more prone to perceive themselves as ambitious and striving. In this connection, the relatively larger percentage of community respondents who choose "Values related to status and status striving" as an "unlike" response may indicate both their awareness of having compromised and given up many previously held goals, and their desire for their children to surpass them in this respect. In other words, community respondents tend to project their own compromised ambitions onto their children. This interpretation is supported by the previous finding (Chapter 3) that community subjects have low goal-striving stress for themselves, but that they raise this level relatively more than the mentally ill with respect to goals for a hypothetical son.

Table 7.7 reveals that for five of the six response categories more mentally ill than community subjects want their children to be unlike them. Only with respect to "Values related to status and status striving" does a reversal occur. The ill do not want their children to be less ambitious than they. Clearly, upward striving seems to be a very salient aspect of self-image for ill respondents.

Analyses also were made of "like" and "unlike" responses for various subgroups within the ill and community populations. In this discussion only significant results will be noted. Because the mentally ill tend to see themselves as more ambitious and striving than the community subjects, as the severity of illness increases we expect a progressive decrease of those who want their children to be unlike them in the area of status striving. The findings confirm this prediction: 70 per cent of the low symptom group, 60 per cent of the high symptom group, 56 per cent of the neurotics, and only 47 per cent of the psychotics select this "unlike" category. This finding also suggests an inverse relationship between the severity of mental illness and the ability to become psychologically involved in the aspirations and hopes of other individuals. It has frequently been observed that the mentally ill are relatively defective in their capacity for identification with others.

If mental illness *is* associated with a more salient self-perception revolving around status achievement, we would predict a direct relationship between the severity of mental illness and the percentage of those who want their children to be like them with respect to status striving. Nine per cent of the low symptom group, 9 per cent of the high symptom group, 20 per cent of the neurotics, and 23 per cent of the psychotics do respond in this manner.

There are few significant differences between males and females as to how they want their children to be like and unlike them. In the community sample both sexes show the same percentage of responses dealing with "Moral and ethical characteristics."

Another measure of self-esteem used in the present study was derived from the position selected by respondents on the self-anchored striving scale described in Chapter 3. Each respondent was presented with a flight of ten diagrammed steps, Step 1 representing the "worst possible way of life," and Step 10 the "best possible way of life." The content of these anchor points was specified by the respondent himself. We assumed that one's perception of his position, using his own value criteria as standards, represented a generalized measure of self-evaluation: the lower the position selected, the lower his self-esteem. Unlike some of the other measures of self-esteem discussed here, this measure avoids the danger that the investigators will impose on the respondent their own value criteria or specifications of the situation in which the self-evaluation is made.

The distribution of step-positions selected by respondents is presented in Table 7.8. For simplification, the responses are grouped into a low

Table 7.8—Perceived Position of the "Self" on the Self-Anchored Striving Scale and

Illness Status, by Sex and Age in Percentages

	TOTAL		MALES		FEMALES		YOUNG		OLD		Low Symp.	High Symp.	Neur.	Psyc
	Ill	Comm.	Ill	Comm.	Ill	Comm.	Ill	Comm.	Ill	Comm.				
Perceived Position														
1-3 (Low)	24	6	27	5	21	6	26	7	20	4	5	10	19	2
4-6	43	33	43	33	43	33	50	38	31	27	31	47	53	4
7-10 (High)	33	61	30	62	36	61	24	55	49	69	64	43	28	3
	100	100	100	100	100	100	100	100	100	100	100	100	100	10
Total N	1383	1435	566	580	808	855	886	768	497	667	1272	163	349	103

Summary of significant chi-square analyses
Total Community vs Total Iᵢₗ, P=<.001
Neurotics vs Psychotics, P= <.02
Low Symptom vs High Symptom, P=<.001
Community Young vs Community Old, P=<.001

self-esteem category (step 1-3), an intermediate category (step 4-6) and a high category (step 7–10). Significantly more community than ill subjects choose high steps on this scale. Twenty-four per cent of the ill sample place themselves in the low self-esteem category, compared to only 6 per cent of the community group. On the other hand, the high self-esteem category contains 61 per cent of the community group and 33 per cent of the mentally ill. Hypothesis 3 (lower self-esteem among the mentally ill) is clearly supported by this measure of self-esteem.

Hypothesis 3a is also supported by the results: on this measure the psychotics manifest lower self-esteem than the neurotics. It is interesting that although a greater percentage of the psychotics fall into the low esteem category, a somewhat higher percentage of psychotic persons are also included in the high self-esteem category. In some of the previous analyses presented in this chapter the psychotics, to a greater extent than the neurotics, tended to cluster around the extremes in measures of self-esteem. The findings on this measure (see Table 7.8) indicate a stronger tendency in this direction than observed previously. Responses to this self-anchored striving scale also show significantly lower self-esteem for the high symptom group than the low symptom group, supporting Hypothesis 3b.

Table 7.8 also supports our general assumption of an inverse relationship between self-esteem and severity of illness. The proportion of respondents with low self-esteem increases from 5 per cent in the low

Other Measures of Self-Esteem 187

symptom group to 26 per cent in the psychotic grouping. The percentage of individuals in the high self-esteem category decreases from 64 per cent in the low symptom group to 33 per cent among the psychotics. Except for the unexpectedly large percentage of psychotics with high self-esteem, the decrease of self-esteem with the increase of severity of mental illness is in the predicted direction.

With respect to the yield issue, there are no differences between community population males and females on the self-anchored striving scale. As predicted for age subgroups in the community, the young respondents show significantly lower self-esteem than the older group $(P = < .001)$.

We now turn to our final method of analyzing self-esteem. Each subject was asked to select one of four responses from a scale representing the degree of success he felt he had achieved in life (Appendix B, Question 195). The precoded responses were: "Very successful," "Fairly successful," "Slightly successful," and "Not successful at all." In analyzing the results, the second and third responses were combined into a "Somewhat successful" category. It was assumed that the perceived degree of success in life was one reasonable operational definition of self-esteem: the higher one's success feelings, the higher his self-esteem. Although the distributions of these responses differ significantly in the community and ill populations, ill individuals are represented with greater frequency in *both* the extreme high and low self-esteem categories (for totals and with sex and age controls—see Table 7.9). This further supports the possibility of more frequent use of psychological

Table 7.9—Perceived Degree of Success in Life and Illness Status, by Sex and Age in Percentages

	TOTAL		MALES		FEMALES		YOUNG		OLD		Low Symp.	High Symp.	Neur.	Psych.
	Ill	Comm.	Ill	Comm.	Ill	Comm.	Ill	Comm.	Ill	Comm.				
Very Successful	18	11	19	12	18	10	17	8	21	14	10	14	15	19
Fairly or Slightly	64	81	63	78	66	84	63	83	67	80	82	77	67	64
Not at all	18	8	18	10	17	6	20	9	11	6	7	9	17	18
	100	100	100	100	101	100	100	100	99	100	99	100	99	101
Total N	1411	1482	573	602	838	880	1000	796	411	683	1309	171	356	1055

Summary of significant chi-square analyses
Total: Community vs Ill, P=<.001
Males: Community vs Ill, P=<.001
Females: Community vs Ill, P=<.001
Young: Community vs Ill, P=<.001
Old: Community vs Ill, P=<.001
Low Symp. vs Neurotics, P=<.001
Low Symp. vs Psychotics, P=<.001
High Symp. vs Psychotics, P=<.005
Community Males vs Community Females, P=<.01
Community Young vs Community Old, P=<.001

defense mechanisms among the mentally ill. As already suggested, perception of oneself as successful has obvious anxiety-reducing properties, since it involves a (motivated) failure to recognize negative aspects of self-functioning. On the other hand, defensively low self-esteem may reduce pressure on the individual to engage actively in competitive situations that might promise new failures and the necessity for more stringent self-evaluation.

If this reasoning is valid, extreme choices on the self-esteem continuum should vary directly with the severity of mental illness. A comparison of the four mental health groupings allows us to explore this idea. Table 7.9 indicates that *both* extremes of self-esteem are least frequent in the low symptom group and become progressively more numerous as severity of illness increases. The proportion of individuals in the "Not successful at all" category (low self-esteem) increases from 7 per cent in the low symptom group to 18 per cent among the psychotics. These differences in low self-esteem compared to the remaining distributions in the four groupings are significant $(P = < .001)$. Similarly, the proportion of subjects in the "Very successful" category (high self-esteem) increases along the continuum from 10 to 19 per cent (see Table 7.9). These differences are also significant $(P = < .001)$.

The responses of males in the community population differ significantly $(P = < .01)$ from those of females, but they are not unidirectional. Males show a higher percentage of responses at both extremes of self-esteem. Our expectation concerning age differences and self-esteem is supported. In the community sample the younger group contains fewer individuals who regard themselves as successful, and more who regard themselves as unsuccessful.

One very consistent pattern emerges from these analyses: an increasing variability of self-esteem responses is frequently associated with increasing severity of illness, although low self-esteem is clearly the predominant extreme. We have already suggested that in a segment of the mentally ill population high or low self-esteem may serve as a psychological defense, or as a means of coping with anxiety. Of course, this phenomenon may also be operative on a reduced scale in the community population. Many individuals who experience emotional difficulties or become mentally ill may attempt to maintain high levels of self-esteem in order to enhance a feeling of security. A sense of low self-esteem may also reduce threat by providing the threatened individual with a rationale for reducing his goals to levels that are easily attainable. This process, in effect, minimizes further threats of failure.

The assumption of the operation of such defensive manipulations reveals nothing about the determinants of high or low self-esteem. We felt that our psychotic subgroup could be utilized in order to explore this issue further. Psychotic individuals tend to manifest both extremes of self-esteem, and presumably psychological defenses are most prevalent in this mental health grouping. The range of self-ideal discrepancies within the psychotic grouping was divided into three categories: low self-esteem (mean discrepancies of .80 and over), medium self-esteem (.40 to .79), and high self-esteem (.00 to .39). We eliminated the medium range group and carried out further analyses with cases in the two extreme self-esteem breakdowns. We hoped that this procedure would indicate whether high or low self-esteem among the psychotics was conditioned entirely by reality factors, whether it was associated with threatening situations that provoked defensive reactions, or whether it involved some combination of these two possibilities.

The first series of analyses reported here considers the relationship between various indices of status (income, education, and occupation) and high or low self-esteem among the psychotics. Although income and education are directly related to self-esteem, these associations are not statistically significant. With respect to occupation, Table 7.10 indicates

Table 7.10—Occupation and Self-

Esteem Among the Psychotics[1]

in Percentages

Occupational Achievement	Low Self-Esteem	High Self-Esteem
1	66	59
2	25	23
3 and higher	9	18
	100	100
Total N	430	175

1. By chi-square, $P = <.02 > .01$

significant differences between the occupational levels of individuals in the high and low self-esteem breakdowns, with the latter group showing lower occupational achievement. Therefore, we cannot accept the assumption that the influence of current reality factors is minimal in a psychotic population. Actually, self-esteem is significantly related to occupational achievement. Individuals with low occupational achievement are characterized by correspondingly low self-esteem, and the converse is true for those with higher levels of occupational attainment. The response of the psychotics may to some extent be determined by objective reality and may not be entirely autistic and defensive.

We also attempted to determine whether the high and low self-esteem pattern among psychotics was related to their view of the societal opportunity structure (Appendix B, Question 195). This questionnaire item, along with its implications, has been discussed in Chapter 3. At that time we reported that the mentally ill were significantly more inclined than the community respondents to perceive the opportunity structure as open. In addition, we found that this perception increased directly with the severity of illness along our mental health continuum. In the present context we assume that an individual who sees the opportunity structure as relatively open is more likely to attribute personal failure to some defect within himself than to shortcomings inherent in the social system. Such an individual internalizes his failures and consequently lowers his self-esteem. This reasoning leads to the expectation of low self-esteem among those psychotics who perceive an open opportunity structure. Table 7.11 presents the findings relevant to this

Table 7.11—Perception of the

Opportunity Structure and Self-Esteem

Among the Psychotics[1] in Percentages

	Low Self-Esteem	High Self-Esteem
Closed	52	63
Open	48	37
	100	100
Total N	429	175

1. By chi-square, $P = <.02$

question. Those who perceive the opportunity structure as relatively open show significantly lower self-esteem than those who see the system as closed. Previously (Table 7.10) we found a significant relationship between the self-esteem of our psychotic population and their objective occupational status positions. In this context, also, we find that the self-esteem of the psychotics is logically related to their view of the societal opportunity structure. Although these analyses do not indicate the extent to which extreme positions on our self-esteem measure represent the operation of psychological defenses, they do show that self-esteem among the psychotics does not reflect merely autistic and irrational responses to questionnaire items.

Summary

IN THIS SUMMARY, reference will be made primarily to the three hypotheses being tested (3, 3a, and 3b), and to predictions based on the relative yields of mental disorder in sex and age subgroups.

Hypothesis 3 predicts lower self-esteem among the mentally ill than among the community population. All four measures used to determine self-esteem show significant differences in the predicted direction. With respect to degree of success in life, the patients *also* tend to select the response category indicating very high self-esteem. They are more likely than community sample individuals to see themselves as having been either very successful or unsuccessful. Those in the community population tend to cluster around an intermediate position of success. We interpret this patterning of extreme responses among the mentally ill as a function of psychological defenses which either maintain or enhance the self-image. However, preliminary analyses indicate that this phenomenon may be explained in terms of perception of the opportunity structure and achievement. Considering all relevant findings in this Chapter, Hypothesis 3 is clearly supported.

We have also been concerned with the relationship between self-esteem and the severity of mental illness. Hypothesis 3a predicts lower self-esteem for the psychotics than for the neurotics. This hypothesis rests on the assumption that these two diagnostic groups lie on a continuum of severity, the psychotics being more severely ill. Although there is little doubt that the psychotics as a group are more seriously impaired in social role performance, the question of whether these two illness conditions differ quantitatively remains unanswered. Of the four major comparisons used to test this hypothesis, only one shows significant differences. But this comparison reveals no single consistent difference in the direction of self-esteem: the psychotics select extreme positions on the striving scale, compared with the neurotics. The psychotics and the neurotics do not differ significantly on the subidentities of the self. We conclude, then, that Hypothesis 3a is not supported by the findings. The nature of the data, however, does suggest that psychological defenses relevant to self-esteem may be more prevalent among the psychotics. In two of the comparisons (position on the striving scale and degree of success in life) the extremes of high and low self-esteem are manifested with greater frequency among the psychotics.

Hypothesis 3b predicts lower self-esteem for those with a high psychiatric symptom score than for those with a low score. Of the four major comparisons presented, two show significant differences. In both cases those in the high symptom group have lower self-esteem. Regarding the four subidentities of the self-image, all the differences are in the predicted direction, two differing significantly. We conclude that the weight of the evidence supports Hypothesis 3b. Even in a population that has not been medically diagnosed (i.e., the community sample), self-esteem appears to be inversely related to degree of psychiatric illness as determined by prevalence of psychosomatic symptoms. This finding attests to the sensitivity of the self-ideal discrepancy and achievement responses on the striving scale as predictors of psychiatric illness.

This discussion of self-esteem and the illness continuum also necessitates a comparison between the high symptom group and the neurotics. The self-esteem of the neurotics is significantly lower than that of the high symptom group on three measures. With respect to the perception of success, the neurotics more frequently give responses signifying both high and low self-esteem. Considering all four of our mental health groupings, high self-esteem is most evident in the low symptom group and becomes progressively less pronounced in the high symptom group and the neurotics. The psychotics as a group do not differ significantly from the neurotics on self-esteem, except that they evidence a greater tendency to choose responses at both extremes of our self-esteem measures.

Although we presented no formal hypothesis to this effect, we did assume that community population males would have lower self-esteem than females, and that the self-esteem of the young community respondents (twenty to thirty-nine years of age) would be lower than that of the older respondents (forty to sixty years of age). These expectations were based on an over-representation in the ill sample of males and of the younger segment of the population. Contrary to expectations, females· have lower self-esteem than males, as gauged by the self-ideal discrepancy. There are no sex differences on the degree to which respondents want their children to "be like" them, and their perception of their position on the striving scale. Although there are significant differences between the sexes on the degree of success in life, the direction of these differences is not consistent. Males select extreme choices more frequently; they are higher than females on the "Very successful" and the "Not successful at all" choices. These inconsistent results suggest that our different operational measures of self-esteem have not tapped similar aspects of the "self" concept. It is also possible that social conditioning involved in learning the two sex roles may cause males and females to use somewhat different criteria of self-esteem. The data indicate conclusively that in the community population the young have larger discrepancies, or lower self-esteem, than the older group. In all analyses the differences between the two age groups are statistically significant, thereby confirming our expectations, at least regarding age.

As mentioned in an earlier chapter, we do not necessarily expect to find differences within the ill population on any given variable when we analyze sex and age subgroups. In regard to our major self-esteem measure (the self-ideal discrepancy), there are, in fact, no sex or age differences among the mentally ill. A few sex differences emerge in the analyses of the four subidentities, but in each instance the direction of difference is erratic and inconsistent.

8

MIGRATORY STATUS AND
MENTAL DISORDER

Chapters 3 through 7 were primarily concerned with differences between the diagnosed mentally ill and community populations with respect to our study variables. These chapters have focused on the relationship between mental illness and such variables as goal-striving stress, stress score components, reference group behavior, and self-esteem. They have discussed only secondarily variations in subgroups within the community population differing in yield of mental disorder. In comparing high yield (males and young subjects) and low yield (females and older respondents) subgroups, we have consistently predicted that the former subgroups would manifest more of the characteristics of the mentally ill than of the community population. If the high and low yield respondents differed from each other in the same way as the ill differed from the community population, the variable under consideration was assumed to be a potential antecedent to mental illness. When the variable did not discriminate between the high and low yield subgroups, it was regarded as a concomitant or resultant condition of illness. In essence, the discussion of differences between these subgroups is directly related to the problem of identifying those social-psychological variables that intervene between sociological factors (independent variables) and differing rates of mental disorder (the dependent variable). The reader should remember that analyses based on the yield issue do not definitively establish antecedents to mental illness—they only help to clarify variables that *may* be antecedents. Only by means of longitudinal studies can the antecedent conditions to mental disorder be specified with any degree of confidence.

The discussion in this and the following two chapters will be primarily concerned with differences between high and low yield subgroups within the community population with respect to our study variables. To what extent can these variables explain such differences? The present chapter will aim at explaining differences between high and low yield migratory status groups in terms of our study variables: perception of the opportunity structure, the goal-striving stress scores in self-related content areas, the aspiration-achievement discrepancy, reference group behavior, and self-esteem.

Migration and Mental Illness:
A Research Review

THIS DISCUSSION will review studies concerned with the relationship between migration and mental disorder and attempt to summarize their relevant findings. An overview of the literature raises four major problems in formulating generalizations about this relationship:

(1) The definitions of "migration" and "mental illness" often differ from study to study. "Migratory status" may be defined in terms of place of birth, intercommunity migration, or even movement from one residential area to another within a single community. Sometimes it is defined in terms of where the major socialization experiences have occurred. Similarly, "mental illness" may be defined in terms of direct psychiatric evaluation, psychological tests, or evaluations of psychiatric symptoms derived from some sort of questionnaire.

(2) The second type of problem involves variations in the data used to determine rates of mental illness—either prevalence or incidence data can be employed. There are at least two definitions of prevalence in current usage: the term may refer either to those individuals *in treatment,* or *in need of treatment,* in a given community during a specified period of time. Similarly, incidence may be defined as the number of first admissions, or the number of first admissions *and* readmissions, to selected facilities during a given time period. It is dangerous to assume that these different ways of viewing mental illness data yield comparable results. Incidence and prevalence studies are designed to answer different questions. In order not to confuse the problems with which each type is concerned, these studies must be treated separately.

(3) Differences in the types of facilities from which data are drawn raise questions about the comparability of these studies and the additive nature of their results. For example, some studies consider only admissions to public mental hospitals; others include data from public and private mental hospitals; still others base their conclusions on data gathered from out-patient clinics.

(4) The procedures employed for analyzing data vary from study to study. In one case, crude rates may be computed, and in another, rates adjusted for sex, age, race, urban-rural residence, national origin, subculture, etc., may be employed. Furthermore, the type of "adjustment" of rates varies considerably. Still other studies, instead of using rates, compare the significance of differences in the distributions of an ill and a "normal" population with respect to a given factor. The lack of comparability of these various procedures poses problems and requires careful consideration and evaluation. Consequently, this review will subdivide the literature according to the type of data utilized and the definition of concepts employed.

Much of the current literature has assumed an association between migration and high rates of mental illness. This view seems plausible on "common sense" grounds, and is supported by the studies of Ødegaard (1932), and Malzberg and Lee (1956). However, reviews of the literature indicate that this relationship has by no means been unequivocally established (Parker, Kleiner, and Taylor, 1960; Kantor, 1965; Kleiner and Parker, 1965; Murphy, 1965). The situation is further complicated by problems in generalizing from findings (to which we have alluded above).

Hollingshead and Redlich (1958) conducted a prevalence study of individuals in treatment during a specified period of time. The criterion of mental illness in their study was direct psychiatric evaluation. These authors were concerned with the differences in rates between foreign- and American-born residents of New Haven, and between individuals born in that city and those moving there from other parts of the country. They found no significant differences in rates for migrants and non-migrants, using either of the two comparisons. Srole et al. (1962: 253–281) also investigated the prevalence of mental illness in a general community population, using level of psychiatric symptoms as their criterion of illness. Each individual's profile was evaluated according to psychiatric appraisal of information gathered in the field by an interviewer with no medical training. The authors of this study were primarily concerned with the mental health ratings (1) of native-born individuals with both parents born in the United States; (2) of native-born individuals with one parent born outside the United States; (3) of native-born individuals with both parents born outside the United States; and (4) of individuals born outside the United States. These investigators found no significant relationship between foreign- and native-born status and mental health. When the differences between the populations were standardized for age and socioeconomic status, the small existing differences were diminished even further.

In the final prevalence study to be considered in this section, Leighton et al. (1963) also used psychosomatic and psychoneurotic symptoms as measures of mental health. They were concerned with the amount of untreated illness in the community. Data obtained in the field by nonmedical interviewers were evaluated by psychiatric personnel. Again, no relationship was observed between migration and mental health, except for individuals who had moved three or more times before twenty-one years of age. Each of these three studies, then, utilized a different definition of mental illness and each showed little relationship between illness and migration (as defined by mobility between countries or within one country).

Relatively few studies accept residential mobility within a given city as a criterion of migration. Faris and Dunham (1939: ix–xx; 161–177) showed that those *areas* within a given city characterized by high rates of first admissions of schizophrenics to mental hospitals, also manifested high rates of residential mobility. However, this study did not involve comparisons of *individuals* with different histories of residential mobility, with respect to rates of mental illness.

In their study of personality disorders, Tietze, Lemkau, and Cooper (1942) concluded that such disorders were related to residential mobility. Lapouse, Monk, and Terris (1956) analyzed first admissions data and found no relationship between residential mobility and rates of schizophrenia. This study, unlike the Faris and Dunham study, compared individuals rather than only geographical areas. Hollingshead and Redlich (1958) also found no relationship between residential mobility and rates of diagnosed illness in their prevalence data.

Clausen and Kohn (1959), studying first admissions to state hospitals and some private facilities in Haegerstown, found, as did Faris and Dunham (1939), high residential mobility among their mentally ill sample. The histories of these patients revealed no greater residential mobility prior to the onset of illness than among a sample of individuals with no mental illness who were studied during this same time period.

Leighton et al. (1963), utilized prevalence data and noted a relationship between residential mobility and symptoms, but only for those individuals who were characterized by three residential changes in a given period of time. In a survey of aid to dependent families, Price (1965) analyzed case workers' evaluations of parent and child mental health. One of the four issues which concerned Price was the relationship between residential stability and the mental health of this sample. Controlling for duration of time during which public assistance was received, he found a U-shaped relationship between the number of residences within a given period and mental health problems. Those with one residence had several problems. The number of problems dropped off for those with two residences, and increased again among those with three residences. This pattern was consistent for whites and nonwhites.

Kantor (1965) considered the consequences of residential mobility for the adjustment of children. A large sample of families was interviewed twice—the interviews were separated by a two-year period. In the initial interview mothers were asked to report on the behavior problems of their children. The families were then separated into two groups: those who had changed residence during the period between the two interviews, and those who had not. Those mothers who subsequently moved reported more symptoms during the first interview than those mothers who did not move. Both the residentially mobile and stable mothers reported a reduction in symptoms at the time of the second interview, but there was no difference between the mobile and stable groups in the amount of change in symptoms. Kantor suggested that the large number of psychological problems reported by subsequently mobile parents during the first interview might have even provided some of the motivation and impetus for the residential mobility. For example, their children's school difficulties and problems with neighbors might have impelled the mobile families to move to areas where these problems would be less evident.

Fried (1965) was interested in the implications of forced housing, or residential relocation, for mental health. Families were interviewed prior to and after relocation. The criterion of mental health was the degree of satisfaction each individual expressed about his current situation. Fried hypothesized that the critical factor in determining the mental health of individuals who relocated was their readiness to accept displacement. A person who was prepared to relocate would presumably have fewer adjustment problems than the person who did not want to move. The individual with strong roots in his former community was expected to resist relocation and to have difficulty in forming new ties. The individual with a weak attachment to his former community was expected to experience little reluctance about moving and to be more oriented toward forming relationships in the new community. In addition, since the relocation would be perceived as upward mobility, Fried expected subjects with strong mobility aspirations to make an easier transition than those with low mobility aspirations. His data confirmed these expectations.

All nine of the studies involving residential mobility differ with respect to (1) the criteria of mental illness or mental health employed; (2) the age of the sample populations; (3) whether the relocation was voluntary or involuntary; and (4) the nature of the populations studied (i.e., white or nonwhite, and those receiving or not receiving public assistance). Consequently, it is difficult to draw any definitive conclusions from these studies. Regardless of these differences, however, five of the studies show no clear relationship between residential mobility and mental illness.

There is a considerable body of literature on incidence studies. Such studies can be subdivided into those dealing with migration from one country to another (international migration), and those dealing with migration from one part of a country to another (intranational migration, or "in-migration"). We consider first those incidence studies investigating the effect of international migration.

Ødegaard (1932) demonstrated that the rate of first admissions among Norwegians in Minnesota was higher for individuals born in Norway than for those born in the United States. The rate of admissions in Norway was lower than either of these. Faris and Dunham (1939) noted a higher rate of first admissions for those sections of Chicago with a large percentage of foreign-born whites, than for areas with a sizeable proportion of native-born whites. Malzberg (1940) investigated the same question and reported that the higher rate of admissions for the foreign born in his sample was not reduced by controlling for national origin.

Dayton's study (1940) of first admissions to Massachusetts mental hospitals revealed a higher rate for foreign-born whites than for native-born whites whose parents had been born in the United States; age and urban-rural residence were controlled. Since the foreign born, as a group, were older than the native born, Dayton felt that their higher rate might be a function of the higher death rate among the foreign born (i.e., this high death rate would result in a comparatively small foreign-born population as a base for computing rates, when compared to the native-born population). Dayton concluded that the differential rates of admissions for the foreign- and native-born whites could not be attributed to this higher death rate.

Lemert (1948) included in his mentally ill population (which was defined by rate of first admissions) not only patients admitted to all Michigan state hospitals, but also admissions to three private mental hospitals. Higher rates of admissions for foreign-born and second generation immigrants, than for native-born individuals, held both for urban and rural areas. A study by Clark (1948), using age-standardized rates for schizophrenia, also showed a higher rate of admissions for foreign-than native-born whites.

The studies cited up to this point unanimously support a relationship between international migration and mental illness. Subsequent studies, which utilized more refined methods of data analysis, have revealed some irregularities in findings relevant to this issue. When Malzberg (1955) used crude rates of first admissions, he found more illness among foreign-born than native-born whites. When these rates were adjusted for sex, age, and urban-rural residence, differences between the two populations disappeared. The rate of admissions for schizophrenia, considered alone, was adjusted for sex, age, and urban-rural residence, but the foreign born still showed a greater incidence of this disease than the native born.

Malzberg and Lee (1956) reported no great overall difference in rates of first admissions to mental hospitals for foreign- and native-born patients when color, sex, and age were controlled. However, as in the previously mentioned study, the rate of schizophrenia remained higher for the foreign born. These findings applied both to whites and Negroes. It should be noted that this was the first study to analyze Negroes with respect to international migration and mental disorder.

Locke, Kramer, and Pasamanick (1960) studied first admissions to Ohio public mental hospitals. Age-adjusted rates for foreign-born whites were higher than for native-born whites. Lazarus, Locke, and Thomas (1963) analyzed rates of first admissions to public and private hospitals in New York State and California, and to public hospitals in Ohio. They also found higher rates among foreign-born than native-born white patients. The final study to be included in this context was carried out by Lee (1963). He examined rate differentials between foreign- and native-born whites, controlling for education, marital status, and occupation. Rates standardized for age and education showed no differences between the foreign and native born, either for males or females.

Several points emerge from this review of studies relating international migration to mental illness:

(1) As already noted, the great majority of the early studies indicated a positive relationship between migration and mental disorder.

(2) Almost all of these studies analyzed white populations.

(3) The studies were based on first admissions to state mental hospitals and in only a few instances dealt also with selected samples of admissions to private hospital facilities.

(4) Some of the studies embraced all categories of mental disorder (including functional and organic disorders), others were concerned only with the functional disorders, and still others were confined to a consideration of schizophrenia.

(5) As the method of data analysis shifted from the use of crude rates to standardized rates, the observed relationship between migration and mental disorder began to break down, although it persisted for schizophrenia. Despite this apparent breakdown with finer methods of analysis, we cannot unequivocally attribute the change in results to this factor. The inconsistency of these results may be a function of the time period during which the data were analyzed. For example, different trends will probably be noted in data collected during a depression period, during wartime, or during a period of prosperity.

We turn now to a final group of studies, which utilized incidence data. These studies were concerned with first admissions only, or with first admissions plus readmissions, during a specified period of time. The final problem area to be considered involves the relationship between in-migration and mental illness. There is a tendency to assume that international migration and in-migration pose the same type of psychological problems for the individual; that studies bearing on the first type of migration apply also to the second type; and that the same explanatory concept (i.e., stresses encountered in the new environment) can account for correlations observed between both types of migration and mental illness (Murphy, 1965). At this point we are particularly concerned with the validity of assuming that differences in rates of illness and the reasons for these differences are the same for both types of migration.

Tietze, Lemkau, and Cooper (1942) investigated the relationship between intranational migration and illness. More specifically, they analyzed the relationship between personality disorders and spatial mobility. They concluded that intracity mobility was related to mental disorder but intercity mobility was not. Ødegaard (1945) showed that rates of illness among migrants within Norway were lower than for the general population (i.e., inferentially, lower than rates for natives to a community). The exception to this finding was the higher rate of illness for migrants to Oslo from other urban centers.

Malzberg and Lee (1956)—probably the most frequently cited study on the question—presented exhaustive data on first admissions to public and private hospitals in New York State for the period 1939 to 1941. The study showed higher rates of functional and nonfunctional disorders for in-migrants than nonmigrants, among the young and older age control groups. This finding applied both to white and nonwhite populations. Malzberg and Lee defined a nonmigrant as an individual who was either born in New York State or lived there for more than five years. Almost all studies cited up to this point used birthplace as the criterion for migratory status. Malzberg and Lee showed that migrants who had lived in the state for less than five years had much higher rates of illness than those who had resided there for more than five years. The illness rates for those who had lived in New York State for more than five years were higher than for those born in New York State, but the differences were smaller. In fact, among patients twenty to twenty-nine years of age, the rate for the native population was higher than for the in-migrants. The authors also pointed out that differences between in-migrants and nonmigrants were sharply reduced when crude rates were standardized for sex and age. Despite these methodological corrections, the rates of illness seemed generally higher for in-migrants than for nonmigrants, regardless of color. Lapouse, Monk, and Terris (1956) found no relationship between in-migration and rate of first admissions of schizophrenics to state hospitals.

Clausen and Kohn (1959) studied first admissions of patients from Haegerstown to public and private hospitals. They found a greater degree of past in-migration among schizophrenics than among a general population group. However, this in-migration activity differential appeared mainly with the onset of illness rather than in the years prior to it, a distinction also observed with respect to intracity mobility. On the basis of this finding, they concluded that in-migration was a symptom, and not an antecedent, of illness.

Kleiner and Parker (1959) studied all Negro first admissions, twenty to sixty years of age, to Pennsylvania state mental hospitals over a five year period. They applied simultaneous sex and age controls to their data and carried out statistical tests of significance. For males and females in this patient population, they found a significant over-representation of natives to Pennsylvania and an under-representation of in-migrants. Similar significant differences were found in age groups twenty to twenty-nine, thirty to thirty-nine, and forty to forty-nine among the males, and thirty to thirty-nine, and forty to forty-nine among the females. There were no differences between natives and in-migrants in the other age intervals. They also reported higher admission rates for in-migrants from other Northern states than for the native born, and lower rates for in-migrants from the South than for the natives. Assuming that the migrants from Northern states to Pennsylvania came primarily from other cities, these findings paralleled those of Ødegaard (1945). (As noted earlier, he found lower rates for in-migrants than for nonmigrants, except for individuals migrating to Oslo from other urban centers.) These findings did not support Malzberg and Lee's study (1956).

Parker, Kleiner, and Taylor (1960) considered whether attitudes toward psychiatry could explain the observed differences in illness rates of migrants and nonmigrants in a Negro population. They suggested that the more educated native-born Negro was more aware of psychiatric facilities and/or less resistant to treatment, and therefore he would appear to manifest more mental illness. It was assumed that persons referred to psychiatric facilities through the police and the courts would generally be less aware of these psychiatric facilities and/or more resistant to treatment than those referred by a social service agency or appropriate medical and/or psychiatric facility. This study also assumed that Negroes with high educational atttainments would be more amenable to psychiatric treatment than Negroes with less education, and therefore would show a lower rate of refusal of psychiatric recommendation for treatment. For both sex groups there were no differences between the natives and migrants on referral source or rate of refusal, however.

In their study of first admissions to Ohio mental hospitals, Locke, Kramer, and Pasamanick (1960) reported that whites and nonwhites and males and females born in Ohio had lower age-adjusted rates than those born in other sections of the United States. Jaco (1960: 60–72) conducted an extensive study of first admissions to public and private psychiatric facilities in Texas. His findings were inconsistent with those of Malzberg and Lee (1956). The crude rates of illness for migrants to Texas were higher than for natives of the state. When rates for all psychoses, as well as for schizophrenia taken alone, were standardized for sex, age, and subculture, rate differences between migrants and natives disappeared. With respect to nonwhites, specifically, rates for natives remained slightly higher than for migrants, for all the psychoses taken together and for schizophrenia considered alone. This finding was in general agreement with Kleiner and Parker (1965). It should also be noted that sex and age controls in the Kleiner-Parker study did not eliminate migratory status differentials, suggesting that subcultural influences are of primary importance.

In a replication of the 1945 Ødegaard study, Astrupp and Ødegaard (1960) again demonstrated higher rates of illness for individuals born in particular communities in Norway than for in-migrants to those communities. "Mental illness" in their study encompassed both organic and functional psychoses.

Lazarus, Locke, and Thomas (1963) attempted to determine whether rate differences between migrants and nonmigrants were constant in different states. Their data were based on first admissions to public mental hospitals, for all disorders and for schizophrenia taken alone, in New York State, Ohio, and California. In each of these states, considering whites and nonwhites and males and females, total admission rates for in-migrants were higher than for natives. These results supported the findings of Malzberg and Lee (1956), and Locke, Kramer, and Pasamanick (1960) but were inconsistent with the studies of Kleiner and Parker (1959) and Jaco (1960). Rates of schizophrenia among male and female whites were higher for migrants than for natives of New York State. There were no differences in Ohio, and in California only white males manifested a slight difference in rates.

Thomas and Locke (1963) controlled for marital status, education, and occupation in these same samples. In Ohio and New York State the rates for nonwhite in-migrants were higher than for nonwhite natives, for males and females, although the differentials were small. Lee (1963), continuing the data analyses reported by Lazarus, Locke, and Thomas (1963), found higher rates of mental disease for migrants than for natives among nonwhite males and females. These differences in rates remained even after standardization. It is important to note that in all instances such increased standardization considerably reduced the differences between in-migrants and natives.

In the last study to be mentioned in this context, Kleiner and Parker (1965) reported on a total incidence count made during a fifteen month period. This count included all Negro first admissions or readmissions to public and private clinics and hospitals, private treatment cases, and those diagnosed as needing treatment but refusing such recommendation.

These investigators found in this ill population a significant over-representation of natives, and an under-representation of migrants to Pennsylvania from the Southern states. They were also interested in determining the degree to which class, status inconsistency, and the discrepancy between aspiration and achievement (which was assumed to be a measure of frustration) could explain the differential rates between the migrant and native populations. On the basis of interview data, they concluded that of these variables only the aspiration-achievement discrepancy could account for the differences; the natives (with higher rates of illness) manifested larger discrepancies than in-migrants.

Although existing studies of intranational migration draw on different populations and use various methods of data analysis, the consensus of these investigations is contrary to the findings noted for international migration. Nine of the fourteen studies of intranational migration cited fail to show higher rates of mental illness for in-migrants than for natives. The implications of international and in-migration for mental illness are apparently dissimilar. In addition, when rates are standardized for different social variables, the importance of migration decreases. This suggests the need for further study of these potentially relevant variables.

Many of the differences noted in this review cannot be explained away by the need for increased methodological sophistication. Another approach to this problem may also be important. If the investigator grants that some of these contradictory studies are valid, he must ask what conditions lead to high rates of mental illness for migrants in one situation and low rates in another. What theoretical and intervening variables can account for these seemingly contradictory studies? Researchers involved in the type of investigation reviewed above do not ignore this problem. Usually, however, the investigator is primarily oriented toward explaining his particular set of findings and does not concern himself with other studies, especially those which contradict his own results. Unfortunately, many attempts to explain one's findings have been speculative and of a *post hoc* nature and have rarely involved the collection of data specifically designed to test hypotheses. The types of speculative explanations most often used are noted below:

(1) Some investigators feel that the high rate of mental illness among the foreign born is a function of selective migration (i.e., those who are already disturbed or potentially ill tend to migrate to new areas (Ødegaard, 1932; Malzberg and Lee, 1956; Locke, Kramer, and Pasamanick, 1960)). This review has described studies both supporting and contra-

dicting the selective migration hypothesis. The interpretations advanced to explain the findings in these studies present a paradoxical picture, however. Investigators who find high illness rates among migrants attribute these rates to some predisposing proneness to illness. Investigators who find lower illness rates for the foreign born say that migrants as a group are *less* prone to illness than nonmigrants.

(2) Other investigators imply selective migration, but instead of assuming some emotional disturbance in the migrant they emphasize the individual's readiness to move or relocate as a determinant of his subsequent adjustment (Weinberg, 1955; Fried, 1965). This explanation presumes a relationship between social isolation and mental illness. Those who migrate from one area to another become mentally ill or disturbed because they lack cultural, interpersonal, and familial ties in their new communities (Faris and Dunham, 1939; Lemert, 1948; Lapouse, Monk, and Terris, 1956; Hollingshead and Redlich, 1958; Jaco, 1960; Last, 1960).

(3) A third major explanation assumes that a person who moves from one area to another is confronted with a cultural or subcultural milieu that conflicts with his original cultural environment (i.e., impact of new situations or "culture shock"). This situation is hypothesized to precipitate stress and mental disorder (Faris and Dunham, 1939; Lemert, 1948; Tyhurst, 1951; Weinberg, 1953c; Malzberg and Lee, 1956; Eitinger, 1959; Listwan, 1959; Last, 1960; Locke, Kramer and Pasamanick, 1960). As is the case for the selective migration hypothesis, the data are too inconsistent to provide firm support either for the social isolation or the culture shock explanation. Each explanation probably applies in some situations but not in others. The task is to determine the circumstances in which a particular explanation is applicable.

The general acceptance of the view that migration leads to mental illness is so widespread that little effort is made to account for studies yielding contradictory findings. Where such inconsistencies are recognized, efforts are made to explain them in terms of differences in receptivity to psychiatric treatment or in sophistication about psychiatry (Dayton, 1940; Murphy, 1965). It has been suggested that the high rates of illness associated with migration may be peculiar only to certain societies (Murphy, 1965). Some efforts have been made to explain obtained relationships between migration and mental disorder in terms of social-psychological variables (Parker, Kleiner, and Taylor, 1960; Kleiner and Parker, 1965).

Yield of Mental Illness
by Migratory Status

EARLIER STUDIES by the present authors (Kleiner and Parker, 1959; Parker, Kleiner, and Taylor, 1960) were limited to census data and first admissions to state hospitals, and migratory status was defined by *birthplace*. In more current research (Kleiner and Parker, 1965) and in the present study we have defined migratory status by *place of socialization* and have attempted to determine its relationship to mental illness. In this study the mentally ill population is not limited to census data and first admissions to state hospitals. It includes all Negro admissions to psychiatric facilities, private and public, and/or those individuals diagnosed as needing treatment during a fifteen-month period. We have used the interviewed community population rather than census data as a basis for computing rates of difference. We shall attempt to explain any rate differences in our migratory status groups in terms of the social-psychological variables of this study.

Our migratory status groups were defined as follows. Native: an individual who spent the majority of his first seventeen years of life in Philadelphia. Migrant: an individual who spent the majority of his first seventeen years of life outside of Philadelphia. The designation of northern or southern migrant was determined by the area in which socialization occurred. If a person spent the majority of his first seventeen years in Georgia, he was classified as a southern migrant. If he spent those years in New Jersey, he was considered a northern migrant. In the present section we shall discuss derived rates and percentage distributions in these migratory status groups, using both place of socialization and birthplace as criteria of classification. The major emphasis, however, will be placed on those migratory status groups classified according to place of socialization. Data based on birthplace are included to show that the differences among the migratory status groups are constant, regardless of the basis for definition. In addition, such data will allow us to link our findings to material on this question reported in the general literature.

The rate of mental disorder for a particular migratory status group was derived by dividing the number of interviewed patients in that group by the number of community population respondents in that same group, and multiplying the quotient by 100. (For example, to derive the illness rate for southern migrants, we divided the count of southern migrants in the patient population by the number of southern migrants in the community sample, and then multiplied by 100.) This figure represented the number of ill individuals in a particular migratory status group in our interviewed ill sample per 100 interviewed community respondents in that same group.[1] Dividing the number of patients in a particular migratory status group in the total incidence population (interviewed ill sample plus noninterviewed potentially eligible ill subjects) by the number of individuals in the corresponding community population group would have represented the number of individuals in that migratory status population in the total ill population per 100 interviewed community respondents.

The major advantage of computing rates such as these, rather than merely considering the proportion of individuals in each migratory status group, is that it provides an index of illness for a given migratory status group independent of the size of the other groups. Analyzing *only* rates gives us no indication of the relative importance of subgroups within the total ill, interviewed ill, and community samples; considering percentage distributions allows us to take this into account. As an instance, although the rate of illness for the northern migrants is very high, this migratory status group constitutes a relatively small proportion of the ill (interviewed and total incidence) and community populations. To ignore the relative contributions of the different migratory status groups to the total picture may result in over- or under-estimation of the importance of certain groups. When we compare the percentage distributions of corresponding migratory status groups in the ill and community populations, we can evaluate the relative over- and under-representation of these categories in the ill population. All migratory status groups are treated simultaneously and rated for their relative importance in the total population under consideration. Given the advantages and disadvantages of

1. Conversion to total population rates would be possible by multiplying our rates ($\frac{\#\text{ill}}{(\#\text{community})}$) by $\frac{1.82}{200}$. The numerator indicates that for every 1.82 patients in the total potentially eligible ill population, we interviewed one. The denominator indicates that for every 200 potentially eligible respondents in the community, we interviewed one. However, if we did convert our rates to total population rates, we would be assuming similar ratios in all subgroups of the community and ill samples. For instance, in analyzing rates in the area of education, we would be assuming that the ratio of interviewed ill to total ill was 1 : 1.82 in all educational control categories, and that the ratio of interviewed community respondents to total community respondents was 1 : 200 in all control groups. If we made such assumptions and they proved incorrect, all our reported figures would be erroneous. Therefore, we decided to present rates only for our known population counts.

these two approaches, both will be utilized in analyzing our data. The significance of the data will be determined by comparing the actual distributions in two given migratory status groups.

REPRESENTATIVENESS OF THE INTERVIEWED ILL SAMPLE

As a first step in data presentation, we consider whether the migratory status distribution of our interviewed ill sample is representative of the total incidence ill population. The curves in Figure 8.1 depict the percentages of the interviewed and total ill populations in each migratory status group (defined by place of socialization). The curves are almost identical.

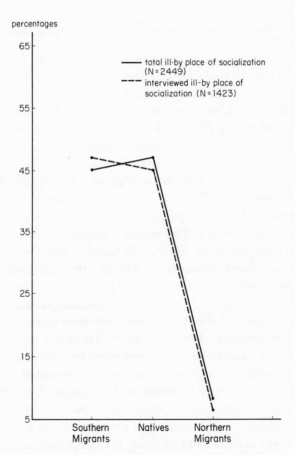

FIGURE 8.1—Representativeness of the Interviewed Ill Sample, by Migratory Status.

Table 8.1—Distributions (in Percentages) and Rates of Mental Illness for

Community, Total Incidence, and Interviewed Ill Samples, 1 by Migratory Status

Definition of Migratory Status

	PLACE OF SOCIALIZATION[2]					BIRTHPLACE[3]					
						Native: Philadelphia-born			Native: Pennsylvania-		
	Comm. (1)	Total Incidence Ill (2)	Rate[4] (3)	Intv. Ill (4)	Rate (5)	Comm. (6)	Intv. Ill (7)	Rate (8)	Comm. (9)	Intv. Ill (10)	Rat (11
Southern Migrant	61	45	123	48	75	68	58	82	68	58	82
Native	33	47	234	45	131	26	33	119	29	36	119
Northern Migrant	6	8	207	7	105	6	9	134	3	6	150
	100	100		100		100	100		100	100	
Total N	1486	2449		1421		1486	1421		1486	1421	

1. Inadequate Information
   Community Sample – 3 cases
   Total Incidence – 42 cases
   Interviewed Sample – 2 cases
2. Community Distribution versus Total Incidence Distribution: By chi-square, P=<.001
3. Analyses were made for natives defined both in terms of city and state in which he was born. For both analyses, by chi-square, P=<
4. Number Ill per 100 community sample

Table 8.1 presents rates of illness by migratory status both for the total ill and the interviewed ill population (columns 3 and 5), and the statistical significance of differences in distribution are also indicated. Clearly, regardless of whether the interviewed or total ill sample is considered, the rate of mental illness is lowest for the southern migrants. In the total incidence population, the northern migrants have a higher rate than the natives, and the opposite relationship applies in the interviewed sample. The distributions of both ill populations differ significantly from the community population ($P = < .001$). The southern migrants are under-represented in both ill populations, and the natives and northern migrants are over-represented. The northern migrants constitute a comparatively small proportion of the two ill samples and the community population. It is difficult to ascertain whether the high rates for the northern migrants are a function of social-psychological factors in the northern migrant group or a function of the small sample size.

In addition to rates, Table 8.1 includes the percentage distributions of the two ill populations (columns 2 and 4). There is a slight tendency for the southern migrants to be over-represented (by 3 per cent), and for the natives and northern migrants to be under-represented (by 2 and 1 per cent, respectively) in the interviewed ill sample. Since the interviewed ill sample contains a larger proportion of hospitalized individuals than the total incidence population, these discrepancies in representation suggest that natives and northern migrants use out-patient facilities more frequently than southern migrants. The differences are very small, however.

Dayton (1940) thought that those who were native to a community (defined by birthplace) used private facilities to a greater degree than individuals migrating into that community. He felt that studies based on admissions to public facilities under-estimated the rates of diagnosed illness among the native born. Murphy (1961) maintained the opposite point of view—that the native born used public facilities to a greater degree than migrants to that area. He felt that records of public psychiatric facilities under-estimated the true rate of diagnosed mental illness for migrants, not natives. When migratory status is defined as place of socialization, our data tend to support Dayton, although the size of the error in under-estimation of rates for natives is not large enough to make any appreciable difference.

The curves in Figure 8.2 represent the rates of illness for the migratory status groups in the two ill populations. Since the ill population under consideration was always divided by the total community sample ($N = 1489$), the rate computed on the basis of the total incidence ill population ($N = 2449$) was always higher than that based on the interviewed ill population ($N = 1423$).

Before we can assume that it makes no difference whether we use the total ill population or the interviewed sample, we must demonstrate that the relative difference in rates for any given migratory status group in the two ill populations is a function only of the relative difference in size of the two populations. If the two curves in Figure 8.2 closely parallel each other, it is very likely that the difference in rates is strictly a function of the size of the populations used to compute the rates, and not of differing proportions of the three migratory status groups within the two populations.

The two curves approximate each other very closely (see Figure 8.2). In fact, the differences in rates for each migratory status group are extremely small. The distribution of the three migratory status groups in the interviewed ill population does not differ significantly from the distribution of these groups in the total ill population. The data presented in the previous paragraph considered together with findings on first admissions previously reported by Parker, Kleiner, and Taylor (1960), suggest that the southern migrants are under-represented and the natives over-represented in Philadelphia's mentally ill population, regardless of whether first admissions or total incidence statistics are used, or whether migratory status is defined in the terms of birthplace or area of socialization. These data also allow us to investigate the relationship between mental illness and migration, defined by birthplace. As mentioned above,

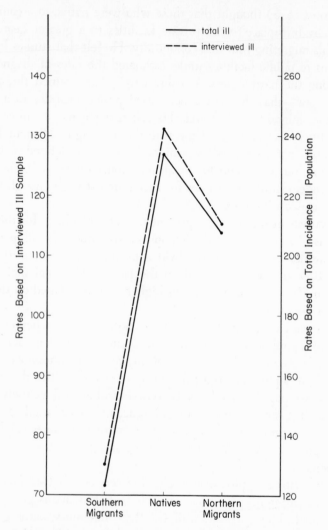

FIGURE 8.2—Rates of Mental Illness for the Total Incidence and the Interviewed Ill Populations, by Migratory Status (Defined by Place of Socialization).

defining migratory status in this way makes our results more directly comparable to findings reported in other studies which use a similar definition of migratory status.

Table 8.1 presents the illness rates and percentage distributions for the three migratory status groups, defined by place of birth. In this context "native" refers to (1) an individual born in Philadelphia; and (2) a person born in Pennsylvania. When Philadelphia-born respondents are considered as natives, the northern migrant group includes those who might have been born in Pennsylvania, but who subsequently moved to Philadelphia. When native means Pennsylvania-born, the total number of northern migrants decreases, since those who would be classified as northern migrants under the previous definition are now included in the native category. In this situation (i.e., decrease in the number of northern migrants) we expect a sharp rise in the illness rates for this group. Table 8.1 (columns 8 and 11) indicates that this expected change in rates occurs. If this reduction in the number of northern migrants is the same for the community and ill samples, the relative difference between the northern migrants in the community and in the ill populations becomes accentuated. The reduction of initially small samples leads to greater variability and instability of rates.

Figure 8.3 represents the illness rates for the three migratory status groups in the interviewed ill population, when "native" is defined as Philadelphia- and as Pennsylvania-born. The rates for southern migrants and natives are the same, regardless of the definition of "native." If we did not also consider the percentage distributions of the migratory status groups in the community and ill samples, we would attribute equal weight to the rate of each migratory status group. Since the northern migrants actually represent a small proportion of the ill and community populations, such an assumption would be misleading. When the percentage distributions are considered, the southern migrants are under-represented and the natives over-represented in the ill population. These differences exist regardless of which criterion of "native" is applied (see Table 8.1). The differences are statistically significant ($P = < .001$).

These findings support our earlier assertion that, regardless of the criterion of migratory status (i.e., place of socialization or birthplace), the natives are over-represented and the southern migrants under-represented in the mentally ill population. Differences emerge when we consider the rate for northern migrants. The rate for interviewed ill northern migrants (defined in terms of place of socialization) is lower than the rate for natives (Table 8.1, column 5), but it is higher than the rate for natives when defined in terms of birthplace (Table 8.1, columns 8 and 11). Apparently, of those born outside of Philadelphia, more individuals from Northern than from Southern states are found in the ill population. Again we emphasize that these results may be a function of the small number of cases in the northern migrant group. (The northern migrants constitute only 6 per cent of the community and 9 per cent of the ill

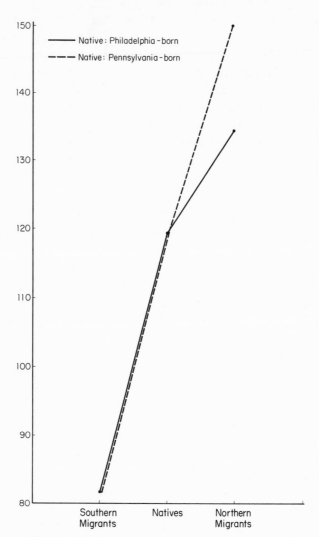

FIGURE 8.3—Rates of Mental Illness for the Interviewed Ill Sample, by Migratory Status (Defined by Birthplace).

sample when "native" refers to Philadelphia-born. The corresponding percentages when "native" is defined as Pennsylvania-born are 3 and 6 per cent.)

Figure 8.4 and Table 8.2 present the illness rates and percentage distributions for the migratory status groups (defined by place of socialization) in the ill and community samples, for males and females and for

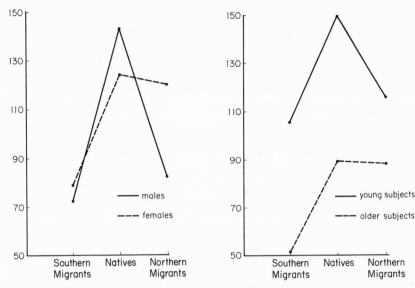

FIGURE 8.4—Rates of Mental Illness for the Interviewed Ill Sample, by Migratory Status, Sex, and Age.

young and older subjects. In the sex and age subgroups the natives are characterized by higher rates of illness than the southern and northern migrants (see Figure 8.4 and Table 8.2). The rates for the northern migrants always fall between those of the southern migrants and the natives, although there is almost no difference between the native and northern migrant rates in the older age groups. Females also manifest a very small difference in rates for these two migratory status groups. Females in the southern and northern migrant groups show higher rates than the males in the corresponding groups. Male natives have a higher

Table 8.2—Distributions (in Percentages) and Rates for the Interviewed Ill

and Community Samples by Migratory Status, Sex, and Age

(Migratory Status Defined as Place of Socialization)

	MALES [1]			FEMALES [1]			YOUNG [1]			OLD [1]		
	Comm. (1)	Intv. Ill (2)	Rate (3)	Comm. (4)	Intv. Ill (5)	Rate (6)	Comm. (7)	Intv. Ill (8)	Rate (9)	Comm. (10)	Intv. Ill (11)	Rate (12)
thern Migrant	61	46	72	61	49	77	49	42	107	75	63	51
ive	32	48	143	33	43	124	44	52	148	20	30	90
thern Migrant	7	6	82	6	8	120	7	6	116	5	7	89
	100	100		100	100		100	100		100	100	
Total N	600	576		885	845		798	1007		684	414	

For each sex and age group, Community distribution vs Ill distribution, by chi-square, $P = <.001$.

Table 8.3—Distributions (in Percentages) and Rates of Mental Illness for Community and Interviewed Ill Samples, Occupation, Income, and Education Groups, by Migratory Status

Occupation	Occ. 1			Occ. 2[2]			Occ. 3			Occ. 4-7[3]		
	Comm. (1)	Ill (2)	Rate (3)	Comm. (4)	Ill (5)	Rate (6)	Comm. (7)	Ill (8)	Rate (9)	Comm. (10)	Ill (11)	Rate (12)
Southern Migrant	72	52	80	50	42	65	42	36	63	50	40	84
Native	25	43	190	42	51	96	45	55	89	38	47	135
Northern Migrant	3	5	226	8	7	66	13	9	56	12	13	150
Total N	708	792		377	296		141	104		60	66	

Income	$0-40/wk[1]			$41-80/wk[1]			$81 and over/wk		
	Comm. (1)	Ill (2)	Rate (3)	Comm. (4)	Ill (5)	Rate (6)	Comm. (7)	Ill (8)	Rate (9)
Southern Migrant	78	52	73	58	47	73	54	48	60
Native	18	43	264	35	47	120	37	42	77
Northern Migrant	4	7	150	7	6	84	9	10	74
Total N	250	277		762	691		307	208	

Education	0-4 yrs.[3]			5-8 yrs.[1]			9-11 yrs.[1]			12 yrs.[1]			13 or more yrs.		
	Comm. (1)	Ill (2)	Rate (3)	Comm. (4)	Ill (5)	Rate (6)	Comm. (7)	Ill (8)	Rate (9)	Comm. (10)	Ill (11)	Rate (12)	Comm. (13)	Ill (14)	Rate (15)
Southern Migrant	95	81	98	84	67	80	53	38	91	40	32	68	46	43	87
Native	5	19	450	12	26	213	40	57	178	52	60	98	39	40	98
Northern Migrant	–	–	–	4	7	192	7	5	81	8	8	89	15	17	106
Total N	83	96		371	372		429	536		336	288		114	107	

1. By chi-square, P=<.001
2. By chi-square, P=<.02>.01
3. By chi-square, P=<.05

illness rate than females socialized in Philadelphia. Rates for the young are higher than for the older subjects in each migratory status group. The rates for northern migrants vary to a greater degree than the rates for the other migratory status groups when the sex and age groups are compared—again this variability (or instability) may be a result of the small sample size.

In each sex and age subgroup within the interviewed ill population, the southern migrants are under-represented and the natives over-represented (see Table 8.2). The findings are more complicated for the northern migrants. This group is under-represented in the ill population among the young, but over-represented in the older group. Northern migrant males are under-represented and females over-represented in the ill population. These trends for the northern migrants are not statistically significant. When the distributions for the ill and community samples for all three migratory status groups are compared in each sex and age group, the differences are significant (all at $P = < .001$). The over-representation of the southern migrants, and the under-representation of the natives in the ill population account for this significance.

Up to this point we have not been concerned with the effects of socioeconomic status on the illness rates and percentage distributions of the three migratory status groups (defined by place of socialization). Figure 8.5 and Table 8.3 present the data for occupational, income, and educational status. The natives clearly have higher illness rates than the southern migrants in each occupational, income and educational status control group. The picture is again inconsistent and complicated for northern migrants (see Figure 8.5 and Table 8.3). In all twelve rate curves, illness rates for natives are higher than for southern migrants. In nine of the eleven curves the rates for northern migrants are lower than the rates for natives, and in ten of the eleven curves the northern migrants have higher rates than the southern migrants. As one moves from low to high status positions on the income and educational hierarchies, the relative rate differences for the southern migrants and natives decrease (see Figure 8.5). This trend appears in the curves for occupation when the lowest status group is compared with the upper three. No systematic status changes can be observed for the northern migrants.

We turn now to the percentage distributions of the migratory status groups in the community and ill samples (see Table 8.3). Among the mentally ill the southern migrants are under-represented and the natives over-represented in each of the occupational status groups. The distributions of the community and ill samples by migratory status differ signifi-

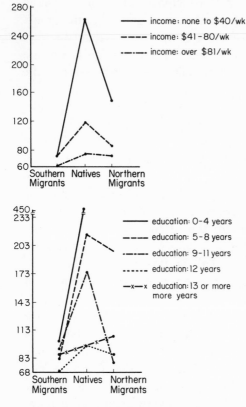

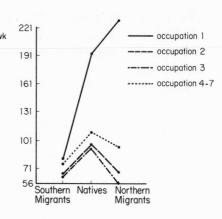

FIGURE 8.5—Rates of Mental Illness for the Interviewed Ill Sample, by Migratory Status, Occupation, Income, and Education.

cantly in three of the four occupational status groups (for occupational level 1, $P = <$ .001; for level 2, $P = <$ .02; and for level 4-and-over, $P = <$ .05).

In each of the three income status groups the southern migrants are under-represented and the natives over-represented in the ill population.

Table 8.4—Distributions (in Percentages) and Rates for Symptom Scores, Diagnosis, and Chronicity by Migratory Status

| | | COMM. SAMPLE | | | ILL SAMPLE [1] | | | | ILL SAMPLE | | | |
	Total Comm. (1)	Low Symp. (2)	High Symp. (3)	Rate [2] (4)	Neur. (5)	Rate (6)	Psych. (7)	Rate (8)	First Adm. (9)	Rate (10)	Chronic Cases (11)	Ra (1
Southern Migrant	61	62	57	12	45	13	47	56	50	52	44	2
Native	33	32	35	14	47	25	46	99	44	85	48	4
Northern Migrant	6	6	8	17	8	22	7	77	6	64	8	4
	100	100	100		100		100		100		100	
Total N	1486	1315	173		258		1060		941		480	

1. Total Community vs Psychotics: By chi-square, $P = <.001$
   Total Community vs Neurotics: By chi-square, $P = <.001$
2. Within the community sample only, rates signify the number of high symptom respondents per 100 community sample.

This same pattern of under- and over-representation emerges in all five educational status groups. The distributions of the community and ill samples differ significantly in the four lowest educational status groups (0–4 years of education, $P = < .05$; 5–8 years, 9–11 years, and 12 years of education, all significant at $P = < .001$). The northern migrants show no consistency from one status group to another on any of the three dimensions of status.

In summary, we note that the southern migrants are over-represented and the natives under-represented in all twelve status groups in the ill population. Nine of the twelve patterns going in the expected direction are significant. No consistent trends emerge for northern migrants, although in eight out of eleven status groups northern migrant rates fall between those of the southern migrants and the natives.

Figure 8.6 presents the curves for rates on migratory status for the psychotics, the neurotics, and the high psychiatric symptom group in the community. Figure 8.6 and Table 8.4 (columns 4, 6, and 8) show higher rates for natives than for southern migrants in each of these three mental health groupings. The rates for northern migrants fall between those of

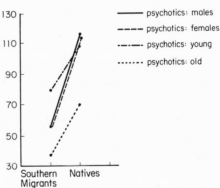

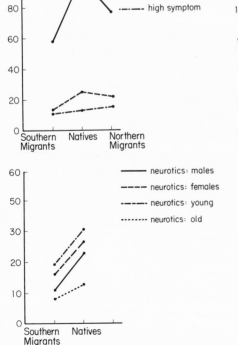

FIGURE 8.6—Rates for Psychotics, Neurotics, and High Symptom Subjects, by Migratory Status, Sex, and Age. Rates for High Symptom Subjects and Northern Migrants Are Limited to Totals.

the natives and southern migrants in the psychotic and the neurotic groupings, but in the high symptom group the rates for northern migrants are higher than rates for natives or southern migrants. We should also point out that in the southern migrant-native comparison, the relative difference in rates increases as one moves from the high symptom group, to the neurotics, to the psychotics (see Figure 8.6).

Figure 8.6 also presents the curves for illness rates among the psychotics and the neurotics, controlling for sex and age. In each sex and age group among the psychotics the natives are characterized by higher illness rates than southern migrants. Rates for males and females are almost identical. The young show higher rates than the older subjects, regardless of migratory status. Rates of neurosis for females are higher than for males in both migratory status groups, and similarly, rates for the young are higher than for the older subjects.

Rates for the neurotics are lower than rates for the psychotics, for each migratory status category. Since the same denominator is used to compute the rates for both of these diagnostic groupings, and since there are fewer neurotic than psychotic respondents in all migratory status groups (i.e., a smaller numerator), the rate is always lower for the neurotics. In view of this common denominator, it is meaningless to attempt comparisons between the rates of the diagnostic groups.

Table 8.4 lists the percentage distributions of the migratory status groups in our four mental health groupings (columns 2, 3, 5, and 7). In the community population the southern migrants are again under-represented and the natives over-represented in the high symptom group, but the difference between the two distributions is not significant. When the distribution of the psychotics is compared to that of the total community population (columns 1 and 7), the southern migrants are under-represented and the natives over-represented among the psychotics. The same pattern emerges for the neurotics compared to the total community population (columns 1 and 5). Both comparisons are significant at $P = < .001$.

The differences observed between migratory status groups may appear only when first admissions or only when chronic cases of mental illness are considered. In this study a "first admission" was defined as an individual diagnosed for the first time in his life as needing treatment in the period during which we conducted the interviews. A "chronic" case was a person who had been diagnosed as needing treatment prior to the interview. Table 8.4 presents the rates and percentage distributions for these populations. In these analyses also, the expected differences in rates between the southern migrants and the natives emerge. Both among first admissions (column 10) and chronic cases (column 12) natives have higher illness rates than southern migrants. Northern migrants fall between these two groups in both instances.

Comparisons of the percentage distributions of first admissions (Table 8.4, column 9) and chronic cases (column 11) with the distribution of the total community sample (column 1) show that the southern migrants are under-represented and the natives significantly over-represented in both ill groups (both comparisons for the natives are significant at $P = < .001$).

In summary, regardless of the criterion of migratory status used, the measure of status employed, diagnosis, sex, or age, the southern migrants are characterized by a lower rate of illness than the natives and are under-represented in the ill sample. The natives show a higher rate of illness and are over-represented in the patient population. The rate for northern migrants falls between those of the southern migrants and the natives when place of socialization is taken as the criterion of migratory status. When birthplace is used as the criterion, the rates for northern migrants are higher than for natives and southern migrants. Findings for northern migrants are rather unstable because of the small number of respondents in this classification.

INTERACTION OF DIAGNOSIS AND MIGRATORY STATUS

We must determine whether the neurotics and psychotics contribute differentially to the rates associated with the various migratory status groups. Since our study variables have shown different patterns for the neurotics and psychotics, it would be misleading to compare mentally ill status groups differing significantly in diagnostic composition. If type of illness is not taken into account, we cannot determine whether observed differences are a result of diagnosis or of our study variables. If significant variations in diagnostic composition in a given set of migratory status groups do emerge, separate analyses must be presented for each diagnostic group.

Table 8.5 shows that 81 per cent of the southern migrants, 80 per cent of the natives, and 77 per cent of the northern migrants fall into the psychotic category. Conversely, 19 per cent of the southern migrants, 20 per cent of the natives, and 23 per cent of the northern migrants are classified as neurotics. These differences are not statistically significant.

Table 8.5—*Distributions of Diagnosis and Chronicity by Migratory Status, Age, and*

Sex for the Interviewed Ill Sample[1] in Percentages

	INTERVIEWED	DIAGNOSIS			INTERVIEWED	CHRONICITY		
	Ill N	Psych.	Neur.	Total	Ill N	First Adm.	Chronic Cases	Total
Total: Southern Migrant	619	81	19	100	680	69	31	100
Total: Native	608	80	20	100	644	66	34	100
Total: Northern Migrant[2]	91	77	23	100	97	61	39	100
Males: Southern Migrant[3]	247	83	17	100	266	67	33	100
Males: Native	269	83	17	100	278	62	38	100
Females: Southern Migrant	382	78	22	100	414	70	30	100
Females: Native	340	77	23	100	366	66	34	100
Young: Southern Migrant	385	81	19	100	421	73	27	100
Young: Native	491	78	22	100	521	63	37	100
Old: Southern Migrant	234	82	18	100	259	63	37	100
Old: Native	117	85	15	100	123	67	33	100

1. Data based only on those cases for which diagnosis and chronicty were known, Unknowns include the 99 cases taken from the original community sample and placed in the ill population because they had been (or still were) in treatment within a year prior to the interview.
2. Analyses for sex and age groups were limited to southern migrants and natives because of the small number of northern migrants.
3. Migratory status vs chronicity, by chi-square, $P = <.01$

Table 8.5 also shows that there is no significant diagnostic variation by sex or age in any of the migratory status groups.

There is little evidence to indicate that these diagnoses are differentially distributed among the various migratory status groups, particularly in the southern migrant and native groups. Consequently, we need not be concerned further with the problems of diagnosis.

INTERACTION OF CHRONICITY AND MIGRATORY STATUS

Although the distribution of diagnoses among the three migratory status groups presents no problem, we must consider whether chronicity is more evident in one group than another. If first admissions and chronic cases exist approximately in the same proportions in all migratory status groups, we need not present separate analyses for each. As with diagnosis, we shall report significant differences in the distributions of first admissions and chronic disorders among the migratory status groups.

The data on chronicity are presented in Table 8.5. Sixty-nine per cent of the southern migrants, 66 per cent of the natives, and 61 per cent of the northern migrants are first admissions. Conversely, 31 per cent of the southern migrants, 34 per cent of the natives, and 39 per cent of the northern migrants are chronic cases. None of the variations between migratory status groups is significant. Similar analyses on chronicity, controlling for sex and age (Table 8.5), show no significant differences between the migratory status groups for males, females, or the older subjects. Among the young respondents, a significantly larger ($P = <.01$) proportion of the southern migrants (73 per cent) than of the natives (63 per cent) are first admissions.

Psychiatric treatment might not have been as available to these southern migrants in their home communities as in Philadelphia. When they migrated to this city they were able to utilize the available facilities. They might also have found greater acceptance of psychiatric treatment in Philadelphia than in their original communities. This would also encourage increased use of the available facilities in the new community. A third possibility is that Southern-born individuals with prior histories of psychiatric illness do not tend to migrate north. All of these possibilities would result in a greater proportion of first admissions among the southern migrants, and all are empirical or testable alternatives.

These possibilities also seem applicable to the older respondents. We present them to explain differences in chronicity among the young subjects, since initial contact with psychiatric facilities is made during the "young" age period. We have already shown that among first admissions and chronics in the young subgroups, southern migrants and natives show the same pattern of rates and over- or under-representation in the ill population as do the older respondents. Therefore, we need not be concerned about young-old differences in first admission and chronic proportions. The significant difference obtained here does not create such a serious problem that data for the two types of admissions must be analyzed separately.

REFERRAL SOURCE, TREATMENT DISPOSITION, AND MIGRATORY STATUS

We have gone to some lengths to establish that the rates of mental illness are higher among natives than among migrants from the South. We have also shown that northern migrants are characterized by illness rates that usually fall between those of the two other migratory status groups. Researchers who report inconsistent findings usually attribute these contradictions to methodological problems on the part of the investigators or to sociocultural artifacts. Thus, Dayton (1940) and Murphy (1961) considered whether natives of a given area tended to use available public facilities more or less frequently than migrants to that area. If such a selective process does occur, then studies based only on data from certain types of facilities (e.g., public hospitals) will come to misleading conclusions. If natives tend to avoid using such public facilities as state mental hospitals, rates based on hospital admission statistics will under-estimate the diagnosed rates for natives, thereby artificially inflating the rates for southern migrants.

Parker, Kleiner, and Taylor (1960) analyzed data on first admissions to Pennsylvania state hospitals and found no evidence of different referral sources for the various migratory status groups. However, the mentally ill respondents in their investigation were already using a selected type of facility, and the study did not include patients being treated at private or other public facilities in the city. The present study utilizes information on the referral sources and treatment disposition of our ill population, including patients seen in all types of facilities: public, private, in-patient, and out-patient (including those in private treatment). These data will provide some answers to the questions raised by Dayton (1940), Parker, Kleiner, and Taylor (1960), and Murphy (1961).

Table 8.6—Referral Source and Disposition for the Interviewed

Ill Sample by Migratory Status in Percentages

	Southern Migrant	Native	Northern Migrant
Referral Source			
Medical, Psychiatric and Social Service Facilities	53	48	46
Self, Family, and Friends	30	34	37
Police, Courts, and Prisons	17	18	17
	100	100	100
Total *N*	615	602	90
Disposition			
Hospitalized (Public and Private)	61	66	63
Outpatient (Public and Private)	34	33	34
Other (Refused Recommendation, withdrew, etc.)	5	1	3
	100	100	100
Total *N*	616	606	91

Table 8.6 presents the percentage distributions of referral sources and treatment disposition for migratory status group totals. Several points emerge with respect to referral source. First, the southern migrants, to a greater degree than the natives and northern migrants, are referred by medical, psychiatric, and social service facilities. Second, there is a tendency for natives and northern migrants to enter psychiatric facilities on their own initiative or through the persuasion of family and friends. Third, all three migration groups contain the same proportion of individuals brought to psychiatric facilities through police and judicial channels. Although these observations are suggested by the data, there are no significant differences in referral source in the three migratory status groups, either for totals or when sex and age controls are considered. Analyses controlling for sex and age clearly confirm the findings obtained for group totals.

Table 8.6 also includes data on treatment disposition in the patient population. Although the "Hospitalized" category includes those admitted to public and private institutions, very few individuals in any of the migratory status groups were admitted to private facilities. This also applies to out-patient clinic dispositions. A greater proportion of natives than of northern or southern migrants are apparently admitted to out-patient facilities. There is also a tendency for a greater proportion of the southern migrants to refuse recommendations for treatment or to withdraw from the treatment process. There is, however, no significant relationship between migratory status and treatment disposition, for any of these groups.

As with referral source, analyses were also carried out in each of the sex and age subgroups. There are no significant differences among the migratory status groups on treatment disposition among females or among young or older respondents. Significant differences ($P = < .05$) do emerge among the males. More male southern migrants than natives are "Hospitalized," whereas a greater proportion of male natives than southern migrants are referred to "Out-patient" facilities. Since most of the studies reported in the literature are based on hospital admissions data, this finding assumes particular importance.

The literature on the relationship between in-migration and mental illness generally reports higher rates of illness for natives than for migrants. Kleiner and Parker (1959) and Parker, Kleiner, and Taylor (1960) have shown this generalization to be particularly applicable to Negroes in Pennsylvania. It has been suggested that natives are more sophisticated than migrants about available psychiatric facilities and are more accepting of admission to psychiatric hospitals. According to this reasoning, southern migrants who are unfamiliar with available facilities and unreceptive to psychiatric treatment are only seen when they are picked up by the police and referred through legal and judicial channels. The data on referral source in the present study do not support these speculations about differences in enforced referral. Male southern migrants tend to be hospitalized more frequently than male natives—the use of hospital data may under-represent the true rates of diagnosed mental illness for natives.

In summary, data pertaining to referral source and treatment disposition provide no basis for questioning the validity of our findings with respect to the distribution of mental illness among the migratory status groups.

*Relationship between our Study
Variables and Migratory Status*

ALL PREVIOUS CHAPTERS have been concerned primarily with determining whether the mentally ill and community populations differed with respect to a number of social-psychological variables. In those chapters we were concerned only secondarily with demonstrating that sub-populations within the community population characterized by high rates (yields) of mental illness manifested more of the characteristics of the mentally ill than did low yield community subgroups. This has been referred to earlier as the "yield issue." Analyses relating to this issue have been limited to comparisons of sex and age subgroups.

Within the present chapter we have begun a series of analyses focusing primarily on comparing community subgroups differing on particular sociological characteristics (e.g., migratory status, socioeconomic status, status mobility), with respect to their rates of mental illness. We are interested in determining to what degree each of the social-psychological variables of this study can be used to explain the high or low rates of illness associated with different subgroups within the community population. A variable that successfully explains differences in yield among these subgroups may be considered antecedent to mental illness, and not merely a concomitant or consequent condition. This reasoning rests on the following assumption: since we are comparing subgroups whose members are not mentally disturbed (as determined by medical evaluation) and who have no history of psychiatric difficulty, differences obtained among these subgroups on our variables cannot be explained in terms of the *effects* of the illness process.

This emphasis on the yield question does not imply a subsequent exclusion of discussions of differences between the ill and community populations. In some situations such discussions will be necessary to the continuity of certain issues introduced earlier in this volume. From this point on, however, our primary emphasis will shift from ill-community comparisons to comparisons of subgroups within the community population.

PREDICTIONS

We may now describe more specifically the kinds of differences we expect among the various migratory status groups, with respect to our social-psychological study variables. The presentation of data on the study variables will be geared toward testing the validity of these expectations.

(1) Since the yield of mental illness is higher for the total native population than for the total southern migrant population, we expect the natives to show more of the characteristics of the mentally ill population. Since the differences in rates between these migratory status groups

apply regardless of sex or age, we make the same prediction for each sex and age subgroup.

(2) Since the yield of mental illness for the total native population tends to be greater than for the total northern migrant population, we expect the natives to show more of the characteristics of the mentally ill.

(3) Since the yield of mental illness tends to be greater for the total northern migrant population than for the total southern migrant population, we expect the northern migrants to show more of the characteristics of the mentally ill. (Predictions of differences in rates between sex and age subgroups cannot be tested in comparisons involving the northern migrants. The small number of cases in this migratory status classification precludes reliable statistical analyses when sex and age breakdowns are made.)

PERCEPTION OF THE OPPORTUNITY STRUCTURE

The mentally ill and community populations have already been compared on perception of the opportunity structure (Chapter 3). The ill were more prone than the community subjects to perceive the opportunity structure as open. The natives tend to view the opportunity structure as more open than the southern migrants, although the difference is not statistically significant. When similar analyses are made comparing males, females, young, and older respondents in the native and southern migrant populations, the natives are more inclined to perceive the structure as open in every situation. The natives also tend to see a more open system than the northern migrants. When the northern and southern migrants are compared, the former group perceives a more open system. In neither analysis are the differences significant.

All seven comparisons with respect to the perception of the opportunity structure show differences in the expected direction, although none of these differences reaches significance. We conclude that there is a slight, but consistent, tendency for the high yield migratory status groups in the community to perceive the opportunity structure as relatively open. We also suggest that a person in a high yield group is still a member of the community because he does not invariably see the opportunity structure as open.

GOAL-STRIVING STRESS SCORES

The present discussion is limited to the three stress scores relating to the individual's own striving (i.e., occupation, income, and the striving

Migratory Status and Mental Disorder

Table 8.7—Mean Goal-Striving Stress Score Comparisons, by High-and Low-Yield

Migratory Status Groups, Sex, and Age[1]

HIGH YIELD LOW YIELD	OCC. STRESS-SELF			INC. STRESS-SELF			STRIVING SCALE STRESS-SELF		
	Mean 1 (1)	Mean 2 (2)	P (3)	Mean 1 (4)	Mean 2 (5)	P (6)	Mean 1 (7)	Mean 2 (8)	(9
Native Comm. vs South Mig. Comm.-Total	8.36	3.36	<.001	21.77	12.38	<.01	19.87	11.05	<.0
Subgroup N	422	788		430	801		479	894	
Native Comm. vs South Mig. Comm.-Males	11.30	4.67	<.001	17.24	15.49	NS	22.24	13.34	<.0
Subgroup N	181	335		174	329		192	364	
Native Comm. vs South Mig. Comm.-Females	6.16	2.38	<.01	24.84	10.22	<.001	18.29	9.48	<.0
Subgroup N	241	453		256	472		287	530	
Native Comm. vs South Mig. Comm.-Young	8.90	4.01	<.01	22.67	14.23	<.01	20.89	10.70	<.0
Subgroup N	304	353		307	357		285	343	
Native Comm. vs South Mig. Comm.-Old	7.27	2.83	<.01	19.34	10.90	<.05	17.35	11.32	<.0
Subgroup N	117	435		121	444		134	509	
Native Comm. vs North Mig. Comm.-Total	8.36	7.44	NS	21.77	21.15	NS	19.87	19.62	N
Subgroup N	422	80		430	87		479	93	
North Mig. Comm. vs South Mig. Comm.-Total	7.44	3.36	.05	21.15	12.38	<.05	19.62	11.05	<.0
Subgroup N	80	788		87	801		93	479	

1. The significance of each comparison was determined by the "t" test. Sex and age controls were not used in comparisons involving T
Northern Migrants because of the small number of cases in this migratory status group.

scale). Stress score comparisons by migratory status are summarized in
Table 8.7. The groups paired in each of the seven rows in Table 8.7
correspond to the three predictions already presented. In all seven comparisons, the high yield migratory status groups show higher occupation
stress scores than the low yield groups (Table 8.7, columns 1 and 2).
The differences between the groups are significant for six of the seven
comparisons. The one comparison that does not reach significance involves the two migratory status groups whose rates of illness also do not
differ significantly.

Stress score differences for the native-southern migrant comparisons
were analyzed within the three lowest occupational status control categories to determine the degree to which these results held at different
status levels. The total native group manifests higher occupation stress
scores than the southern migrants at all three achievement levels. Two
of these three comparisons are significant (both at $P = < .01$). Comparisons between these two migratory status groups with sex and age
controls provide twelve additional tests of the prediction. Eleven of these
twelve comparisons go in the expected direction (by sign test, $P < .01$).
Six of these eleven comparisons are significant (three at $P = < .05$,
one at $P = < .01$, and two at $P = < .002$).

The average income stress scores are clearly higher for the high yield
migratory status groups in all seven comparisons (Table 8.7, columns 4
and 5). Five of these seven comparisons are significant. Again, one of
the two nonsignificant analyses involves the natives and northern migrants, who, as pointed out earlier, do not differ significantly in yield of
mental illness. Analyses between natives and southern migrants were

also carried out in each of the three income achievement control groups. The native group is characterized by higher stress scores than the southern migrant group at two of the three income achievement levels. Both of these differences are in the predicted direction and are significant ($P = < .01$ and $< .05$, respectively). Comparable native-southern migrant analyses in each of the sex and age groups provide twelve additional evaluations of our prediction. Ten of these twelve analyses are in the predicted direction. Five of these ten comparisons are significant (four at $P = < .05$, and one at $P = < .002$).

The average striving scale stress scores are higher within the high yield migratory status groups for all seven comparisons (Table 8.7, columns 7 and 8). Six of these seven analyses are significant. As noted for the occupation and income stress scores, the one nonsignificant comparison involves the natives and northern migrants. Control group analyses between natives and southern migrants were carried out in only two striving scale achievement groups (because of the limited number of cases). In both control categories the total native population is characterized by higher stress scores than the southern migrant population; both comparisons are significant ($P = < .05$ and $< .01$, respectively). Applying the same control group comparisons to each sex and age group furnishes eight additional comparisons, all of which go in the expected direction. Five are significant (one at $P = < .05$, and four at $P = < .01$).

A brief summary of the analyses carried out up to this point will provide the reader with an overview of the findings. Only two of the sixty-three analyses fail to go in the predicted direction. Forty of the sixty-one comparisons that do conform to expectations are statistically significant. High stress scores in these three self-striving areas are clearly associated with high yield migratory status groups within the community population—this evidence supports the view that these three goal-striving stress scores can be considered possible antecedents to mental illness.

DISCREPANCY BETWEEN LEVEL OF ASPIRATION AND ACHIEVEMENT

In previous research, the present authors (Kleiner and Parker, 1959; Parker, Kleiner, and Taylor, 1960; and Kleiner and Parker, 1965) attempted to use the aspiration-achievement discrepancy concept as an intervening variable to explain the higher illness rate for natives than southern migrants. This aspiration-achievement discrepancy was also considered to be the stressor factor in the computation of goal-striving stress scores (Chapter 3). Because of the central role assigned to the discrepancy concept, it is important to determine whether high and low yield migratory status groups differ on this measure. We predict larger aspiration-achievement discrepancies for the high yield than for the low yield groups. We limit this discussion to the discrepancy scores used as components of the three self-related stress scores. The relevant data are summarized in Table 8.8.

Table 8.8—Mean Aspiration-Achievement Discrepancy, Mean Reference Group Discrepancy, and Mean Self-Ideal Discrepancy, by High - and Low-Yield Migratory Status Groups, Sex, and Age[1]

High Yield	Low Yield	OCC.-SELF DISCREP.			INCOME-SELF DISCREP.			STRIVING SCALE DISCREP.			REF. GRP. DISCREP.[2]			SELF-IDEAL DISCREP.[3]		
		M1 (1)	M2 (2)	P (3)	M1 (4)	M2 (5)	P (6)	M1 (7)	M2 (8)	P (9)	M1 (10)	M2 (11)	P (12)	M1 (13)	M2 (14)	(15)
Native Comm. vs South-Mig. Comm.-Total		1.50	1.22	<.001	3.42	4.38	<.02	2.74	2.38	<.001	.46	.42	N.S.	.53	.52	N.
Subgroup N		422	786		438	819		480	894		479	874		487	904	
Native Comm. vs South Mig. Comm.-Total		1.80	1.11	<.001	3.33	3.34	N.S.	2.83	2.42	<.01	.39	.38	N.S.	.49	.51	N.
Subgroup N		181	334		183	343		192	365		188	357		194	368	
Native Comm. vs South-Mig. Comm.-Females		1.31	1.28	N.S.	3.49	2.89	<.001	2.67	2.35	<.01	.51	.46	N.S.	.55	.52	<.0
Subgroup N		241	452		255	476		288	525		291	517		293	536	
Native Comm. vs South-Mig. Comm.-Young		1.52	1.25	<.01	3.58	3.27	<.05	2.95	2.85	N.S.	.52	.45	N.S.	.53	.54	N.
Subgroup N		305	352		315	370		345	386		343	374		348	391	
Native Comm. vs South-Mig. Comm.-Old		1.41	1.20	<.05	3.01	2.91	N.S.	2.18	2.02	N.S.	.33	.40	N.S.	.51	.50	N.
Subgroup N		116	434		123	449		133	508		.34	500		137	513	
Native Comm. vs North-Mig. Comm.-Total		1.50	1.38	N.S.	3.42	3.67	N.S.	2.74	2.46	N.S.	.46	.40	N.S.	.53	.50	N.
Subgroup N		422	80		438	85		480	93		479	92		487	93	
North Mig. Comm. vs South Mig. Comm.-Total		1.38	1.22	N.S.	3.67	3.08	<.02	2.46	2.38	N.S.	.40	.42	N.S.	.50	.52	N.
Subgroup N		80	786		85	819		93	894		92	874		93	904	

1. See footnote to Table 8.7.
2. The larger the discrepancy, the further the respondent is below his reference group.
3. The larger the discrepancy, the lower the self-esteem.

In all seven comparisons, the high yield groups are characterized by larger discrepancies between occupational aspirations and achievements (Table 8.8, columns 1 and 2). Four of these differences are significant, all of which involve comparisons between natives and southern migrants. Data on the income discrepancy (Table 8.8, columns 4 and 5) again disclose higher average discrepancies for high yield than for low yield migratory status groups. Six of the seven comparisons go in the expected direction, and four of the seven analyses are significant. Finally, the data on the striving scale discrepancy indicate larger average discrepancy scores for the high yield groups in all seven comparisons (Table 8.8, columns 7 and 8). The reader will recall that the yields of mental illness for the natives and northern migrants did not differ significantly—none of the three discrepancy scores differentiates significantly between these two migratory status groups.

The data on the three discrepancy scores for each of the seven comparisons provide twenty-one tests of the discriminating value of the discrepancy concept. Twenty of these twenty-one tests show larger discrepancy scores for the high than for the low yield migratory status groups. Eleven of these twenty tests are significant. The data clearly provide considerable support for regarding the discrepancy concept as a potential antecedent to illness, as an intervening variable to explain differences in yield between migratory status groups, and as the stressor factor in our goal-striving stress scores.

REFERENCE GROUP BEHAVIOR

Two major measures were used to contrast the reference group characteristics of the ill and community populations (Chapter 6): the perceived discrepancy between the achievement level of one's "close friends" and oneself, and the three blue/white-collar occupation choices in which the subject indicated a preference between a high-salary blue-collar position and a low-salary white-collar job. This blue/white-collar choice implies a discrepancy between achieved and aspired occupations. Since the overwhelming majority of our samples are at blue-collar occupational levels, the selection of a white-collar alternative reflects both a dissatisfaction with one's current occupational achievement, and an orientation toward more prestigious occupations.

Since mentally ill individuals placed themselves further below their reference group than did community respondents (Chapter 6), in this context we expect high yield migratory status groups in the community population to manifest larger reference group discrepancy scores than low yield groups. This expectation is confirmed for five of the seven comparisons (Table 8.8, columns 10 and 11), but none of the seven comparisons is significant. These findings provide little support for expecting the reference group discrepancy to discriminate between high and low yield migratory status groups.

The data on preferences for blue- or white-collar occupations were analyzed only for migratory status group totals—sex and age were not taken into account. The percentage distributions of the choices are shown in Table 8.9. In previous analyses of the blue/white-collar items (Chapter 6), the ill selected white-collar occupations more frequently than did

Table 8.9—*Preferences for Blue Collar or White Collar*

Occupations by Migratory Status in Percentages

	CHOICE					
	1[1]		2[2]		3[2]	
	Blue	White	Blue	White	Blue	White
Southern Migrant	43	57	52	48	63	37
Native	31	69	42	58	54	46
Northern Migrant	22	78	46	54	51	49

1. By chi-square, P=<.001
2. By chi-square, P=<.01

community subjects. On this basis we predict that more natives than southern migrants will choose white-collar occupations. The data support this expectation for each of the three paired occupational choices. In each occupational choice, the natives select the white-collar alternative significantly more often than the southern migrants (for the first set of choices, 69 per cent of the natives and 57 per cent of the southern migrants prefer the white-collar job; the corresponding percentages are 58 and 48 per cent for the second choice, and 46 and 37 per cent for the third choice).

We also predict more white-collar choices among the natives than among the northern migrants, although not necessarily to a significant degree. Only in the second choice situation is this expectation supported: 58 per cent of the natives and 54 per cent of the northern migrants prefer the white-collar alternative. Since the natives and northern migrants do not differ significantly in yield of illness, these results merely reflect this lack of difference between the two migratory status groups.

Our third hypothesis predicts that more northern than southern migrants will choose the white-collar alternatives. In all three choices the data go in the predicted direction, but none of the differences is significant. We should indicate at this point that the three migratory status groups differ significantly in their choice of white-collar alternatives in each of the three choices (for the first set of choices, $P = < .001$; for the second and third choices, $P = < .01$).

The first reference group discrepancy measure fails to discriminate between high and low yield migratory status groups. The hypothesis that this discrepancy measure constitutes an antecedent to illness is not supported. The data on preference for blue- and white-collar occupations do support the view that reference-group orientation may be an antecedent to illness. The inconsistency observed between these two reference group measures in the present context suggests the necessity for a more systematic analysis of what these measures actually reflect.

SELF-ESTEEM

The principal method used to measure self-esteem was the self-ideal discrepancy (Chapter 7). It was found that the patients always manifested higher self-ideal discrepancy scores (i.e., lower self-esteem) than the community respondents. If low self-esteem is an antecedent to illness, we expect high yield migratory status groups in the community to show lower self-esteem (i.e., higher self-ideal discrepancies) than low yield migratory status groups. Only four of the seven comparisons relevant to this prediction (Table 8.8, columns 13 and 14) indicate higher self-ideal discrepancy scores for the high yield migratory status groups. Three of these seven comparisons show higher discrepancy scores for the low yield groups. Only one of the seven comparisons reaches significance, although this one does confirm our expectations: female natives (with a relatively high yield of illness) show lower self-esteem than southern migrant females. These findings provide little support for our prediction of a relationship between self-esteem and high and low yield migratory status groups.

Summary

FINDINGS with respect to the usefulness of our social-psychological study variables in explaining differences between migratory status groups differing in yield of mental illness are summarized below:

(1) The data on the perception of the opportunity structure indicate that the high yield migratory status groups differ from the low yield groups in the same way as the ill differs from the community population, although the differences are not striking.

(2) The data on all three goal-striving stress scores show larger scores for the high yield migratory status groups than for the low yield groups.

(3) The data on the discrepancy between level of aspiration and achievement in three self-striving areas indicate that the discrepancy concept may be considered an antecedent to illness as well as a stressor factor in our theoretical framework.

(4) Our two measures of reference group behavior do not show comparable results. The reference group discrepancy fails to discriminate between the high and low yield groups. Changes in this discrepancy apparently reflect the effects of illness. The second measure of reference

group behavior (i.e., preferences for blue- or white-collar occupations) does show that reference group behavior can be considered a potential antecedent condition to illness. The differences between the two measures, however, indicate that in the context of this study, measures of reference group behavior may reflect more than one phenomenon.

(5) The data relevant to our measure of self-esteem (the self-ideal discrepancy) do not discriminate among the high and low yield migratory status groups. It appears that low self-esteem may be a concomitant, and not an antecedent, of mental illness.

MENTALLY ILL VERSUS COMMUNITY POPULATION, CONTROLLING FOR MIGRATORY STATUS

As mentioned above, neither the reference group discrepancy nor the self-ideal discrepancy discriminates at all between the high and low yield migratory status groups. We decided to compare the ill and community populations on these variables, controlling for migratory status as well as for sex and age. In the two chapters on reference group behavior and self-esteem, no controls other than sex and age were used. Therefore, we felt that at least one series of analyses with some status controls was necessary to see whether the two populations still differed on these study variables.

Eleven comparisons were made between the ill and community samples. The southern migrant group in the ill population was compared to the corresponding group in the community population, both for totals and with sex and age controls (five comparisons). The same five comparisons were made between the natives in the ill and community samples. The northern migrant group was compared only for the total patient and community samples—because of the small number of cases no sex and age controls were applied (one comparison).

All eleven analyses show significantly larger reference group discrepancies for the ill than for the community groups (all at $P = < .001$). The same eleven analyses were carried out with data on the self-ideal discrepancy. In all eleven comparisons the ill show significantly larger self-ideal discrepancy scores (i.e., lower self-esteem) than their community counterparts (all at $P = < .001$).

The consistency of these ill-community differences, regardless of the type of controls imposed, indicates unquestionably larger reference group discrepancies and lower self-esteem among the patients. The contrast between the significance of these data and the lack of significance in the discussion of migratory status groups differing in yield supports the possibility that these two variables are consequences of the illness process.

INTRACITY MOBILITY AND MENTAL ILLNESS

Our review of the literature earlier in this chapter failed to draw any definitive conclusion about the relationship between intracity mobility and mental illness. In order to investigate this question, we divided our mentally ill and community populations into (1) those who had not moved at all (i.e., had only one address) during the three years prior to our contact; (2) those who had moved only once; (3) those who had moved twice; and (4) those who had moved three or more times. We compared the distributions of these categories in the ill and community populations, controlling for migratory status. Among the southern migrants and natives, the number of intracity residential moves is significantly higher for the patients than for the community respondents $(P = < .001$, for both migratory status categories). In the northern migrant group there is also a tendency for the mentally ill to move more frequently than the community subjects, but this difference is not significant $(P = < .10 > .05)$.

A second group of analyses controlled for respondents' educational achievements. The control groups were: o to 4 years of education, 5 to 8 years, 9 to 11 years, and 12 or more years of education. In all four control groups the intracity mobility is greater for the mentally ill population (all at $P = < .001$).

A third group of analyses controlled for occupational achievement. The achievement categories were: occupation level 1 (on our seven step scale), level 2, level 3, and level 4-or-higher. Again, within all occupational control groups, the amount of intracity mobility is higher for the mentally ill population (for levels 1 and 2, $P = < .001$; for level 3, $P = < .01$).

In a final group of analyses we controlled for income achievement. Our control groups were: no income to $40 per week, $41 to $80 per week, and $80 or more per week. In all control groups the number of moves is significantly higher for the ill population (all at $P = < .001$).

The mentally ill show more intracity residential mobility than their community counterparts in all fourteen analyses. Twelve of these comparisons reach significance. Clearly, the patients are characterized by greater intracity residential instability than the community respondents.

Can the greater intracity mobility among the ill population help to explain high and low yields of mental illness among migratory status groups in the community? We must determine whether this variable can be considered a potential antecedent to illness. When the migratory status groups within the community population are compared on amount of intracity mobility, significant differences are obtained ($P = < .001$), but the direction of these differences is not as predicted. The natives (with the highest illness yield) show less mobility than either the southern or northern migrants. The northern migrants, who tend to have a higher yield of illness than the southern migrants, show the same amount of mobility. The evidence indicates that intracity mobility cannot explain differences in yield of mental illness among the migratory status groups in the community population.

9

SOCIAL STATUS AND
MENTAL DISORDER

This chapter will investigate the relationship between mental disorder and each of three status indices: occupation, income, and education. If an association between yield of illness and these status measures is found, an attempt will be made to determine whether the social-psychological variables used in this study, whose relationship with mental disorder has been established in previous chapters, can account for this association.

Review of the Literature

A RECENT COMPREHENSIVE REVIEW of the literature on the relationship between socioeconomic status and mental illness (Kleiner and Parker, 1963) indicated numerous and confusing research findings on this relationship. Findings reported in the literature since that time confuse the picture even further. Aside from ambiguity in the substantive findings and in attempts to pinpoint the causes of the reported relationships, investigators frequently fail to distinguish between prevalence and incidence studies. Prevalence rates, which encompass first admissions, continuations, and readmissions, during a specified time period, provide valuable general information about the frequency of mental disease. When interest is focused on etiological factors, however, incidence rates, which usually include only first admissions during a specified time period, are superior because new cases are temporally close to the precipitating conditions.

A number of studies have shown an association between low socio-economic status and a high incidence of schizophrenia. In a study of the distribution of first admissions to mental hospitals in the Chicago area during the 1930's, Faris and Dunham (1939) found that low-status sections of the city admitted more of their residents to mental hospitals than those areas designated as middle- or upper-status. Although schizophrenia conformed to this pattern, manic-depressive psychosis showed a relatively uniform distribution throughout the various status groups. A subsequent study in Chicago (Clark, 1949) generally confirmed these findings but noted that the inverse relationship between social status and mental disorder was considerably more marked for whites than for Negroes.

Similar findings have since been reported for a number of different areas. Tietze, Lemkau, and Cooper (1941) reported an association between high rates of schizophrenia and lower-class status in Baltimore. Manic-depressive disorders were slightly more common in upper-class groups. Kaplan, Reed, and Richardson (1956) found a higher incidence of undifferentiated hospitalized psychosis in a lower- and lower middle-class area of Boston than in an upper- and upper middle-class section. This inverse relationship between the incidence of schizophrenia and social class was also found in England and Wales (Morris, 1959).

Hollingshead and Redlich's well-known study (1958: 194–249) of mental disorder in New Haven has often been cited as definite evidence of this inverse relationship. Their findings presented no simple linear pattern, however. Incidence rates revealed a slightly different picture than the other studies mentioned above. Although the lowest class was characterized by the highest rates of psychosis, there was little rate differentiation in the four other social class groups. Schizophrenia taken alone increased linearly from the highest to the lowest class. Rates of neurosis were not related to social class.

No relationship between socioeconomic position and the incidence of schizophrenia was reported by Clausen and Kohn (1959; 1960) in their study of mental illness in Haegerstown. Jaco (1960: 178) found a curvilinear relationship between social status and the incidence of all psychoses in Texas. Rates were high among individuals at the lowest *and* at the highest occupational and educational positions and were low at the middle status positions. Among nonwhite males, specifically, illness rates were highest among the professional, semi-professional, and clerical-sales occupations (Jaco, 1960: 127–132). Nonwhite females showed the highest rates in the service, professional, and semi-professional occupations.

Using education as his status measure, Jaco found that nonwhites with the highest educational achievements also showed the highest rates of mental disorder. He obtained a negative correlation between educational status and rates of mental disorder in the Anglo-American population, and a positive correlation among nonwhites (Jaco, 1960: 151–155).

Kleiner, Tuckman, and Lavell (1960) noted no relationship between occupational status and incidence of schizophrenia among Negroes in Pennsylvania during the period 1951 to 1956, but there was evidence of an inverse relationship between status and illness among whites. These findings, as well as those of Clark (1949) and Jaco (1960), suggest that the status-mental illness relationship differs in white and nonwhite populations. We may also infer from Jaco's study a close association between social mobility and rates of mental disorder in a Negro population. Even many studies of illness rates among white populations, however, fail to confirm the inverse relationship between status and schizophrenia, manic-depressive psychosis, or psychoneurosis. This is particularly true of investigations conducted in foreign countries (Bremer, 1951; Cade, 1956; Ødegaard, 1956; Stein, 1957).

Hollingshead and Redlich (1958: 210) found the highest prevalence rate in the lowest social class, when all types of treated mental disorder were considered together. There were no statistically significant differences in morbidity rates among the other classes, however. The reported inverse relationship was due entirely to a particularly high rate at the lowest level. At all social class levels except the lowest, patients were under-represented (Hollingshead and Redlich, 1958: 199), and the degree of under-representation increased progressively from the highest class through the next three lower classes. If class position and mental disorder were inversely related, under-representation should have *decreased*. Although the prevalence of psychosis was inversely related to class position, the prevalence of neurotic disorders was directly related. Any discussion of class and mental disorder must therefore evaluate the distributions of the different types of illness separately. An examination of the components of prevalence (i.e., incidence, continuations, and reentry) in the Hollingshead and Redlich study indicates that the reported relationships between class position and both psychosis and neurosis could be attributed to continuations alone—that is, if continuation cases had been omitted from their analyses, no clear pattern would have emerged.

Although all of the studies mentioned above are based on diagnosed mental disorder, it is generally recognized that many undiagnosed conditions among community individuals are not brought to medical attention. Since the picture presented by hospital statistics may be biased, there has been widespread interest in determining whether the inverse status-mental illness relationship would emerge in studies of undiagnosed pathology in the general community. Attempts to resolve this issue must deal with the complex problems of defining and identifying "mental disorder" in such a community population. It is extremely difficult to diagnose even a small sample of the community population by accepted psychiatric diagnostic procedures. For this reason, various questionnaire methods have been developed to obtain information on psychosomatic and other psychopathological symptoms, and deviant role performance (Macmillan, 1959).

Srole et al. (1962: 230) used such methods in their extensive prevalence study of a nonhospitalized population in Manhattan. They found fewer high-status individuals in their "Impaired" group than in their "Well" category. Another prevalence study of psychiatric disorder in a representative sample of the nonhospitalized population was conducted in Baltimore by Pasamanick, Roberts, Lemkau, and Krueger (1959). The majority of respondents were examined by nonpsychiatric physicians, and a diagnosis was derived through clinical evaluation procedures. Psychotic disorders generally increased as income decreased, except among individuals in the lowest status group. Rates at this level dropped below those at the previous status level. Rates for neurosis yielded a U-shaped curve—they were high in the low-status group, declined in the middle-status groups, and increased again in the high-status group. There was a direct relationship between the prevalence of psychosomatic complaints and economic status.

Many other studies (e.g., Hyde and Kingsley, 1944; Lin, 1953; Kaplan, Reed, and Richardson, 1956), carried out in the United States and in other parts of the world, merely add to the existing ambiguity about the relationship between status and mental disorder. This literature is characterized not only by contradictory findings, but also by a failure to investigate in a systematic fashion the reasons for observed relationships between these variables. A notable exception to this generalization is the recent study by Langner and Michael (1963). These authors attempted to explain the inverse relationship between status and psychiatric symptoms in a community population by means of ten "stress" factors that were found to be independently associated with psychopathology. However, careful analysis of the relationship between these stress factors and social status position failed to yield an explanation for the decrease in illness rates with increasing status levels. On the basis of existing evidence, it is difficult to specify an invariant relationship between social status and mental disorder. In addition, status-associated factors which would explain high or low rates of mental disorder have not yet been identified.

Definition of "Status"

IN THE PRESENT STUDY we utilized three different measures of social status: occupation, income, and education. A composite multi-status index (see Appendix D) was not used because these three individual status measures did not correlate with mental disorder in the same manner. Since, in fact, their respective degrees of association to mental disorder were quite dissimilar, merely averaging these disparate measures to derive a single composite estimate would not have provided a meaningful overall status measure.

These three independent measures will be considered throughout this chapter. At this point we shall briefly note the various status gradations in the occupational, educational, and income hierarchies. In all cases, ascending numbers assigned to the status levels correspond to ascending positions in the given hierarchy.[1]

OCCUPATIONAL STATUS POSITIONS

Level 1: Unskilled laborers, farm workers, service and janitorial personnel, messengers, etc. For the most part, these occupations require no special education or training.

Level 2: Semi-skilled laborers and sales positions in retail establishments.

Level 3: Skilled laborers, clerical positions, minor government clerks, and proprietors of small retail establishments.

Level 4: White-collar positions requiring special education and training: professionals, semi-professionals, managerial personnel, entertainers, athletes, etc.

1. Originally, each of the three status indices was categorized on the basis of a seven-step scale. However, because of the small number of cases falling into certain categories, some of these steps have been combined for the purposes of this analysis.

INCOME STATUS POSITIONS

Level 1: No income to $40 per week.
Level 2: $41 to $80 per week.
Level 3: $80 or over per week.

EDUCATIONAL STATUS POSITIONS

Level 1: No education to four years of education.
Level 2: Five to eight years of education.
Level 3: Nine to eleven years of education (some high school).
Level 4: Twelve years of education (graduated from high school).
Level 5: Thirteen or more years of education (some college).

Relationship between Social Status Position and Referral Source, Diagnosis, and Treatment Disposition

THIS CHAPTER will be concerned with the distributions of mental disorder by the three different status measures and with determining whether the nature of these distributions can be explained by the social-psychological variables underlying this study. First, we must consider the influence exerted on the existing status distribution of *diagnosed* illness by nonpsychopathogenic factors. This problem has often been raised in the epidemiological literature (Clausen, 1961). For example, status-linked attitudes toward psychiatric treatment, attitudes of psychiatrists toward individuals at various status positions, and differential knowledge about available facilities may very definitely affect the number of individuals entering treatment, the diagnoses that are made, and the type of treatment patients subsequently receive. The complexities of accounting for such factors have led some investigators to conclude that statistics on diagnosed mental disorder are useless in determining the actual amounts of illness at different status levels. They feel that these distributions are so affected by extraneous social and cultural factors that spurious conclusions about relevant etiological factors can easily be drawn.

Hollingshead and Redlich (1958) showed that social status was a determinant of (1) referral source for treatment; (2) the diagnosis made; and (3) the treatment disposition. They noted that individuals in lower socioeconomic groups were more likely to be referred to treatment facilities by the police and courts, more apt to be diagnosed as psychotic than neurotic, and more likely to be treated in public state hospitals than in private sanatoriums or out-patient clinics. In order to see whether such social artifacts did influence the distributions of mental disorder in our study, we determined to what extent our status measures were associated with differences in referral source, diagnosis, and treatment disposition.

SOCIAL STATUS POSITION AND REFERRAL SOURCE

Table 9.1 shows the relationship between the three measures of status and referral source for our patient population. Any significant dif-

Table 9.1—Referral Source and Treatment Disposition, by Status

		REFERRAL SOURCE				TREATMENT DISPOSITION		
	Total Intv. Ill N	Medical Facility or Social Service	Self-Ref. or Family Per Cent	Police, Courts or Prisons	Total Intv. Ill N	Hospi-talized	Out-patient Per Cent	Other[1]
Occupational Status Position								
1	830	51	30	19	838	64	33	3
2	301	52	34	14	302	65	33	2
3	111	42	43	15	111	61	34	5
4	62	42	44	14	62	58	42	0
Income Status Position								
1	250	50	34	16	279	63	34	3
2	648	54	31	15	621	61	36	3
3	254	43	35	22	260	67	30	3
Educational Status Position								
1	87	55	24	21	88	65	30	5
2	347	52	31	17	347	67	31	2
3	499	47	33	20	505	61	35	4
4	273	53	33	14	272	63	35	2
5	99	44	39	17	101	61	38	1

1. Other includes social service, discharged, private Physician, refused recommendation, etc.

Summary of significant chi-square analyses.
For Referral Source, by Occupation, P=<.02
For Referral Source, by Income, P=<.01

ferences in referral source among respondents at various status positions may stem from status-linked attitudes toward psychiatry rather than from pathology itself. Referral sources are grouped into three categories: (1) medical facility or social service agency; (2) self or family; and (3) police, courts, or prisons. We assume that referrals in category (2) reflect the most knowledge about, and/or receptive attitudes toward, psychiatric treatment, and referrals in category (3) the least.

Significant differences in the distributions of the three referral sources occur for the occupational status positions ($P = < .02$). The lowest occupational level (level 1) contains the largest proportion of referrals from police, courts, or prisons (Table 9.1, column 4), but the difference between level 1 and the other occupational levels taken together is not statistically significant for this referral source. Referrals by self or family (Table 9.1, column 3) become progressively more numerous with increasing occupational status position, although this tendency is not significant. The greater willingness of higher status individuals to seek psychiatric help tends to over-estimate illness rates at the high end of the status continuum, and to under-estimate rates at the lower occupational positions, for this referral source.

The analyses by income status position also yield significant differences in the distributions of the three referral sources ($P = < .01$). In contradiction to the corresponding findings for occupational status, the lowest income position contains a smaller proportion of referrals from the police and courts than does the highest income status group. There are no systematic directional differences by income status position for the two other referral sources. The differences in referral source by educational status are not significant.

An overview of these findings indicates no systematic relationship between status position and referral source on any of the three status dimensions.

SOCIAL STATUS POSITION AND DIAGNOSIS

The relationship between status and diagnosis will be discussed more fully in a later context. At this point we shall merely note those findings which pertain to the present issue. When the various psychiatric diagnoses are combined into two broad categories ("psychosis" and "neurosis"), neither occupational nor educational status is significantly related to diagnosis. The inverse relationship between income position and psychosis ($P = < .05$), may be attributed to the large number of psychotics at the lowest income level. Neither educational nor occupational status is significantly related to diagnosis, but in both content areas the highest status group contains the smallest number of psychotics.

SOCIAL STATUS POSITION AND TREATMENT DISPOSITION

Table 9.1 also presents data on the relationship between social status and treatment disposition. Three types of treatment disposition are considered: (1) hospitalization; (2) out-patient treatment; and (3) other disposition (recommendations to social service agency or private practitioner, refusal of recommendation, or discharged as not in need of treatment). This residual category shows little systematic variation among the different status groups. In effect, we must deal only with hospitalization and out-patient disposition.

Based on previous reports of trends in the white population, we predict an inverse relationship between status position and recommendations for hospitalization: the lower the status, the greater the percentage of hospitalized individuals. This relationship may emerge because low-status patients often cannot afford out-patient care, particularly private care.

No statistically significant difference in treatment disposition by status position emerges for any of the three status hierarchies. An increase in occupational and educational status position is accompanied by a slight decrease in the proportion of hospitalized respondents. There is an unexpected increase in hospitalization in the highest income status group. On the whole, however, there is little relationship between status position and type of treatment disposition in the Negro sample used in his study.

In summary, there is no strong relationship between social status position (as determined by each of the three measures) and referral source, diagnosis, or treatment disposition. This finding reduces the possibility that social artifacts associated with status position markedly influence the distribution of diagnosed mental disorder in our Negro sample. A close association between status position and these social and cultural factors has often been reported in a white population. Why is this association less marked in our Negro sample? Status differences that do exist may not be associated with attitudes affecting receptivity to psychiatry. Although such differences possibly exist among Negroes, they may be ordered by factors other than hierarchically arranged social status positions determined by the usual measures.

Occupational Status and Mental Disorder

THE RATES of mental disorder by occupational status position in the total incidence population and the interviewed ill sample form a crude U-shaped curve (see Figure 9.1 and Table 9.2, columns 3 and 5). For both ill populations, the rates at the three lowest positions decrease progressively, but at the fourth position they rise sharply to a point above level 1. The status distribution of the total incidence ill population does not differ significantly from that of the community sample (Table 9.2, columns 1 and 2). The difference between the interviewed ill and the

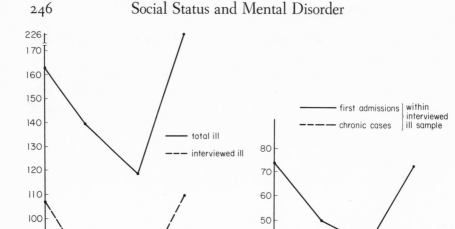

FIGURE 9.1—Rates of Mental Illness, by Occupational Status.

community samples (Table 9.2, columns 1 and 4) does reach significance ($P = < .01$). As suggested previously, this disparity between the total incidence and interviewed ill populations may be attributed to the effects of status differences in referral source.

Since the "new" cases comprising the interviewed ill sample consist of both first admissions and chronic cases (i.e., readmissions who reported at least one previous psychiatric diagnosis), we must see whether the curves representing rates of mental illness are parallel in both illness categories at each occupational status level. The rate curve for first admissions roughly parallels the status curves for the total incidence and

Table 9.2—Illness Status and Chronicity, by Occupation

	COMMUNITY SAMPLE	TOTAL INCIDENCE ILL		INTERVIEWED ILL SAMPLE					
				Total		First Admissions		Chronic Cases	
	Per Cent (1)	Per Cent (2)	Rate (3)	Per Cent (4)	Rate (5)	Per Cent (6)	Rate (7)	Per Cent (8)	Rate (9)
Occupational Status Position									
1	57	60	163	64	107	66	74	59	33
2	28	25	139	23	78	22	50	24	29
3	11	9	119	8	73	7	42	11	34
4	4	6	226	5	110	5	73	5	41
	100	100		100		100		99	
Total N	1486	2292		1423		941		480	

Summary of significant chi-square analyses
Community vs Interviewed Ill, $P = <.01$
First Admissions vs Chronic Cases, $P = <.02$

interviewed ill populations (see Figure 9.1). Among first admissions there are virtually no rate differences between the lowest and highest occupational status groups. The curve of rates for chronic cases, on the other hand, indicates somewhat higher rates of illness at levels 3 and 4 than at levels 1 and 2 (see Figure 9.1).

We now consider the types of pathology and their distributions within the four occupational status groups among the interviewed mentally ill sample, and psychiatric symptoms among the community respondents (see Figure 9.2 and Table 9.3). The psychotics manifest

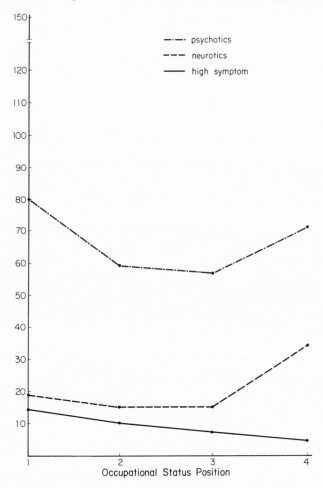

FIGURE 9.2—Rates of Mental Illness for Psychotics, Neurotics, and High Symptom Subjects, by Occupational Status.

Table 9.3—Psychiatric Symptoms and Diagnosis, by Occupation

	COMMUNITY SAMPLE				INTERVIEWED ILL SAMPLE			
	Total Per Cent (1)	Low Symptom Per Cent (2)	High Symptom Per Cent (3)	Rate (4)	Neurotics Per Cent (5)	Rate (6)	Psychotics Per Cent (7)	Rate (8)
Occupational Status Position								
1	57	56	69	14	60	18	65	80
2	28	29	23	10	23	15	23	59
3	11	11	6	7	9	14	8	57
4	4	4	2	5	8	34	4	71
	100	100	100		100		100	
Total N	1489	1314	175		225		1060	

1. Within the community sample only, rates signify the number of high symptom respondents per 100 community sample.

Summary of significant chi-square analyses
Low symptom group vs high symptom group, P=<.01
Total community vs neurotics, P=< .05
Total community vs psychotics, P=<.02

the same crude U-shaped rate curve previously found for both ill samples, with high rates at occupational status positions 1 and 4. Rates for the neurotics, show little variation at the three lowest status positions, and then rise sharply at level 4. The status distributions of the psychotics and the neurotics both differ significantly from the community sample distribution ($P = < .02$ and $< .05$, respectively). The illness rates for the high symptom individuals in the community sample decrease progressively as status position increases (Table 9.3, column 4). The distributions of high and low psychiatric symptom scores by occupational status in the community population differ significantly ($P = < .01$).

Although the rate curve for the high symptom community group does not resemble the curves for the psychotics and the neurotics, all three groupings are characterized by a progressive drop in illness from occupation level 1 through 3. Only at the highest status level do they deviate. This difference is contrary to our expectation that the rate of high psychiatric symptoms would closely parallel the status-associated yield of diagnosed mental disorder. The availability of financial resources and more favorable attitudes toward, or knowledge about, psychiatric treatment at the highest occupational status level may account for the rise in rates of diagnosed illness. This possibility accounts for the seemingly contradictory fact that relatively few community respondents at occupation level 4 manifest high psychiatric symptom scores, but that these high-status individuals do show a high rate of diagnosed mental illness.

Are the status variations in rates and percentage distributions of mental illness maintained at the four occupational status levels within sex and age subgroups? The U-shaped curve is maintained for males and females (see Figure 9.3 and Table 9.4, columns 3 and 6)—the highest rates occur at status positions 1 and 4 in both sex groups. Distributions by

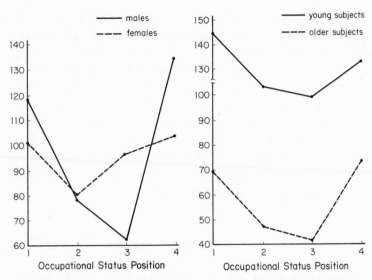

FIGURE 9.3—Rates of Mental Illness for the Interviewed Ill Sample, by
Occupational Status, Sex, and Age.

occupational status differ significantly for ill and community sample
males but females show no significant difference (see Table 9.4, columns 1 and 2, and 4 and 5).

The young and older segments of the ill population both show rate
curves similar to the curve for the interviewed ill sample. The major
difference between the two age subgroups is a greater rise in rates at
occupation level 4 among the older respondents.

In summary, rates of mental disorder by occupational status decline
progressively from occupational level 1 through 3, and then increase at
level 4. Levels 1 and 4 show higher rates than either of the two middle-
status groups. In his analysis of a Negro sample in Texas, Jaco (1960:

Table 9.4—*Illness Status, Sex and Age, by Occupation*

	MALES			FEMALES			YOUNG			OLD		
	Comm. Per Cent (1)	Ill Per Cent (2)	Rate (3)	Comm. Per Cent (4)	Ill Per Cent (5)	Rate (6)	Comm. Per Cent (7)	Ill Per Cent (8)	Rate (9)	Comm. Per Cent (10)	Ill Per Cent (11)	Rate (12)
Occupational Status Position												
1	47	58	118	65	68	101	54	61	145	62	70	69
2	35	28	78	24	20	80	30	24	103	26	20	47
3	15	10	62	8	8	96	12	9	99	9	6	41
4	4	5	133	4	5	103	5	5	133	3	4	75
	101	101		101	101		101	99		100	100	
Total N	597	574		881	843		788	1010		676	413	

Summary of significant chi-square analyses
Males: Community vs Ill, $P = <.001$
Young: Community vs Ill, $P = <.01$
Old: Community vs Ill, $P = <.02$

178) also found high rates of diagnosed mental disorder in the lowest and highest status groups. Our data suggest that the height of the curve at level 1 is attributable mainly to psychotic males in both age categories. The major contributor to the rate increase at level 4 is the number of neurotic males in the older age group. It should be emphasized that almost every population subgroup is characterized by a variation of the rate curve described for the total incidence ill population. Only the rates for the high symptom subjects deviate at occupational status level 4. This rise in illness at the highest level may be an artifact of attitudes toward treatment and the availability of financial resources, or it may represent a true increase in types of psychopathology.

Income Status and Mental Disorder

SINCE INFORMATION about income was collected only for the interviewed segment of the ill population, we cannot compare the interviewed and total incidence ill samples on the relationship between income status and mental disorder. The shape of the rate curve for the interviewed ill sample by income status does not resemble that of occupational status (see Figure 9.4 and Table 9.5, column 6). The essential difference between the two curves lies in rate differences at the highest status levels. While the illness rate increases in the highest occupational group, it decreases at the highest income position.

The overall occupational and income status rate curves may not be as different as they appear at first glance, however. The fact that the highest income level is numerically so much larger than the highest occupational level means that many individuals with high income fall into occupational categories 2 and 3, which show relatively low rates of mental disorder. This may explain why the rate curve for income continues to decline at the highest status position, instead of rising as it does for occupation.

The income status distributions in the community and interviewed ill populations (Table 9.5, columns 1 and 5) are significantly different $(P = < .01)$. Therefore, both the rates and distributions of mental disorder show an inverse relationship to income status.

Rates for both first admissions and chronic cases are inversely related to income status position. The percentage distributions of these two groups are not significantly different (see Figure 9.4 and Table 9.5).

Like the curve for the interviewed ill sample, the rate curves for

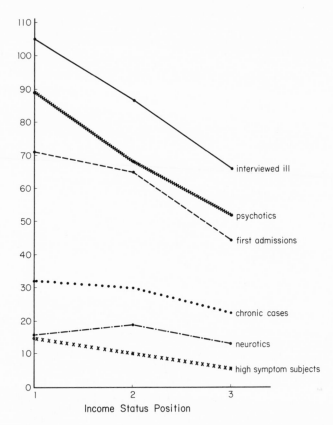

FIGURE 9.4—Rates of Mental Illness, by Income Status.

the high symptom group and the psychotics show an inverse relationship to income status, although this relationship is not marked for the high symptom group (see Figure 9.4 and Table 9.5, columns 4 and 13). There is a significant difference between the percentage distributions by status for the psychotics and the total community population ($P = < .001$). The rates for the neurotics do not show the same inverse relationship observed for the psychotics. Rates for this mental health grouping are slightly higher in the middle income status group than at either of the two extremes. The percentage distribution for the neurotics by status does not differ significantly from the distribution of the total community sample. Illness rates thus decrease progressively as income status level increases, for the interviewed ill sample, first admissions, chronic cases, high symptom individuals, and the psychotics. Only the neurotics do not conform to this pattern.

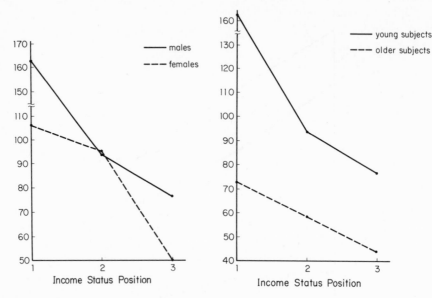

FIGURE 9.5—Rates of Mental Illness for the Interviewed Ill Sample, by Income Status, Sex, and Age.

The rates and distributions of mental disorder at each income status level by sex and age are presented in Figure 9.5 and Table 9.6. Rates for males and females both show the characteristic inverse relationship with income status position. The high rates at the lowest income position are accounted for mainly by males, however. The rates for both age groups also show an inverse relationship with status, with the young at status level 1 showing particularly high rates.

This discussion of income status and rates of mental disorder indicates

Table 9.5—Psychiatric Symptoms, Chronicity, and Diagnosis, by Income

	COMMUNITY SAMPLE				INTERVIEWED ILL SAMPLE									
	Total Per Cent	Low Symp. Per Cent	High Symp. Per Cent	Rate1	Total Per Cent	Rate	First Admissions Per Cent	Rate	Chronic Cases Per Cent	Rate	Neurotics Per Cent	Rate	Psychotics Per Cent	Rate
	(1)	(2)	(3)	(4)	(5)	(6)	(7)	(8)	(9)	(10)	(11)	(12)	(13)	(14)
Income Status Position														
1	20	19	26	15	24	105	24	71	22	33	18	16	26	89
2	52	52	54	11	54	87	56	65	55	31	59	19	52	68
3	29	30	20	7	22	66	21	45	23	24	24	14	22	52
	100	100	100		100		100		100		100		100	
Total N	1363	1221	147		1163		826		409		234		929	

1. Within the community sample only, rates signify the number of high symptom respondents per 100 community sample.

Summary of significant chi-square analyses
Total Community vs Total Interviewed Ill, P=<.01
Low Symp. Group vs High Symp. Group, P=<.01
Total Community vs Psychotics, P=<.001

Table 9.6—*Illness Status, Sex and Age, by Income*

	MALES			FEMALES			YOUNG			OLD		
	Comm. Per Cent (1)	Ill Per Cent (2)	Rate (3)	Comm. Per Cent (4)	Ill Per Cent (5)	Rate (6)	Comm. Per Cent (7)	Ill Per Cent (8)	Rate (9)	Comm. Per Cent (10)	Ill Per Cent (11)	Rate (12)
Income Status Position												
1	6	11	163	27	32	106	16	22	162	22	28	73
2	57	58	94	59	61	95	59	60	124	57	57	59
3	37	31	77	14	8	50	25	18	84	21	15	44
	100	100		100	101		100	100		100	100	
Total N	542	502		783	715		722	864		600	353	

Summary of significant chi-square analyses
Males: Community vs Ill, P=<.01
Females: Community vs Ill, P=<.001
Young: Community vs Ill, P=<.001
Old: Community vs Ill, P=<.10>.05

an almost consistent inverse relationship between the two variables. The high illness rate at the lowest status level can apparently be attributed mainly to young male psychotics. It is also interesting that rates for the psychotics and the high symptom individuals are inversely related to income status, but rates for the neurotics are highest in the middle-income status level.

Educational Status and Mental Disorder

EDUCATIONAL ACHIEVEMENT is the third measure of social status utilized in this study. The rates and distributions of mental disorder by educational status for the total incidence and interviewed ill populations and for first admissions and chronic cases in the interviewed sample, are presented in Figure 9.6 and Table 9.7. The rates by educational status for the interviewed ill sample and total incidence ill population (see Figure 9.6 and Table 9.7, columns 3 and 5) both form crude W-shaped curves, with the high points at educational status levels 1, 3, and 5. Rate curves for first admissions and chronic cases parallel each other— they are also W-shaped.

There are significant differences between the distributions of the community sample and both the total incidence population and the interviewed ill sample (Table 9.7, columns 1, 2, and 4). The difference between the community and the interviewed ill sample can be mainly attributed to (1) those respondents at level 3, who received some high school education but failed to graduate—these respondents are significantly over-represented in the ill sample; and (2) those respondents at level 4, who graduated from high school but did not go on to college— these respondents are significantly under-represented in the ill sample.

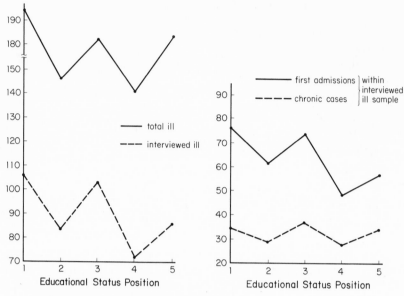

FIGURE 9.6—Rates of Mental Illness, by Educational Status.

The rates and distributions of mental disorder for the high symptom individuals, the psychotics, and the neurotics are presented in Figure 9.7 and Table 9.8. The rates for the psychotics and neurotics by educational status form the same W-shaped curves. The rate curve for the high symptom individuals by educational status is consistent with the curves obtained for these respondents on the two other measures of social status —the higher the status the lower the rates of high symptom scores. This curve is clearly different from the curves characteristic of the diagnosed illness groups.

A consideration of sex and age differences by educational status (see

Table 9.7—Illness Status and Chronicity, by Education

	COMMUNITY SAMPLE	TOTAL INCIDENCE ILL		INTERVIEWED ILL SAMPLE					
	Per Cent (1)	Per Cent (2)	Rate (3)	Total Per Cent (4)	First Admissions Rate (5)	Per Cent (6)	Rate (7)	Chronic Cases Per Cent (8)	Rate (9)
Educational Status Position									
1	6	7	195	7	106	7	77	6	35
2	28	25	146	27	84	28	62	25	29
3	33	37	183	38	103	39	74	38	37
4	26	22	141	21	72	19	49	22	28
5	9	9	184	8	86	7	57	9	34
	100	100		100		100		100	
Total N	1489	2421		1421		941		480	

Summary of significant chi-square analyses
  Community vs Total Incidence, P=<.05
  Community vs Interviewed Sample, P=<.005

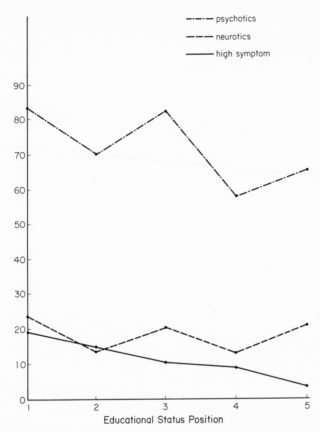

FIGURE 9.7—Rates for Psychotics, Neurotics, and High Symptom Subjects, by Educational Status.

Figure 9.8 and Table 9.9) indicates that males contribute more heavily than females to the high illness rate at the lowest educational status level. In addition, this status position contains a majority of young individuals. The high rate at educational level 1, then, can be attributed to young male psychotics, a pattern also noted for occupation level 1.

Social Status and Mental Disorder:
a Summary Statement

Some of the more salient conclusions emerging from these data will be briefly discussed at this point. The curves representing illness rates by status position are generally dissimilar for the three status measures. This implies that these three measures are not very highly correlated.

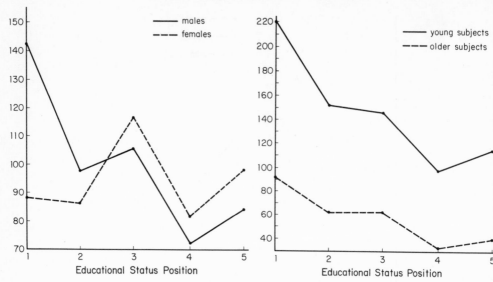

FIGURE 9.8—Rates of Mental Illness for the Interviewed III Sample, by
Educational Status, Sex, and Age.

The lack of consistency in predictability of these status measures suggests
that status factors are relatively unimportant in ordering the distribution
of mental disorder. In this study, migratory status (Chapter 8) and social
mobility (Chapter 10) definitely influence the distribution of mental disorder in our study population. A number of studies on psychopathology
among Negroes support the idea that status may not be an important
contributory factor (Kardiner, and Ovesey, 1951: 301–317; Prange and
Vitols, 1963).

Although our three status measures are not related to the distribution

Table 9.8—Psychiatric Symptoms and Diagnosis, by Education

| | COMMUNITY SAMPLE | | | | INTERVIEWED ILL SAMPLE | | | | | |
	Total Per Cent (1)	Low Symp. Per Cent (2)	High Symp. Per Cent (3)	Rate[1] (4)	Total Per Cent (5)	Rate (6)	Neurotics Per Cent (7)	Rate (8)	Psychotics Per Cent (9)	Rate (10)
Educational Status Position										
1	6	5	9	19	7	106	8	23	7	83
2	28	27	35	15	27	84	22	14	28	70
3	33	33	32	11	38	103	40	21	38	82
4	26	26	21	10	21	72	20	14	21	58
5	9	9	4	5	8	86	10	22	7	64
	99	100	101		101		100		101	
Total N	1489	1316	176		1321		260		1061	

1. Within the community sample only, rates signify the number of high symptom respondents per 100 community sample.

Summary of significant chi-square analyses
Total Community vs Total Interviewed I11, P=<.005
Low Symptom Group vs High Symptom Group, P=<.01
Total Community vs Neurotics, P=<.05
Total Community vs Psychotics, P=<.05

Table 9.9—Illness Status, Sex and Age, by Education

	MALES			FEMALES			YOUNG			OLD		
	Comm. Per Cent (1)	Ill Per Cent (2)	Rate (3)	Comm. Per Cent (4)	Ill Per Cent (5)	Rate (6)	Comm. Per Cent (7)	Ill Per Cent (8)	Rate (9)	Comm. Per Cent (10)	Ill Per Cent (11)	Rate (12)
Educational Status Position												
1	7	10	144	5	4	88	2	3	219	10	15	91
2	27	27	97	29	26	87	17	20	149	41	43	63
3	33	37	105	33	40	116	37	42	144	29	30	64
4	24	18	72	27	22	81	34	26	95	16	8	33
5	9	8	85	7	7	98	10	9	112	5	3	42
	100	100		101	99		100	100		101	99	
Total N	602	577		888	848		800	1010		687	415	

Summary of significant chi-square analyses
Males: Community vs Ill, $P < .05$
Females: Community vs Ill, $P < .05$
Young: Community vs Ill, $P < .001$
Old: Community vs Ill, $P < .001$

of mental disorder in the same way, some further aspects of the data should be noted.

(1) Despite some variability by position, status is not clearly related to referral source or treatment disposition (Tables 9.1 and 9.2). This finding provides increased assurance that data to be presented subsequently on status and mental disorder are not merely artifacts of status differences in attitudes toward psychiatric treatment, or of differences in how decisions about treatment were made at various agencies. This is not to say that such influences are not operative at all—for example, upper-status individuals are more inclined to come to the psychiatric facility via either self or family referral.

(2) Illness rates for first admissions, compared to chronic cases, are for the most part, similar to those obtained for the total incidence ill population. As mentioned previously, first admissions data are more conducive than readmissions data to speculations about etiological factors. We have also shown that there are no significant status differences between the mentally ill sample used in this study and the relevant universe of mentally ill.

The most consistent finding is the relatively high rate of mental disorder in the lowest status group on each of the three status dimensions. This high illness rate is also present, but is not as marked, in the high status position of two of the three status measures. The data also consistently show that the higher the status position, the lower the representation of the various status positions in the high psychiatric symptom category. In the lower status group there is a tendency for the number of psychiatric symptoms and the amount of diagnosed mental disorder to be relatively high, while at the highest occupational and educational status positions, the rate of diagnosed mental disorder is high, but the number of psychiatric symptoms is low.

The coincidence of diagnosed mental disorder and high psychiatric symptoms at the lowest status positions indicates a greater prevalence of illness at these levels. The situation is more complex with respect to the highest status positions, where there is no coincidence between the two measures of pathology. High-status individuals are more often diagnosed as ill (especially neurotic) by virtue of a greater receptivity to psychiatric treatment, but in fact they are psychiatrically healthier than our statistics imply. One may also argue that psychiatric symptoms as measured in this study are not really on the same illness continuum as the bulk of diagnosed psychiatric disorders.

Social Status, Mental Disorder, and Goal-Striving Stress

NOW WE EXAMINE the status distributions of some of the social-psychological factors reported to be associated with mental disorder in previous chapters. Again we assume that a given status position in the community population with a relatively high yield or rate of mental disorder, will also be characterized by a comparatively high prevalence of pathology-linked factors. In considering these expectations, however, we must remember that there are no significant differences between the occupational status distributions of the community and total incidence ill samples. Differences occur only between the community and the interviewed ill samples. This suggests a sample bias with respect to occupational status, which argues against a prediction of status differences in goal-striving stress (as well as in the reference group and self-ideal discrepancies).

We should note that the perception of the opportunity structure (an item that differentiated clearly between the community and ill populations) is not consistently related to status variations of mental disorder on any of the three status dimensions.

Table 9.10 presents the three mean goal-striving stress scores by status position for goals in self-striving content areas: occupation, income, and goals specified on the striving scale as representing one's "best way of life." At most status levels the diagnosed mentally ill show significantly higher scores in these areas of goal striving than their community counterparts.

An examination of Table 9.10 reveals very little consistency between occupational status-linked rates of mental disorder and the three stress scores. This is not unexpected, however, since the occupational status dis-

Table 9.10—Mean Scores for Selected Social Psychological Variables, by Status

	Occup.-Self Stress-Score	Income-Self Stress Score	Striving Scale-Self Stress Score	Reference Group Discrepancy	Self-Ideal Discrepancy
Occupational Status Position					
1	5.47	13.63	13.40	.51	.54
2	4.62	20.83	15.00	.34	.38
3	6.37	19.79	17.30	.27	.43
4	3.98	26.55	13.90	.29	.44
Income Status Position					
1	.97	7.67	11.50	.52	.52
2	5.77	13.41	12.20	.44	.50
3	7.96	24.55	23.50	.31	.49
Educational Status Position					
1	2.67	12.01	9.50	.68	.57
2	2.95	10.14	12.80	.30	.54
3	4.69	13.68	14.60	.48	.52
4	7.73	24.37	15.60	.43	.49
5	8.95	32.14	17.90	.51	.47

tributions of the total incidence ill and community samples do not differ significantly.

Income status (Table 9.5) is inversely related to mental disorder, and the distributions of the community and ill samples differ significantly. The three sets of stress scores for the income status groups all show a direct relationship between goal-striving stress and status (see Table 9.10): as the yield of mental disorder decreases, the goal-striving stress scores increase.

The analysis of the relationship between mental disorder and educational status (Table 9.7) shows that two educational positions differ significantly in their percentage distributions in the community and ill samples. Status level 3 is over-represented among the ill and is associated with high rates of illness, and level 4 is under-represented and has relatively low rates. Table 9.10 indicates lower goal-striving stress scores for status level 3 than level 4 in all three goal areas. This finding again supports the association of high yields of mental disorder and low goal-striving stress. Education level 5 is characterized not only by high rates of mental disorder (Table 9.7) but also by the highest mean stress scores in all three goal-striving areas. Thus, the findings for educational status are inconsistent.

An overview of the analyses on the relationship between goal-striving stress and status-linked rates of illness suggests that high yield community status groups show relatively low goal-striving stress scores. As already noted, however, there are inconsistencies in these data and no conclusive generalizations can be made.

Some related points may be mentioned at this point. For the most part, the mean goal-striving stress scores for the income and educational status groups increase directly with status position, indicating that high-status community groups tend to be more involved in goal striving than low-status community groups. Since relevant analyses show that this increase which accompanies higher status cannot be attributed to the discrepancy component of these scores, we conclude that stress scores tend to increase because higher probabilities of success and/or higher valences of success predominate at these higher status levels. In this context we indicated earlier that rates of high psychiatric symptom scores clearly tend to decrease as status increases, using each of the three status measures. Apparently goal-striving stress is not consistently related to yield of diagnosed mental disorder associated with various status levels in the community, but is inversely related to psychiatric symptoms associated with these levels. In other words, at the upper status levels, relatively high goal-striving stress scores tend to be associated with low symptom rates. Conversely, the uniformly high rates of diagnosed mental disorder and psychiatric symptoms at the lowest positions of all three status hierarchies are associated with relatively low goal-striving stress scores.

In order to investigate why low levels of goal-striving stress are associated with high yields of psychopathology at the lowest socio-economic positions, we considered two additional questionnaire items related to the goal-striving behavior of the different status groups. The first of these items elicited the respondent's opinion about whether his present ambitions were "Higher," "The same," or "Lower" than in the past (Appendix B, Question 196). Presumably, individuals who had been most successful in striving for goals in the past would also have relatively high ambitions for the future. Using status achievement as a criterion of success, we expect that perception of present ambitions as "Higher" than in the past will increase with status position. This expectation is confirmed for the income and educational status measures (see Table 9.11). There is also a progressive increase in "Higher" responses at the first three occupational levels but a decrease at the highest position.

We cannot explain the deviation of responses at this high occupational level. Perhaps occupation itself is the major criterion of present ambitions in this population, in which case many respondents already at occupation level 4 do not expect to obtain better jobs than their current ones. In effect, the question of occupational ambitions is irrelevant to them. If the interpretation of these findings is valid, we can speculate that the high rates of psychiatric symptoms generally found at the lowest status levels in the community are associated with low self-

Table 9.11—Ambitions and Expectations, by Status in Percentages

	TOTAL N	PRESENT RELATIVE TO PAST AMBITIONS		EXPECTIONS OF BETTER JOB		
		Higher	Same or Lower	Yes	No	Don't Know
Occupational Status						
Position						
1	611	33	67	41	56	3
2	380	46	54	44	53	3
3	138	52	48	54	41	5
4	53	36	64	43	53	4
Income Status						
Position						
1	267	25	75	25	69	6
2	706	38	62	38	56	6
3	395	50	50	50	47	3
Educational Status						
Position						
1	65	25	75	37	60	3
2	338	30	70	29	68	3
3	293	43	57	57	40	3
4	150	47	53	63	34	3
5	103	50	50	61	36	3

esteem and a painful curtailment of present ambitions. This explanation also suggests that those respondents with present low levels of goal-striving stress *do* perceive that their ambitions have been higher in the past.

How does this questionnaire item on present ambitions relate to rates or yield of mental illness on the three status hierarchies? Illness rates for the occupational status groups form a U-shaped curve—similarly, respondents' ambitions decline at the two extreme occupational positions characterized by high rates of mental disorder. Illness rates show a perfect inverse relationship with income status. Ambitions also decline progressively with increasing income position. There is no consistent relationship between present ambitions and yield of mental disorder for educational status (see Table 9.11). The data for occupation and income, then, indicate an association between status groups with high current ambitions or hope for the future, and a low illness yield.

Another questionnaire item provides a more direct gauge of hope for the future, at least in the area of occupational goals. Individuals were asked if they expected to "be in a better job" sometime in the future (Appendix B, Question 46).[2] For the first three occupational status levels, where illness rates decline progressively, there is a steady increase in hope for a better job (see Table 9.11). There is a decline in hope at the highest occupational status level, which shows an increase in yield of illness. In the area of income, the expectations of obtaining a better job increase as the status-associated illness rates decrease.

When the data on expectation of a "better job" and "present ambitions" are considered together, the low occupational and income status groups (which both have high rates of illness and psychiatric symptoms)

2. Housewives were asked about their expectations for their husbands.

manifest a temporal pattern of progressively lowering their goal-striving levels from the past to the present, and of expressing even less hope for the future. The responses at the various educational status levels do not conform to this pattern.

Social Status and Mental Disorder Related to the Reference Group and Self-Ideal Discrepancies

IN THIS SAME CONTEXT we now consider two additional study variables previously found to be associated with diagnosed mental illness: discrepancy from one's reference group, and self-ideal discrepancy used as a measure of self-esteem. The data pertaining to these factors are summarized in Table 9.10.

Neither reference group discrepancy nor self-ideal discrepancy varies significantly by any of the three status measures. On the occupational status hierarchy, the U-shaped pattern of mean reference group discrepancy scores parallels the rate curve associated with these status positions (see Figure 9.1). Similarly, income status level is inversely related both to discrepancy from reference group and rates of mental disorder. The mean reference group discrepancy scores of the educational status groups again show the W-shaped curve characteristic of illness rates for this status measure. All three of our status measures thus show a dramatic congruence of yields of mental disorder and mean discrepancies from reference group.

Throughout this volume, a high self-ideal discrepancy has been taken to imply low self-esteem. The distribution of mean self-ideal discrepancies among the occupational status groups (Table 9.10) shows the familiar U-shaped curve, again roughly similar to the rate curve obtained for occupational status yields of mental disorder. Self-esteem is lowest in the two groups associated with the highest illness rates. For income status there is also a perfect fit between self-ideal discrepancy scores and the status-associated illness rates reported earlier. The yield of mental disorder decreases progressively as status and self-esteem increase. Self-ideal discrepancy is inversely related to educational status position (see Table 9.10). This pattern does not coincide with the status-linked illness rates.

Summary and Discussion

FINDINGS RELATED to status show both consistent and inconsistent patterns and do not lend themselves to simple interpretations. Here we attempt to accomplish something very difficult: to explain illness rates at different socioeconomic status levels in a general community population by means of social-psychological factors previously found to be associated with the diagnosed mentally ill population. We assume that these social-psychological factors will be more prevalent in a community subpopulation with a high yield of mental disorder than in its low yield counterpart. Since we are comparing essentially "normal" individuals, we anticipate some difficulty in demonstrating differences in the distributions of these pathological factors. However, since a similar approach met with considerable success in analyzing data on migration and mental disorder (Chapter 8), its failure in this instance suggests that status position is not an important predictor of mental illness.

In broad outline, rates of diagnosed mental illness are high both at the lowest and highest occupational and educational status positions. A high rate characterizes only the lowest income status level. The high rates at the low end of the status scale for the interviewed ill population are due to an over-representation of young male psychotics, who were first admissions and who were referred to the treatment center by the police or courts. Rates of high psychiatric symptom scores in the community population decrease progressively as status increases.

Are the social-psychological variables underlying this study at all useful in helping us to explain variations in rates of mental disorder associated with the different status positions, particularly with the lower positions? Respondents at the lowest status levels are characterized by the lowest mean goal-striving stress scores in seven out of nine cases (see Table 9.10). Apparently individuals at low status levels are relatively uninvolved in active goal striving. But if these subjects experience a minimal amount of goal-striving stress, why should they yield high rates of psychosis and psychiatric symptoms? To say that these respondents are below the optimum stress level tells us little about the nature of their psychological state. The crucial question is whether the low goal-striving stress scores of community individuals in the lowest status groups indicate a psychological adjustive compromise (i.e., coming to terms with a reality situation), or a painful awareness of personal failure and lack of hope for the future. The mental health consequences of these alternative interpretations are undoubtedly quite different. The former state is probably associated with a relative absence of psychiatric symptoms, and the latter with a comparatively large number of symptoms. We shall probe this issue further as we continue to examine the findings.

The reader will recall that the largest proportions of respondents who reported that their present ambitions were "The same" or "Lower" than in the past, and who said they had no expectations of obtaining a better job in the future (see Table 9.11), were in the lowest positions on all three status dimensions. These responses may also indicate a lack of concern over achievement strivings. However, individuals at the lowest status levels have the largest reference group discrepancies—they compare their position on the striving scale with friends whom they perceive as being considerably above them. This suggests that the pattern of low-goal-striving stress among the lowest-status groups represents a painful awareness of failure and a giving up of the "American dream" rather than an indifferent, easy-going attitude. This interpretation is supported by the fact that the self-esteem of these low-status individuals is lower (i.e., the self-ideal discrepancy score is higher) than at any other status level (see Table 9.10). This provides a possible explanation of why very low levels of goal-striving stress in a community population are associated with high rates of psychiatric symptoms.

It is interesting to compare this pattern to that characteristic of the diagnosed mentally ill, who manifest high levels of goal-striving stress, a large mean reference group discrepancy, and low self-esteem. Negroes at the lowest status positions in the community population perceive the reality of their low position and the small likelihood of achieving future success. The process of reducing their goal-striving levels results in psychological stress and a loss of self-esteem in a society that places such a high value on success. It is this process that leads to the development of psychiatric symptoms.

On the other hand, low-status individuals who do not diminish their early high investment in goal striving, or who perhaps even raise it in accordance with the ideal prescriptions of the larger society or as a reaction to perceived failure, incur a high risk of developing mental illness, especially psychosis. In this connection, it is noteworthy that the patients are more prone than the community individuals to regard the opportunity structure as open, but they have much lower personal expectations of improving their situation.

We may consider these conclusions in light of some research reported in the literature. Meyers and Roberts (1959: 129–171) noted that actual mobility strivings were psychopathogenic in their middle-class sample, but not in the lowest socioeconomic group, despite the fact that perceived aspiration-achievement discrepancies were high at both status levels. They noted that patients in the lowest class of their sample did virtually nothing to reach their stated goals. For them, the struggle for existence was such a meaningful reality that the satisfaction of daily subsistence needs assumed paramount importance. Mobilty strivings played little part in their development (Meyers and Roberts, 1959: 167).

The findings of the present study suggest a modification of this interpretation. Although individuals at the lowest status levels in our samples do have low goal-striving stress, we cannot agree that mobility strivings are of little importance to them and play no role in their psychic problems. The fact that these low-status respondents manifest the highest perceived discrepancy from reference group and the lowest self-esteem indicates that their mobility strivings may be extremely relevant, although perhaps associated with little actual effort at implementation. As noted previously, the crucial factor may not necessarily be the amount of actual effort individuals expend in goal striving, but rather their perception of, and the psychological meaning they attach to, their achievement experiences.

Meyers and Roberts' study implies that the low striving level in the lowest status group is a stress-reducing mechanism. Hyman (1953b) offered a similar interpretation in his study of the values of the different social classes: "The lower-class individual doesn't want as much success, knows he couldn't get it even if he wanted to, and doesn't want what might help him get success."

On the other hand, Sewell and Haller (1959) found that the evidence of relatively high levels of psychopathology (among low-status individuals) was associated with great dissatisfaction with their achievement levels and status positions. Our data suggest that low-status individuals may not maintain a simple attitude toward goal striving. Their frequently reported lack of actual active mobility strivings and *seemingly* indifferent attitudes towards success may not simply reflect the actual psychological significance of their low position and failure to achieve in a society that places a high value on achievement. Although Hyman may correctly conclude that the individual at a low-status level is aware that he "couldn't get it even if he wanted to," the data in this chapter suggest that the low-status person does "want it" but believes he cannot "get it." In fact, in another article, Hyman (1953a) reported that more individuals in the lowest of four economic classes saw their position as one or more classes higher than it actually was. He interpreted these results in terms of the greater need for psychological compensation at lower status levels. If his previous allegation about the lack of motivation for success in the lower classes is valid, then we must ask the reasons for this compensatory reaction. Our data indicate that such low-status individuals are involved in goal striving but feel that active striving is futile.

The data discussed in this chapter show that social status position does not significantly or consistently order the distribution of mental disorder. We have suggested that status position is not an important psychopathogenic factor in the Negro community. This issue will be explored further in the chapter on social mobility and its relationship to mental illness.

10

SOCIAL MOBILITY AND
MENTAL DISORDER

In this chapter we shall investigate the relationship between social mobility and mental disorder, and the extent to which this relationship can be explained in terms of goal-striving stress, reference group discrepancy, and self-esteem. Again we assume that community population subgroups associated with high yields of illness will tend to show response patterns for these three social-psychological variables similar to those of the diagnosed mentally ill population.

A Review of the Literature

THE REVIEW of the literature and the presentation of findings on migration and on social status position (Characters 8 and 9) suggest that an invariant relationship between these sociologically conceptualized variables and mental disorder cannot be assumed. Does this general conclusion apply also to the relationship between social mobility and mental illness?

Most of the empirical studies of this problem offer *post hoc* explanations of relationships found between social mobility and mental disorder. Attempts to explain the findings systematically by means of hypothesized intervening variables are seldom built into the research design.

Warner (1937) merely assumed that both upward and downward mobility in American society were responsible for many mental ailments. Implicit in this reasoning were assumptions of a positive relationship between social mobility and interpersonal disturbances, and between the latter factor and mental illness.

These assumptions have continued to characterize much of the literature on social mobility. Blau (1956) reviewed the general subject of social mobility and interpersonal relations and cited studies showing that socially mobile individuals (in either direction) manifested more racial prejudice (Greenbaum and Pearlin, 1953) and greater concern over their health (Litwak, 1956) than nonmobile persons. Blau assumed that these types of behavior resulted from interpersonal disturbances characteristic of socially mobile individuals, and he implied that such disturbances might be psychopathogenic.

In a more recent theoretical paper on this subject, Lipset and Bendix (1963) suggested that extreme mobility was accompanied by a greater likelihood of inconsistencies or discrepancies between the different factors comprising one's social status position. These inconsistencies would lead to role conflict and disturb social relationships.

The few analyses of the psychological dimension of this problem that have been made indicate that status discrepancies may cause difficulties in personal adjustment because high self-evaluations in one sphere of life conflict with low ones in another. Durkheim, for example, suggested that both upward and downward mobility result in increased suicide rates by increasing the number of persons who find themselves in an *anomic* situation, one in which they do not know how to react to the norms involved (Lipset and Bendix, 1963:65).

Janowitz and Curtis (1957) presented a closely related point of view. They hypothesized the greatest primary group interpersonal strains (family, friendship cliques, etc.) for those who had experienced the most upward and downward mobility, and the least strains for stable and moderately upwardly mobile families. This hypothesis remains unverified, however.

Research on social mobility and mental disorder must deal with two major problems. (1) Can social mobility itself, regardless of direction, and the degree of such mobility, differentiate between community and ill individuals, or between diagnostic subgroups among patients? (2) Can the high rates of mental disorder often reported for the lower socioeconomic groups be explained by the "downward drift" of individuals who were already ill prior to this mobility? If the high illness rates often reported for low-status groups can be explained on the basis of the "downward drift" hypothesis, then factors associated with the way of life of lower-class individuals may have little relevance for the etiology of mental disorder. This question has been discussed many times since it was first raised by Faris and Dunham (1939).

Tietze, Lemkau, and Cooper (1941) reported that the inverse relationship between schizophrenia and social class could not be explained by the movement to lower socioeconomic levels of those who were already ill. Lapouse, Monk, and Terris (1956) also found that "for first admissions of schizophrenics to state hospitals from Buffalo, the concentration in the poor areas is not the result of downward drift from higher areas." On this basis, these authors rejected the "downward drift" hypothesis as an explanation of their data.

More recently, Hollingshead and Redlich (1955) reported similar findings. Using a composite social class index, they were unable to account for the status distribution of mental disorder by social mobility. A considerable body of available data casts doubt on the validity of ascribing high illness rates in low-status groups to occupational "downward drift." Clausen and Kohn (1959) found no indication of higher rates of schizophrenia and more occupational drift among lower-class patients than among a "normal" control group of comparable status. The absence of differences in drift was noted both for inter- and intragenerational mobility. These investigators also found no significant differences prior to, or at the onset of, illness. This finding, however, was based not on a longitudinal study but on past hospital records.

Although the evidence cited above indicates no significant relationship between mental illness and upward or downward mobility, not all studies reach this conclusion. Lystad (1957) took the difference between a respondent's occupational level and that of his father as a measure of social mobility; schizophrenic patients were more downwardly mobile than a control group of neurotics matched for occupational achievement.

In their study of a nonhospitalized population in New York City, Srole and his associates (1962) reported that a relatively large proportion of individuals with severe psychiatric symptoms were occupationally downwardly mobile (compared to the occupational levels of their fathers). The upwardly mobile were slightly over-represented in the "Well" category. Futher analyses of these same data (Langner and Michael, 1963) confirmed Srole's conclusion that the downwardly mobile were characterized by the poorest mental health, and the upwardly mobile by the least mental illness. Nonmobile individuals fell between these two groups. This finding applied to "psychotic types" but not to "neurotic types." The latter, in fact, were most often upwardly mobile and least often downwardly mobile.

In contrast to Hollingshead and Redlich and other studies reported above, the data analyzed by Srole, and by Langner and Michael depended on "diagnoses" made from questionnaire responses of a general community population. Medically diagnosed patients were omitted from this study. Langner's measure of mobility also differed somewhat from that employed in other studies: a respondent's social status level was determined by a composite rating of his present occupation, education, rent, and family income; his father's status level was indicated by a composite score of the father's highest educational achievement and the occupation he held when the respondent was eight years of age. Differences of this kind among studies underline a serious methodological consideration in comparing findings. The widely differing criteria often used to define social mobility and mental illness render the results of many studies incomparable.

Jaco (1959) investigated social mobility in *communities* yielding different rates of mental disorder and noted that areas with high rates of illness were characterized mainly by downward mobility. In a study conducted in England, Morris (1959) reported a heavy concentration of schizophrenic patients in his low-status group but pointed out that the fathers of these patients were randomly distributed throughout all social classes. He referred to a downward "drop" as opposed to "drift," observing that many schizophrenics in his sample dropped to the lowest class immediately after leaving school.

The studies just discussed indicate that downward mobility in particular, rather than mobility per se, is associated with high rates of mental disorder. Srole's findings (1962) actually indicated the greatest mental health for the upwardly mobile. None of these studies tells us about the temporal relationship of these two variables, however: does downward mobility precede or result from mental disorder?

Some of the studies mentioned up to this point indicated no relationship between social mobility and mental disorder, and others reported an association between downward mobility and illness. This inconsistent picture is still more complicated by findings of a relationship between *upward* mobility and illness. Although Hollingshead and Redlich (1954) found no significant relationship between mobility and mental disorder, they noted that most of the patients who did change social position were upwardly mobile.

Hollingshead, Ellis, and Kirby (1954) explored mobility and diagnosis at two different status levels. At the lower status level they found no relationship between mobility and illness, but at the higher status position neurotics were more upwardly mobile than nonpatients, and schizophrenics were the most upwardly mobile of all groups. The authors inferred that neurotic and schizophrenic individuals at relatively high status levels were strivers who had actually experienced more upward movement from parental level than had nonpatients.

Ellis (1952) determined the occupational mobility of sixty career women, relative to their fathers' levels. The upwardly mobile women were significantly more prone than the nonmobile respondents to manifest severe psychosomatic symptoms. Self-ratings of adult happiness failed to differentiate between the mobile and the nonmobile women. Ruesch (1946; 1956) and Ruesch, Jacobson, and Loeb (1948) also concluded that "social climbers" were more subject to chronic psychosomatic disorders than those who were either socially nonmobile or downwardly mobile.

The research reported in this review permits few generalizations about a relationship between social mobility and mental disorder. The serious methodological inconsistencies in the operational definitions of mobility and mental disorder have already been mentioned. The difficulty in defining social mobility is further compounded by the problems involved in measuring status itself. A single status measure such as education or income may be used as the basis for determining mobility, or a composite status index may be utilized. The researcher must also determine to what extent the measures of status or social class differ from population to population. All of these difficulties make the mere combining of the results of many studies a questionable procedure.

In addition to these questions, the literature suggests a varying relationship between social mobility and mental disorder at different status levels and for different diagnostic groups. Psychosomatic symptoms and perhaps neurosis seem to be associated with upwardly mobile individuals, while psychotics tend to be downwardly mobile. These facts suggest the importance of using samples large enough to permit careful controls in data analysis. In this respect, too, existing studies vary widely and are often seriously lacking.

Another problem to which we alluded in passing is the lack of conclusive data on the temporal relationship between mobility and mental disorder. Even if consistent relationships could be determined between these variables, the nature of the causal relationship between them would be difficult to infer. Until this relationship is known, the hypothesis that interpersonal disturbances constitute an intervening variable between mobility and mental disorder cannot be adequately evaluated. Longitudinal studies may provide an answer.

A final problem is that very few epidemiological investigations of social mobility and mental illness have incorporated systematic attempts to study the social-psychology underlying the relationship of these variables. Perhaps these data will be more consistent when we understand the psychological concomitants of mobility, and how these factors change according to the direction of the mobility and the social context in which it occurs. We suggest that the concept of social mobility in itself is too gross a structural factor and too variable in its psychological implications to relate to mental disorder in a simple manner. A more sophisticated typology of mobility, encompassing additional aspects of the social situation or associated psychological factors, may yield greater consistency in the research findings.

Occupational Mobility
and Mental Disorder

IN ORDER to analyze the relationship between occupational mobility and mental illness, the occupation which the respondent (or head of household) had held for most of his life, and the occupation of either parent (whichever was higher on our occupational scale) were placed on a seven-step continuum of occupational prestige (see Appendix C). The difference between these two occupational levels for a given subject indicated whether that respondent was occupationally upwardly or downwardly mobile, relative to the occupational achievement of his parent. If there was no difference between the respondent's and his parent's occupational levels, he was classified as "nonmobile," or "stable."

Table 10.1 presents the relative amounts, or rates, of psychopathology for each mobility category. When the illness rates of the three mobility types are considered for the total group without occupational status controls, the upwardly mobile show the lowest rates, the stable subjects somewhat higher rates, and the downwardly mobile the highest illness rates.

Table 10.1 also includes the percentage distribution for each mobility type in the ill and community samples with no occupational controls. Among the mentally ill, the stable and upwardly mobile individuals are under-represented and the downwardly mobile over-represented. The differences between the community and ill populations are statistically significant ($P = < .001$).

We must now consider whether these findings, based on an analysis

Table 10.1—Occupational Mobility¹ and Illness Status,

by Status Position

Occupational Status Position (of respondent)	Mobility Type	ILL	COMM.	RATE	P VALUE (by chi-square)
		Per Cent			
1: Low	Up	—	—	—	
	Stable	49	72	69	<.001
	Down	51	28	186	
		100	100		
Total N		785	772		
2	Up	33	59	43	
	Stable	29	21	106	<.001
	Down	38	20	141	
		100	100		
Total N		292	382		
3	Up	63	65	71	
	Stable	28	24	85	N.S.
	Down	9	11	63	
		100	100		
Total N		105	143		
4: Highest	Up	91	63	263	
	Stable	9	37	24	<.001
	Down	—	—	—	
		100	100		
Total N		58	52		
Total	Up	17	25	63	
	Stable	41	52	72	<.001
	Down	42	23	168	
		100	100		
Total N		1240	1349		

1. Refers to the direction of the difference between the occupational achievement of the respondent and the occupational achievement of either his father or mother. The higher of the two parental achievements was used to determine the mobility type to which a respondent belonged. If only one parental achievement was known, it was used for determining the mobility type.

of the total samples, also apply at particular occupational status levels. In two of the three available comparisons, the downwardly mobile show higher rates of illness than the nonmobile respondents at the separate occupational status levels (see Table 10.1). The exception to this pattern (at level 3) shows no significant differences in the distribution of mobility types in the ill and community populations. Similarly, the upwardly mobile show lower illness rates than the nonmobile subjects at two of the three occupational levels where comparisons are possible. Only at the highest status level is this trend reversed. Rates of mental illness are apparently influenced by whether the individual has been socially mobile occupationally, by the direction of his mobility, and by his current occupational status position.

It is possible that the *degree,* or amount, of mobility, and not only its pervasiveness, is related to mental disorder. When the total ill and community samples are compared, the average downward occupational mobility for the patients is 1.87 steps, and for the community respondents, 1.68 steps ($P = < .01$). The comparable figures for the upwardly mobile are 1.41 and 1.28 steps ($P = < .02$). Clearly, among individuals in both populations who have been occupationally mobile, the amount of upward and downward mobility is significantly greater for the patients.

Evidence for a relationship between degree of occupational mobility and rate of mental disorder may also be inferred by a less direct method. Are the relatively high illness rates among the upwardly and downwardly mobile also associated with relatively high average degrees of upward and downward mobility? Illness rates for the downwardly mobile are highest at occupation level 1 and decline progressively through levels 2 and 3. The converse holds for the upwardly mobile: illness rates are lowest at status level 1, and increase progressively as one ascends the occupational hierarchy (see Table 10.1). The average number of steps moved by the downwardly mobile is 1.72 steps at occupational level 1, 1.42 steps at level 2, and 2.38 steps at level 3. No consistent relationship between illness rates and degree of downward occupational mobility emerges, but the increasing rates of illness observed with rising occupational status among the upwardly mobile are paralleled by a progressive increase in the average number of steps moved: 1.00 steps at level 2, 1.62 steps at level 3, and 2.15 steps at level 4.

In summary, the degree of upward occupational mobility is directly related to rates of mental disorder among the upwardly mobile but is not consistently related to the amount of downward occupational mobility.

Up to this point we have discussed only the relationship between occupational mobility and rates or yield of *diagnosed* mental disorder associated with community status groups. Do the findings relevant to occupational mobility and diagnosed illness also apply to psychiatric symptom scores within the community population itself? Table 10.2

Table 10.2—Psychiatric Symptoms by Mobility Type in a Community Population in Percentages

| | OCCUPATIONAL MOBILITY | | | | EDUCATIONAL MOBILITY | | | |
	Total N	Low Symp.	High Symp.	Rate[1]	Total N	Low Symp.	High Symp.	Rate
Mobility Type								
Upwardly	318	93	7	7	828	88	12	14
Stable	670	87	13	14	425	90	10	12
Downwardly	311	86	14	15	185	85	15	17

1. Within the community sample only, rates signify the number of high symptom respondents per 100 community sample.
2. By chi-square, High Symptom vs Low Symptom, $P=<.01$ (for Occupational Mobility).

indicates that rates of high symptom scores are lowest among the upwardly mobile, increase among the nonmobile, and reach their highest point among the downwardly mobile. These psychiatric symptom rates parallel the illness rates for the three mobility groups with no occupational status controls (see Table 10.1).

INTRAPERSONAL OCCUPATIONAL MOBILITY
AND MENTAL DISORDER

Data were obtained from respondents in both populations on the type of work they had done "most of their lives" and the type of work they had done during the "last year" (Appendix B, Questions 30 and 37, respectively). A person who held a job "last year" which was higher on our seven-step occupational scale than the work done "most of his life" was classified as upwardly mobile. If the job held "last year" was lower, he was classified as downwardly mobile, and if it was at the same level, he was considered to be occupationally stable. Analyses of the data for mobility status show no significant relationships with mental illness. These findings are consistent with the study of Clausen and Kohn (1959).

CONTRIBUTION OF OCCUPATIONAL MOBILITY TO AN
UNDERSTANDING OF THE RELATIONSHIP BETWEEN
OCCUPATIONAL STATUS AND MENTAL DISORDER

Data on occupational mobility may be considered in relation to the findings on occupational status position and mental illness discussed in the previous chapter. In that context, the rates of mental disorder associated with occupational status formed a crude U-shaped curve, with the high illness rates occurring at the lowest and highest occupational status levels. When this finding is considered together with the occupational mobility data summarized in Table 10.1, it appears that the high illness rates at the lowest occupational level can be accounted for by the downwardly mobile, and at the highest level by the upwardly mobile. The fact that the psychotics seem to contribute more heavily to the high illness rates at the lowest level, and neurotics to the high rates at occupational level 4, suggests that downward mobility is associated with, or antecedent to, psychosis, and similarly for upward mobility and neurosis.

In order to investigate this point more fully, we analyzed the distributions of the psychotics and the neurotics in the three mobility groups, for the total interviewed ill sample and for each occupational status level. The psychotics tend to predominate among the downwardly mobile at the low end of the scale. For the total sample, there is only a tendency for the neurotics to predominate among the upwardly mobile. An examination of the separate occupational status levels shows that the overall tendency for the neurotics to be concentrated among the upwardly mobile (although not significant) becomes progressively more marked as one ascends the occupational status hierarchy.

Educational Mobility and Mental Disorder

DATA ARE ALSO AVAILABLE on educational mobility from parental educational level. Each respondent's school grade achievement and the average grade achievement of both parents were placed on a continuum of seven educational status levels. (If information was available only for one parent, this educational status was used.) The difference between the respondent's and the average parental educational level was determined. The respondent was then categorized as upwardly mobile, downwardly mobile, or stable, relative to his parental achievement level.

For all educational status levels considered together, the downwardly mobile have the highest, and the stable individuals the lowest illness rates (see Table 10.3). The rates for the upwardly mobile fall between the two other mobility groups. Both downward and upward educational mobility are associated with illness to a greater extent than is nonmobility. The reader will remember that in the occupational area, the upwardly mobile showed *lower* rates than the nonmobile. Whichever mobility measure is used, however, the downwardly mobile clearly manifest the highest illness rates.

When percentage distributions of the three mobility groups in the ill and community samples are evaluated, the community sample contains a larger proportion of individuals either with the same (stable) or higher (upwardly mobile) educational attainments than their parents (see Table 10.3). The downwardly mobile predominate among the ill. The distributions of the three mobility types in the community and ill samples differ significantly $(P = < .001)$.

As suggested in the review of the literature, different mobility types may vary in their association with mental illness at particular status levels. Therefore, analysis of illness rates and percentage distributions among the three mobility types at the various educational status levels may enlarge our understanding of the findings on educational status and mental disorder reported in Chapter 9. Although the downwardly mobile have higher rates than the upwardly mobile for the total group without educational status controls, this relationship only holds at educational status levels 1 through 3 (see Table 10.3).

The ill sample contains fewer stable respondents than the community

Table 10.3—Educational Mobility[1] and Illness Status,

by Status Position

Education Status Position (of respondent)	Mobility Type	ILL	COMM.	RATE	P VALUE (by chi-square)
		Per Cent			
1 (Low)	Up	—	—	—	
	Stable	55	73	87	<.01
	Down	45	27	196	
		100	100		
Total N		100	86		
2	Up	45	44	95	
	Stable	30	42	66	<.001
	Down	25	14	172	
		100	100		
Total N		381	412		
3	Up	61	70	98	
	Stable	17	17	111	<.001
	Down	22	13	178	
		100	100		
Total N		543	491		
4	Up	71	68	80	
	Stable	21	24	68	N.S.
	Down	8	8	80	
		100	100		
Total N		291	380		
5 (Highest)	Up	74	71	99	
	Stable	26	29	79	N.S.
	Down	—	—		
		100	100		
Total N		108	178		
Total	Up	56	59	92	
	Stable	25	30	79	<.001
	Down	19	11	177	
		100	100		
Total N		1423	1469		

1. Refers to the direction of the difference between the educational achievement of the respondent and the educational achievement of either his father or his mother. The higher of the two parental achievements was used to determine the mobility type to which a respondent belonged. If only one parental achievement was known, it was used for determining the mobility type.

sample at all educational status levels except level 3, but the proportion of downwardly mobile individuals is higher among the patients at three of the four levels where comparisons are possible. Although some differences are evident, the findings reported for all educational levels taken together and for each of the individual status levels show a general correspondence. The percentage over-representation of the downwardly mobile is greatest at educational level 1, but it becomes progressively smaller as one ascends the educational status ladder. The differences finally disappear at level 4 (graduation from high school). Upward mobility is not over-represented among the patients at educational levels 2 and 3, although there is a tendency for over-representation at levels 4 and 5.

When degree, or amount, of mobility is considered, the average downward educational mobility on the seven-step scale is 1.75 steps for the ill, and 1.60 steps for the community sample. Although the amount of mobility among downwardly mobile individuals is greater for the ill, the difference does not reach statistical significance. The comparable figures for the upwardly mobile in the two samples are 1.59 and 1.45 steps, respectively ($P = < .01$). Both the upwardly and downwardly mobile patients show a greater degree of educational mobility than the community respondents.

We have already noted that downwardly mobile individuals in the area of education are characterized by relatively high rates of mental disorder at the lower educational status levels. No consistent pattern emerges for the upwardly mobile. As in the case of occupational mobility, we now consider whether these comparatively high rates of illness among the downwardly mobile are associated with a high degree of downward mobility. The findings indicate that this is the case: the average number of steps moved down is 1.21 at educational level 4, 1.47 steps at level 3, 2.29 steps at level 2, and 1.57 steps at the lowest educational level. Although this relationship is not perfect, high rates of illness do tend to be associated with large degrees of downward educational mobility. This trend is unlike that observed for occupational mobility, where illness was related only to the degree of upward mobility.

When educational mobility is considered in relation to psychiatric symptoms within the community population itself, we find the lowest rate of psychiatric symptoms among the nonmobile, a somewhat higher rate among the upwardly mobile, and the highest rate of symptoms among the downwardly mobile (see Table 10.2). Various mobility types apparently manifest similar trends in rates of diagnosed mental disorder and psychiatric symptoms.

COMPARISON OF OCCUPATIONAL AND EDUCATIONAL MOBILITY

In the areas of occupation and education the downwardly mobile are characterized by considerably higher illness rates than either of the two other mobility groups. The upwardly mobile have lower illness rates than the nonmobile respondents in the area of occupation. This is not true for the upwardly mobile in the area of education. Our data do not allow any further investigation of the reasons for this difference, but in this connection it should be noted that a much higher proportion of ill and community sample individuals are upwardly mobile educationally (56 and 59 per cent, respectively) than occupationally (17 and 25 per cent, respectively).

Some of this disparity is undoubtedly due to existing patterns of occupational discrimination experienced by Negroes. Many Negroes who have been upwardly mobile educationally have not experienced concomitant upward mobility in the occupational hierarchy. This situation may create high levels of stress in these individuals, an issue that will be explored in greater detail later in this chapter. In any case, the differences in the illness-mobility relationship obtained when the two dimensions of mobility are employed indicate the complexity of the problem and suggest the need for incorporating intervening social-psychological variables into future studies of this relationship.

CONTRIBUTION OF EDUCATIONAL MOBILITY TO AN
UNDERSTANDING OF THE RELATIONSHIP BETWEEN STATUS
AND MENTAL DISORDER

The curve representing rates of mental disorder at the various educational status levels formed a W-shaped curve, with the high points at educational levels 1, 3, and 5 (Chapter 9). Table 10.3 indicates a much higher proportion of downwardly mobile community respondents at educational level 1 than at any other status level. This may account partially for the high rates of mental disorder at this level. The high illness rates at education level 5 can probably be partly attributed to the 71 per cent of upwardly mobile community subjects at this level. Education level 3 is associated with the largest proportion of mobile individuals in the community population (83 per cent). This mobility may account for the high illness rates at this level.

An additional analysis of our data supports the speculation that educational mobility may partially explain the relationship between educational status and mental disorder. When all the mobile individuals are removed from our samples, and only the nonmobile, or stable, respondents are compared, significant differences between the ill and community samples disappear. This means that the significance of the difference between the distributions of mobility types in the ill and community populations ($P = <$ .001, see Table 10.3) is carried by respondents who have experienced some social mobility.

TEMPORAL RELATIONSHIP BETWEEN MOBILITY
AND MENTAL ILLNESS

Although both upward and downward educational mobility are associated with higher rates of mental disorder than is nonmobility, we must determine whether mobility is antecedent to mental illness, or whether illness itself is responsible for the observed mobility patterns. The assumption that mobility is primarily a consequence of illness involves certain logical inconsistencies. Downward mobility is relatively simple to explain when this assumption is made, but upward mobility constitutes more of a problem. In addition, most individuals in our sample population probably terminated their schooling in their mid-teens. If we assume that either of the mobility patterns is a consequence of illness, we must also assume that most of these individuals were already mentally ill in early adolescence. While this possibility may in fact be true in some cases, it is unlikely that it can account for the majority of cases. Therefore, the assumption of mobility as an *antecedent* condition of illness becomes the more tenable one.

This issue can be clarified by considering the distribution of high psychiatric symptom scores associated with the different mobility types in the community population. The rates and distributions of high symptom scores for the upwardly mobile, stable, and downwardly mobile groups parallel the rates of diagnosed illness associated with these mobility types. This similarity in rates supports the view that social mobility is antecedent to mental disorder: since this analysis evaluates mobility groups in a community sample, illness cannot be responsible for the results obtained. Implicit in this reasoning is the further assumption that any undiagnosed disorders that may exist in the community are minimal and therefore unlikely to account for mobility. At this point, however, our most sophisticated guess is that these factors are mutually interactive, and it may be impossible to separate completely the antecedent and consequent aspects of mobility. When occupational mobility is considered, the rates of high symptom scores in the community population provide similar support for considering mobility as antecedent to illness.

Income Mobility and Mental Disorder

OBTAINING RELIABLE INFORMATION on income which would be comparable to the data obtained for the other two measures of mobility from parental achievement level involved certain difficulties. Therefore, we decided to focus on the income mobility the individual had experienced within his own lifetime. If a respondent reported that he had ever had a higher yearly income than the previous year, he was classified as downwardly mobile; if his answer to this question was "No," he was placed in a category containing both stable and upwardly mobile individuals.

Downward mobility in the income area is clearly associated with higher rates of illness than is the case for the combined mobility category (see Table 10.4). The distributions of downwardly mobile and stable-

Table 10.4—Income Mobility and

Illness Status[1]

Mobility Type	ILL	COMM.	RATE
	Per Cent		
Upwardly Mobile and Stable	47	65	61
Downwardly	53	35	125
	100	100	
Total N	1014	1220	

1. By chi-square, $P = < .001$

or-upwardly mobile individuals also differ significantly in the ill and community samples ($P = < .001$). Although income mobility was determined in a different manner than mobility on the previous two dimensions of status, all three mobility measures show the highest rates of mental illness for the downwardly mobile. No analyses were carried out for separate income status levels.

Subjective Mobility and Mental Disorder

THE READER MAY WONDER about the degree of correspondence between a respondent's subjectively perceived mobility and his mobility based on his stated achievements in various content areas. Much speculation about the psychological effects of social mobility tacitly assumes that the individual perceives and defines his situation in terms of such objective criteria as we have used here. In some situations this correspondence may in fact be minimal. It is possible that the criteria of mobility employed by social scientists have only peripheral significance for the respondent, who may gauge his own mobility by other factors. This issue is particularly relevant for the present study, since half of the studied population are mentally ill individuals whose perception of objective reality may be distorted in varying degrees. This ill population may not perceive their social mobility in the manner suggested by the findings presented up to this point.

The comparison of objective and subjective mobility among the patients has important implications for another issue. How are the responses of the mentally ill affected by interviewing them soon after they become patients? Does the interview situation tend to accentuate the pessimism in some of their answers? Using occupational mobility as a criterion, virtually the same proportion of the mentally ill have *actually* been downwardly mobile (42 per cent, see Table 10.3) as have *perceived* a downward direction to their movement (44 per cent, see Table 10.5).

Table 10.5—Subjective Mobility and

Illness Status[1]

	ILL	COMM.	RATE
	Per Cent		
Mobility Type			
Upwardly	37	53	68
Stable	19	31	58
Downwardly	44	16	259
	100	100	
Total N	1014	1473	

1. By chi-square, P=<.001

As discussed in earlier chapters, all ill and community respondents were asked to estimate their position on a ten-step striving scale (Appendix B, Question 180), the top step labeled the "best possible way of life," and the bottom the "worst possible way of life." After selecting the step representing his present position on this scale, each respondent was asked to designate the step representing his position "a few years ago" (Appendix B, Question 181). In this situation the respondent himself chose the criteria by which to judge his mobility. If the step representing his present position was higher than that of a few years ago, the individual was categorized as subjectively upwardly mobile. If it was lower, he was considered downwardly mobile. If both steps were the same, he was classified as stable.

Table 10.5 presents illness rates in the three subjective mobility categories. Again, the highest illness rate is associated with the downwardly mobile. The lowest rate characterizes the nonmobile, and the upwardly mobile fall between the two other groups.

The percentage distributions of the three different subjective mobility categories in the ill and community populations indicate that more community than ill respondents perceive themselves as upwardly mobile or stable. Only 16 per cent of the community respondents regard themselves as downwardly mobile, compared to 44 per cent of the patients. The ill-community difference in the distributions of the three categories of subjective mobility is significant ($P = < .001$). The relative differences in mobility in the two populations, using subjective criteria, roughly parallel the previous findings on social mobility defined in terms of stated achievement levels on specific status dimensions.

The Relationship Between Social Mobility and Selected Social-Psychological Study Variables

THE PRESENT SECTION has a dual purpose. First, it will investigate the extent to which the rates of mental disorder associated with the different types of mobility can be explained by certain of our social-psychological study variables (namely, goal-striving stress, discrepancy from reference group, and self-ideal discrepancy). Our procedures and predictions concerning the yield of mental disorder have already been discussed. Since high levels of goal-striving stress, large discrepancies from reference group, and large self-ideal discrepancies (i.e., low self-esteem) are associated with diagnosed mental disorder, we hypothesize that these patterns will also characterize mobility groups in the community with high yields, or rates, of mental disorder. The confirmation of such predictions will indicate that these social-psychological variables can explain the rates associated with different types of mobility, and will also support the idea that social mobility is an antecedent condition of mental disorder.

Second, this section will determine the extent to which the findings on social mobility help to explain some of the data on status position reported in the previous chapter. We speculated in Chapter 9 that the nature and the extent of social mobility at different status levels might clarify some of the problems encountered in investigating the status-illness relationship.

The relationships between social mobility and each of the three social-psychological study variables were analyzed, considering both occupational and educational mobility from parental level. Since the latter mobility measure showed no consistent relationship to the three variables, however, we shall present only the data on occupational mobility. In addition, since analyses of group totals actually masked significant differences that emerged from analyses of separate status positions, only findings using occupational status controls will be presented.

Findings on social mobility as gauged by occupational movement from parental level, and the three social-psychological study variables are presented in Table 10.6. The illness rates associated with the three mobility

Table 10.6—Relationship between Social Mobility and Selected Social-Psychological Factors in a Community Population, by Occupational Status Levels

| | Rates [1] (1) | Mean Stress Score | | | Mean Ref. Grp. Discrep. (5) | Mean Self-Ideal Discrep. (6) |
		Occ.-Self (2)	Income-Self (3)	Striving Scales (4)		
OCCUP. LEVEL 1						
Up	—	—	—	—	—	—
Stable	69	10.6	26.6	24.8	3.2	.552
Down	186	11.9	30.6	30.9	3.0	.554
P. "t" test						
Up vs Stable		N.S.²	N.S.	<.05	N.S.	N.S.
Down vs Stable		—	—	—	—	—
Up vs Down		—	—	—	—	—
OCCUP. LEVEL 2						
Up	43	10.2	32.4	24.4	3.0	.498
Stable	106	10.1	30.7	26.4	2.8	.490
Down	141	16.0	39.7	21.3	2.9	.492
P. "t" test						
Up vs Stable		N.S.	N.S.	N.S.	N.S.	N.S.
Down vs Stable		<.05	<.03	N.S.	N.S.	N.S.
Up vs Down		<.05	N.S.	N.S.	N.S.	N.S.
OCCUP. LEVEL 3						
Up	71	11.9	30.9	30.3	2.9	.435
Stable	85	4.7	44.6	26.6	2.8	.494
Down	63	4.7	28.8	30.3	2.7	.318
P. "t" test						
Up vs Stable		<.01³	<.03	N.S.	N.S.	<.05
Down vs Stable		N.S.	<.03	N.S.	N.S.	<.001
Up vs Down		<.01	N.S.	N.S.	N.S.	<.01
OCCUP. LEVEL 4						
Up	263	6.6	53.5	27.4	2.4	.495
Stable	24	2.2	35.9	11.6	2.7	.286
Down	—					
P. "t" test						
Up vs Stable		N.S.	<.03	<.001	N.S.	<.001
Down vs Stable		—	—	—	—	—
Up vs Down		—	—	—	—	—

1: Taken from Table 10.1.
2: The italicization of significance values indicates that the differences in the scores are in the predicted direction.
3: By two-tailed test

types at each occupational level are listed in column 1. We predict that mobility types characterized by high illness rates will also manifest high scores on these three variables.

SOCIAL MOBILITY AND PERCEPTION OF
THE OPPORTUNITY STRUCTURE

We have already shown (Chapter 3) that, compared with the community respondents, the patients tend to see the opportunity structure as very open to goal achievement. In terms of the yield issue, we expect those community subgroups with high rates of mental illness to see a more open opportunity structure than those with low rates. In Chapter 8 we reported a weak but consistent tendency for the high yield migratory status group (the natives) to perceive a more open structure than the low yield group (the southern migrants). In Chapter 9 we found no consistent relationship between perception of the opportunity structure and rates of illness.

Do socially mobile individuals with high rates of illness perceive a more open system than those groups with low rates? Table 10.6 (column 1) lists the illness rates of the upwardly mobile, the stable, and the downwardly mobile respondents, controlling for occupational status position. Since none of the differences between mobility groups is significant, we shall be concerned with consistency of direction.

At occupational status level 1, the rate for the downwardly mobile exceeds that for the stable subjects. On this basis we expect more downwardly mobile than nonmobile respondents to see a very open opportunity structure. The difference is in the predicted direction.

At occupational status level 2, the illness rate for the downwardly mobile is higher than that for the stable or upwardly mobile group. As expected, more downwardly mobile than stable subjects see a very open system, but contrary to expectations, more upwardly mobile than downwardly mobile subjects at this level perceive a very open system. Since the opportunity structure has *in fact* been more open for the upwardly mobile, these individuals may be inclined to perceive the system as open. The stable subjects have a higher illness rate than the upwardly mobile, but fewer of these nonmobile subjects perceive a very open structure, again contrary to expectations.

At status level 3, the highest rate is associated with the stable group, the next highest with the upwardly mobile, and the lowest rate with the downwardly mobile. The proportions of those seeing a very open system increase in that order, as expected. Therefore, predictions for the downwardly-upwardly, upwardly-stable, and downwardly-stable comparisons on perception of the opportunity structure all go in the expected direction.

At occupation level 4, the upwardly mobile have a higher illness rate than the nonmobile and also see a more open system, consistent with expectations.

In summary, six of the eight comparisons show differences in the expected direction. It is important that at occupation level 1 the downwardly mobile, with the higher illness rate, perceive a more open system than the stable subjects. At occupation level 4, the upwardly mobile have a higher rate of illness and perceive a more open system than the stable respondents. As was the case for migratory status, there is a tendency for the perception of the opportunity structure to fit the variations in illness rates, but this trend is a weak one.

SOCIAL MOBILITY AND GOAL-STRIVING STRESS

Table 10.6 (columns 2, 3, and 4) presents the three goal-striving stress scores relating to self-striving for the three mobility types at each occupational control level. For the occupation stress score at occupational status level 1, the only comparison available is that between the downwardly mobile and the stable respondents. The rate of mental disorder is higher for the former mobility group. As predicted, the occupation goal-striving stress score is also higher for the downwardly mobile than for the nonmobile, although these two groups do not differ significantly.

At level 2, the downwardly mobile have a higher rate of illness than either the stable or the upwardly mobile respondents. Again, the downwardly mobile show significantly higher occupation stress scores than either of the other mobility groups. Although the stable subjects have a higher rate of illness than the upwardly mobile, there is virtually no difference between these two groups on the occupation stress scores.

At level 3, the downwardly mobile show a *lower* rate of illness than either of the other two mobility groups. Their mean stress score is the same as that of the stable group but significantly lower than that of the upwardly mobile. The magnitude of the mean stress scores of the upwardly mobile and the stable group are not in the predicted direction, and the difference between the two groups is significant. At occupational status level 4, the upwardly mobile have a higher illness rate than the stable subjects and also manifest a larger (but not significantly) mean occupation stress score.

In summary, six of the seven comparisons go in the predicted direction, and three of these six comparisons reach significance. One comparison that goes in the opposite direction is also significant.

In the area of income goal striving (Table 10.6, column 3), the downwardly mobile at occupational status level 1 have higher mean stress scores than the nonmobile, as predicted from their relative rates of illness. At level 2, the downwardly mobile, with the highest illness rate, also have a higher mean income stress score than either the stable or upwardly mobile subjects. The comparison with the latter mobility group is not significant, however. There is very little difference between the mean scores of the stable and upwardly mobile respondents.

At occupational status level 3, the stable subjects manifest both the highest illness rate and the highest mean income goal-striving stress score. They differ significantly from the downwardly mobile but not from the upwardly mobile in this content area. The relative magnitudes of the mean stress scores coincide perfectly with the relative rates of illness. At occupation level 4, the higher rate for the upwardly mobile compared to the nonmobile is paralleled by their higher mean income stress score.

In summary, seven of the eight comparisons are in the predicted direction (by sign test $P = < .04$). All four significant differences are also in the predicted direction. The upwardly mobile-stable comparison for the income stress score at occupational status level 3 goes in the predicted direction, but the comparable analysis for the occupation stress score is contrary to expectation. This difference suggests that income is more salient than occupation to these respondents.

In the area of the striving scale (Table 10.6, column 4) the mean stress score data show little consistency in the direction of the predictions, except for the comparison of the downwardly mobile and stable subjects at occupation level 1, and between the upwardly mobile and stable subjects at level 4 (both comparisons are significant and in the predicted direction).

Some interesting facts emerge when all three stress scores are considered. Although not perfectly consistent, there is a clear tendency for these stress scores to vary directly with the rates of mental disorder associated with the three mobility types. Nine of the ten comparisons that show significant differences are in the predicted direction. By analyzing each stress score separately, we do not necessarily intend to imply that we expected all the stress scores to conform in like degree to expectations for each of the eight comparisons. Since the three stress scores relate to different content areas which may be differentially important to respondents, we should see how many of the eight comparisons fulfill this criterion.

It seems reasonable to conclude that the association between mobility and mental disorder can be at least partially explained by goal-striving stress. In addition, these stress scores are capable of predicting yield of diagnosed mental disorder in community subgroups. This further supports the idea that mobility and its social-psychological concomitants constitute an antecedent condition of mental disorder.

These findings indicate that low-status downwardly mobile *and* high-status upwardly mobile subjects are characterized by high goal-striving stress scores. For whatever reason this is so, it appears that those who are most prone to mental illness at the low and high ends of the occupational status continuum also apparently have relatively high levels of goal-striving stress.

The findings on stress scores presented in Table 10.6, help us to understand rates of mental disorder associated with status position itself. First, the difference in distributions of the occupationally stable respondents in the ill and community populations barely reaches significance ($P = < .05$). The distributions of the educationally nonmobile respondents are not significant. On the other hand, distributions of all three mobility types for occupation and education do differ significantly in the ill and community populations ($P = < .001$). Apparently, the mobile portion of these populations accounts mainly for differences in rates of mental disorder. Social mobility seems to be more clearly linked to goal-striving stress than does social status per se. The isolation of the mobility effect permits us to understand rates of mental illness associated with different community subpopulations.

In Chapter 9 we noted that low-status community subgroups were generally associated with high illness rates and relatively low goal-striving stress scores. The small proportion of downwardly mobile respondents at occupation level 1 (28 per cent), who are characterized by high illness rates and high stress scores, seem to exert relatively little influence on the mean stress scores at this status level. The stable respondents at level 1 (72 per cent), who are characterized by low rates and low stress scores, apparently account for the low overall mean stress scores initially associated with low-status position. Although a high rate of illness at status level 1 is associated with low mean stress scores, it is the relatively healthy individuals at this stress level (the nonmobile) who apparently account for these low means. Occupation level 4 is associated with relatively high illness rates, and also high mean stress scores. The upwardly mobile (37 per cent), who are characterized by high rates and high goal-striving stress scores, seem to account for the elevated mean scores at this status level.

SOCIAL MOBILITY AND DISCREPANCY FROM REFERENCE GROUP

Another social-psychological variable to be considered in this context is one's discrepancy from his reference group (see Chapter 6). Data on one of the two measures of this discrepancy (i.e., the difference between one's estimate of his present position and that of his "close friends") are presented in Table 10.6, column 5. There is no consistent relationship between type of mobility and mean discrepancy from reference group when this reference group measure is utilized. None of the eight comparisons is statistically significant.

A second and less direct measure of reference group orientation, also discussed earlier, involves the respondent's preferred choice of two paired occupations: a blue-collar occupation with a relatively high wage, and a white-collar position with a relatively low wage. Since most of our community respondents actually held blue-collar jobs, we assumed that individuals choosing the white-collar occupation with its associated wage penalty were more discrepant from their occupational status reference point than those choosing the blue-collar, higher-paying job. We also noted that this technique did not represent a sufficiently sensitive reference group measure for respondents at the upper educational levels, who actually did hold white-collar positions. Since comparisons of occupational choice would obviously be influenced by current occupational status position, for these analyses, educational mobility from parental level was used to determine the three mobility types. Comparisons were made for each separate educational status level, as well as for the total community population.

The findings relevant to occupational blue/white-collar choice are summarized in Table 10.7. Consistent with the assumptions (1) that a white-collar choice represents a larger discrepancy from a reference group (at least at the lower-status levels) than a blue-collar choice, and (2) that the ill are characterized by more white-collar choices than the community respondents, we predict that the illness rates associated with the different mobility types will vary directly with the proportion of white-collar occupational preferences.

The distributions for the total community group (Table 10.7, bottom)

Table 10.7—Blue-Collar White-Collar Occupational Choices, Educational

Mobility and Rates of Mental Disorder, by Status Position

Educational Status Position	Mobility Type	Rate	WITHIN THE COMMUNITY POPULATION Blue-Collar	White-Collar	P VALUE (by chi-square)
			Per Cent		
1 (Lowest)	Up	–	–	–	
	Stable	87	69	31	<.01
	Down	196	47	53	
2	Up	95	57	43	
	Stable	66	68	32	<.001
	Down	172	50	50	
3	Up	98	50	50	
	Stable	111	49	51	N.S.
	Down	178	44	56	
4	Up	80	44	66	
	Stable	68	36	64	N.S.
	Down	80	37	63	
5 (Highest)	Up	99	31	69	
	Stable	79	33	77	N.S.
	Down	–	–	–	
Total (all Groups)	Up	92	53	47	
	Stable	79	63	37	<.001
	Down	177	47	53	

show a perfect correspondence between the rates of illness and the relative proportions of respondents choosing white-collar jobs.

These distributions differ significantly ($P = < .001$). The downwardly mobile group, with the highest illness rate, also contains the largest proportion of white-collar choices. The nonmobile group, with the lowest illness rate, is characterized by a smaller proportion of white-collar preferences. The upwardly mobile fall between these other groups in rate and proportion.

At education level 1, the downwardly mobile show both a higher rate of illness and a larger number of white-collar choices than the nonmobile ($P = < .01$). At status levels 2 and 3, a perfect correspondence between illness rates and percentage of white-collar choices is observed, although the difference in distributions is significant only at level 2. This correspondence breaks down at levels 4 and 5. For the group as a whole and for each of the three lowest educational status levels, all of our predictions tend to be supported. There is reason to believe that at the two highest status levels this type of data is an insensitive measure of reference group orientation.

The large number of white-collar choices among the downwardly mobile at the three lowest educational status levels (i.e., high discrepancy from an aspired reference group) probably indicates that these individuals are moving downward in the educational status hierarchy, but that they have failed to lower their reference point to the level prevailing at the lower status position. They still reflect patterns internalized at the earlier, higher positions. The findings suggest that mental illness is related to individuals' inability to adjust their status aspirations in accordance with reality.

The higher number of white-collar choices among the upwardly mobile, compared to the nonmobile at education levels 2, 3, and 4, probably reflects a high achievement orientation and a desire to move up still further in the occupational status hierarchy. Reference group discrepancy derived on this basis indicates that reference group orientation may constitute an antecedent condition of illness.

SOCIAL MOBILITY AND THE SELF-IDEAL DISCREPANCY

The final social-psychological variable with which we are concerned in this context is self-esteem, as measured by the self-ideal discrepancy (see Chapter 7). At occupation level 1 (Table 10.6, column 6) the downwardly mobile, with the higher rate of illness, also manifest a higher mean self-ideal discrepancy than the stable group, although these differences are not statistically significant. At status level 2 none of the differences in self-esteem reaches significance, and only one of the three comparisons goes in the predicted direction. All three predictions of differences between mobility groups at level 3 are significant and in the predicted direction. The nonmobile, with the highest rate, also have the largest mean discrepancy, and the downwardly mobile, with the lowest illness rate, show the smallest mean discrepancy. The upwardly mobile fall between these two groups. At the highest occupational status level, the one possible comparison (upwardly mobile vs. stable) is significantly different in the predicted direction—the upwardly mobile have both the higher illness rate and the larger self-ideal discrepancy (or lower self-esteem).

Six of the eight comparisons are in the predicted direction, and all four of the statistically significant analyses are in the expected direction. The self-ideal discrepancy clearly varies directly with illness rates associated with the three mobility types. It is interesting that self-esteem is relatively low both among the downwardly mobile at the lowest educational status level, and among the upwardly mobile at status level 4. At level 3 the stable group is characterized by the lowest self-esteem. These observations reemphasize the fact that pathogenic effects of a structurally defined variable are not universally uniform, and that such a variable can be fully understood only within its social-psychological context.

STATUS INCONSISTENCY AND MENTAL DISORDER

Closely related to the phenomenon of social mobility is that of status inconsistency. An individual may experience greater social mobility in one status dimension than in another. As a result, he may be in a relatively high position on one hierarchy (e.g., education), and in a low position on another (e.g., income). It has been suggested in the literature that such status inconsistencies are psychologically disturbing, since the social roles associated with one status position may conflict with those of another, and since conformity to one whole pattern may interfere with the individual's conformity to another set of roles (Hughes, 1945; Lenski, 1954). Such types of interpersonal disturbances may be psychopathogenic; therefore, in the present study we determined whether there were differences between the community and ill populations in status inconsistency. We hypothesized that the mentally ill would be characterized by greater inconsistencies between their status rank attributes than the community population.

Each of the three attributes of status employed in this study (occupation, income, and education) was ranked on a seven-step scale. The inconsistencies (i.e., the differences) between rank positions on each status dimension were totaled for each subject, disregarding sign.

$$(Occupation\text{-}Income) + (Occupation\text{-}Education) + (Income\text{-}Education)$$

If, for example, a respondent was at occupational status level 2, income level 5, and educational status level 4, his total status inconsistency score would be $(2\text{-}5) + (2\text{-}4) + (5\text{-}4)$, or 6. Individuals' total scores were averaged to obtain group means. Although the mentally ill do have higher mean inconsistency scores than community individuals, the differences are not statistically significant. Separate analyses by sex and age also indicate greater status inconsistency among the patients, but again the differences are not significant.

This method of determining status inconsistency tells us nothing about an individual's actual status profile. It merely represents a mathematical derivation from this profile. The consequences of status inconsistency to the individual may vary, however, depending on his high or low rank in particular status dimensions. Low educational achievement coupled with a high income or occupational achievement level may not be as stress-provoking in our society as the reverse situation—high educational level and low income or occupational achievement. Although it is possible that the uneducated person with a relatively

high occupational rank experiences some consequent interpersonal difficulty, this particular status discrepancy offers some compensations. The
self-made man, with little education but with the ambition and personal
qualities necessary to succeed, is an object of considerable approval in
American society. To most Americans, education represents merely the
means to success, while occupation and income constitute actual criteria
of success. Thus, the individual with a high educational level who
occupies a menial, unskilled job may be under considerable stress. A
person characterized by this pattern of status inconsistency is likely to be
considered a failure by himself and by his peers. Since education is
probably closely linked to level of aspiration, the highly educated individual with relatively low occupational and/or income attainments will
probably be characterized by a larger aspiration-achievement discrepancy
than the individual with little education but with comparatively high
occupational and/or income achievement levels. Previous research indicates that this former type of discrepancy is, in fact, associated with
mental illness (Kleiner, 1959; Parker, Kleiner, and Taylor, 1960; Tuckman and Kleiner, 1962).

A comparison of Tables 10.1 and 10.3 suggests that the consideration
of a *particular* status inconsistency profile is quite relevant to an understanding of mental disorder in the present study. Although only 25 per
cent of the community respondents and 17 per cent of the patients are
occupationally upwardly mobile, the corresponding percentages for
educationally mobile individuals are 59 and 56 per cent. Although we
did expect to find more educational than occupational mobility, the
discrepancy between these two status dimensions is extremely large. It is
well known that discriminatory practices often force the Negro to accept
a lower status occupation than the white person of comparable educational achievement. It seems reasonable that the highly educated Negro,
who is characterized by high levels of aspiration but who has not attained
correspondingly high occupational and/or income levels, experiences
frustration and is possibly prone to psychopathology. This situation is
akin to the idea of status inconsistency, except that here we are specifying the nature of the inconsistency profile.

Our hypothesis that a particular inconsistency profile is associated
with illness stems from the assumption that the opportunity structure is
more open to the American Negro in the area of education than in the
areas of occupation and income. In order to explore this issue, the community and ill samples were combined, and the educational mobility of
each respondent was correlated with his occupational and income achieve-

ment levels. The correlations for educational mobility with occupational and with income status are .11 and .03, respectively. These very low correlations indicate that a Negro who has advanced educationally in relation to his parents has not necessarily attained correspondingly higher occupational or income levels. We must now consider the psychic consequences of this uneven opportunity structure to the American Negro.

Hollingshead and Redlich (1958: 394) found a correlation of .72 between the educational and occupational levels of a sample of predominantly white families in New Haven. Kahl and Davis (1955) reported correlations of .77, .70, and .65 between education and each of three occupational status scales in a white sample. These four correlations for predominantly white populations are fairly similar. The corresponding figure in our combined community and mentally ill Negro sample is .44, reaffirming the much lower correlation often noted between education and occupation among Negroes. In a comparison of the relationship between education and occupation among whites and nonwhites in the 1950 census figures, Glick and Miller (1956) concluded:

Among nonwhite men in the same age group [45–54], on the other hand, the proportion employed as service workers or laborers decreases very little for successively higher education groups. Even a college education has not been a sufficient qualification to elevate a majority of the nonwhite men above the occupational level of service workers or laborers.

If our speculation about the pathogenic potential of this profile of status inconsistency is valid, the mentally ill should show a lower correlation, or higher discrepancy, than the general population between educational and occupational achievement. Since the majority of community sample individuals were in the low symptom group, and most of the patients were psychotic, correlations for the community and ill populations were corrected for the disproportionately low number of high symptom subjects in the community and neurotics in the ill sample. The corrected correlations are .44 and .40, respectively. Our hypothesis is apparently supported.

These correlations between educational and occupational status levels do not directly disclose *which* of these variables is relatively high or low. We may safely infer from previous findings on the amount of mobility on these two status dimensions that achieved educational level exceeds occupational level in the vast majority of cases.

In a subsequent analysis we attempted to test this inference more directly. It was hypothesized that at each educational status level above level 1 (since no status inconsistency could be involved at the lowest educational level), more patients than community subjects would be found at the lowest occupational status position. Only young males (twenty to thirty-nine years of age) were considered for this analysis, since we felt that these subjects were the most likely to manifest this type of status discrepancy and to be most affected by its psychological consequences. In order to avoid a distortion of data on occupational level among the patients (because of possible downward mobility just prior to becoming a patient), we considered in this context the occupation held by the respondent for "most of his life" (Appendix B, Question 30).

At every educational status level from 2 to 5 more mentally ill than community respondents hold unskilled jobs at the lowest occupational status level. The percentages of ill and community respondents at the various status positions are: level 2, 64 and 60 per cent, respectively; level 3, 65 and 52 per cent, respectively; level 4, 54 and 23 per cent, respectively; and level 5, 21, and 6 per cent, respectively. These findings provide additional support for associating this particular profile of status inconsistency with psychopathology.

The same pattern seems to emerge when other status variables are considered. For example, Kahl and Davis (1955) found a correlation of .36 between education and income in a white population, compared to a correlation of .20 between these variables for our combined ill and community Negro samples. When corrections are made for the disproportionately fewer high symptom subjects in the community sample and neurotic individuals in the ill sample, correlations of .25 and .15, respectively, are obtained for the education-income discrepancy in these samples. These corrected correlations support the assumption of a larger discrepancy between education and income among the patients.

We have noted very low correlations between educational *mobility* and both occupational and income status (.11 and .03, respectively) but have reported correlations of .44 and .20, respectively, between educational *status* and both occupational and income status. The higher correlations obtained with educational status than with educational mobility can apparently be attributed to the educationally stable segment of our Negro population. In addition, the educationally mobile seem particularly likely to experience the stress resulting from the inconsistency between education and occupation, or between education and income. This fact may be partly responsible for the higher levels of mental disorder among Negroes native to Philadelphia than among migrants from the South. Although we have not yet investigated this point, the native born have probably experienced more educational mobility than the Southern migrants. The findings already analyzed suggest that this is an important variable to consider in studying the psychological effects of the migration experience.

We cannot determine to what extent the high illness rates among educationally mobile Negroes can be attributed to mobility itself, or to the status inconsistency to which these individuals are particularly prone. This poses an important social and theoretical problem. Investigation of this problem involves determining illness rates for groups with different degrees of status inconsistency, while controlling for direction of social mobility and for status position. Clinical case studies should also throw some light on this problem.

Summary and Discussion

ANALYSES PRESENTED in this chapter have indicated that (particularly downward) occupational mobility is associated with higher rates of illness than occupational stability, although the upwardly mobile do have a somewhat lower rate than the stable subjects. In the area of education also, the highest illness rates are manifested by the downwardly mobile.

An examination of results at the separate status levels indicates that for occupation *and* education the downwardly mobile show relatively high rates at the lower end of the status continuum and the upwardly mobile manifest high rates at the higher status positions. The high rates among the upwardly mobile at the upper-status levels are consistent with some studies (e.g., Ruesch, 1946; Ruesch, Jacobson and Loeb, 1948; Hollings-head, Ellis, and Kirby, 1954), but inconsistent with others (e.g., Srole et al., 1962; Langner and Michael, 1963). The distributions of stable individuals in the community and ill populations barely reach significance for occupation and are not significant for education. This suggests that the varying rates of mental disorder associated with status position can be explained mainly by social mobility.

This conclusion can also be utilized to account for some contradictory results in the research literature. In a previous publication (Kleiner and Parker, 1963) the present authors noted that high rates of mental disorder seemed to be associated with low status in large cities, but that this relationship did not hold for smaller communities. It is possible that individuals occupying the lowest status position in large urban areas have experienced considerably more downward mobility than individuals of comparable status in less highly urbanized areas. In these smaller communities there is probably less social mobility in either direction.

The social-psychological variables of goal-striving stress and self-esteem (as measured by the self-ideal discrepancy) are systematically related to differences in rates of illness associated with different types of occupational mobility. Only the blue/white-collar measure of reference group orientation is related in this manner to educational mobility. Since these findings pertain to a community population, they suggest that social mobility, goal-striving stress, and low self-esteem are antecedent conditions of mental disorder. Undoubtedly, however, continuous interaction between such behavior variables exists, and it is not usually feasible to maintain a sharp distinction between antecedent and consequent conditions of illness.

The findings on the relationship between social mobility and our social-psychological study variables allow us to explain in part the patterns of high illness rates observed at both extremes of the occupational status continuum (Chapter 9). The downwardly mobile, who are concentrated at the lowest occupational level, manifest relatively high goal-striving stress scores, coupled with low self-esteem. The highest occupational level contains a concentration of upwardly mobile respondents who are also characterized by a pattern of relatively high goal-striving stress scores and low self-esteem. Reference group discrepancies are not systematically related to mobility. The tendency for the downwardly mobile to show higher goal-striving stress than their status peers is explained as a failure to reduce high levels of aspiration associated with past status affiliations. The persistence of such high levels may be maladjustive.

Individuals at the highest level, who have risen in the occupational status hierarchy despite the considerable barriers facing the Negro, are probably characterized by chronic achievement striving and dissatisfaction with self—an inability to reduce their striving even after they have achieved considerable success. This continued achievement striving suggests the anomic effects of the differentially restricted opportunity structure the Negro faces in American society. A high level of goal striving in the context of a relatively restricted opportunity structure apparently takes its psychological toll. This idea is supported by the fact that a status inconsistency profile of relatively high educational achievement, and low occupational and/or income achievement is more characteristic of ill than community respondents.

These findings on mobility may also explain why Langner and Michael (1963) could not isolate the stress factors that could explain their reported inverse relationship between psychopathology and social status. The present discussion underlines the importance of understanding how social-psychological variables intervene in the relationship between sociological factors and mental disorder.

Our data also show that both upwardly and downwardly mobile patients have experienced a significantly greater degree, or amount, of mobility than community subjects (in agreement with Janowitz and Curtis, 1953). Among the community subjects degree of mobility shows somewhat different relationships with yield of mental disorder depending on whether occupational or educational mobility is considered. Degree of occupational mobility in the community is related to the rate or yield of mental disorder for the upwardly mobile, but not for the downwardly mobile. For the Negro in particular, upward occupational mobility is accompanied by considerable achievement strivings. The parental occupational levels of most of our respondents were already so low that it would have been difficult for these respondents to manifest any downward occupational mobility.

The yield of mental disorder is directly related to educational downward mobility, but is not consistently related to upward mobility. This probably reflects the fact that higher educational achievement than the parental level is almost automatic and therefore obscures any possible relationship between upward mobility and yield of disorder. The extent to which the individual's educational achievement falls short of his parental level is the more realistic indicator of psychopathology.

We cannot explain why our major measure of reference group discrepancy fails to distinguish between the various types of mobility at the different status levels in the community population. Either the use of "close friends" as a reference group does not provide a sensitive enough measure to permit accurate predictions, or else reference group orientation as measured by this discrepancy is a concomitant and not an antecedent condition of illness.

Chapter 9 concluded with speculations about the goal-striving behavior of individuals at the lower socioeconomic levels, and the relationship of such behavior to mental disorder. Although low-status respondents showed comparatively low goal-striving stress scores, their reference group discrepancies and self-ideal discrepancies tended to be larger than those of high-status respondents. The inconsistent pattern of these variables suggested that low-status individuals were not reconciled to their low striving and were manifesting an ambivalent and unstable adjustment. We further speculated that this situation might lead to emotional disturbance and mental disorder.

The present findings on mobility necessitate some revision of these speculations. Although the above paragraph may describe a large proportion of lower status Negroes, it is not characteristic of that segment of the low-status group responsible for the high rates of psychopathology. As already noted, it is the downwardly mobile at the low end of the scale who have a particularly high illness rate and considerably higher goal-striving stress and lower self-esteem than their peers. Hyman (1953a) has suggested that many low-status persons have given up striving for higher occupational and income levels. Our data indicate that these individuals may not be psychologically reconciled to this situation. The fact that low-status stable subjects with low goal-striving stress scores are not characterized by a particularly high illness rate, supports Hyman's speculation that the reduction of active striving in this segment of the low-status group is adjustive. The downwardly mobile, who do not make this adjustment and who maintain high levels of striving, manifest high psychiatric symptom scores and high rates of mental illness. While the reasons for this rigid maintenance of high striving levels may lie partly in the individual's personal history (which is beyond the scope of this investigation), we must remember that American society emphasizes the belief in an open opportunity structure and the value of striving for high achievement levels. In the context of this study, the ill are more prone than the community respondents to perceive an open opportunity structure. Given the social realities of Negro life, this belief may be maladaptive.

High illness rates at the upper status levels are also consistent with the above rationale. At occupation level 4, the upwardly mobile have a higher illness rate and considerably higher mean stress scores than the nonmobile subjects. Upward mobility into the higher status levels particularly among Negroes, who are socially disadvantaged, probably requires considerable drive and striving. The apparent inability of many high-status individuals to reduce their striving even after reaching these higher positions supports the idea of a link between rigidly held aspirational levels and mental disorder.

Our findings underline the importance of using samples large enough to institute control groups in data analysis. Gross correlations can lead to erroneous conclusions. In this study, only by analyzing mobility groups at each status level did the relationships among our variables become clear.

Community vs Ill Sample: Controlling
for Occupational Mobility and
Occupational Status

IN EARLIER CHAPTERS we controlled for sex, age, migratory status, and social status position, while comparing the ill and community samples with respect to our social-psychological study variables. Each of these control factors is basically a classification system with no necessary implication of social movement or goal striving. When we compare the two study populations controlling for direction of social mobility, we gain some insight into the interaction effect of our study variables with mental illness. When in addition, we control for the four occupational status positions, we are provided with three status levels at which comparisons of the upwardly mobile ill and community respondents are possible, and three levels at which the downwardly mobile in these two populations can be compared. Consequently, we have six tests of the hypothesized difference between the ill and community samples for each of four social-psychological variables (perception of the opportunity structure, goal-striving stress, reference group discrepancy, and self-ideal discrepancy).

We have assumed that the mentally ill will see a more open opportunity structure than the community subjects. In all six comparisons using mobility and status controls, the differences are in the expected direction (by sign test, $P = <.02$).

In line with our theoretical point of view, we predict higher goal-striving stress scores for the mentally ill sample. The stress score based on the self-anchored striving scale is higher in every instance for the ill respondents (by sign test, $P = <.02$). Most of the comparisons for the occupation and income stress scores show higher mean scores for the ill than the community sample, but the consistency of direction is not significant.

We also expect the ill sample to manifest a larger mean reference group discrepancy than the community sample. In five of the six comparisons the differences are in the expected direction (by sign test, $P = <.03$). One comparison yields equal reference group discrepancies for the two samples. Consistent with expectations, the ill show larger self-ideal discrepancies in all six comparisons (by sign test, $P = <.02$).

The consistency of the data clearly supports all our expectations with respect to differences between the ill and community populations on these social-psychological variables. The stable ill subjects show these same differences when compared to the stable community subjects. These findings have implications over and above their relevance to our theoretical orientation. The upwardly mobile ill individual not only shows greater occupational movement than his community sample counterpart, but also manifests higher goal-striving stress, sees himself as further from his reference group, and is characterized by lower self-esteem. Apparently his greater upward mobility is associated with greater striving and lower self-esteem than his less upwardly mobile community counterpart. He presents a picture of perpetual driving dynamism that cannot be easily, if at all, satisfied in the context of a relatively closed opportunity structure. Despite his upward mobility, he is continually driven by striving that cannot be tempered. His inability to reduce this striving is associated with low self-esteem, self-blame for not having moved further upward, and an incapacity to consider that the social system might be limiting his movement.

The downwardly mobile ill respondent has moved significantly further down the status hierarchy than the downwardly mobile community subject. Like the upwardly mobile ill person, he also manifests higher goal-striving stress, a larger reference group discrepancy, and lower self-esteem than his downwardly mobile community counterpart. This pattern indicates that the downwardly mobile patient is aware of his greater loss of status, but he increases rather than decreases his goal-striving stress (as does the upwardly mobile patient) and continues to believe in an open opportunity structure. Again we see a picture of a driving dynamism that persists even with further downward movement in the status hierarchy.

11

THE STUDY VARIABLES: THEIR INTERDEPENDENCE AND INTERRELATIONSHIPS

Chapters 3 through 7 were concerned primarily with relating each of our social-psychological study variables (perception of the opportunity structure, goal-striving stress and its components, reference group behavior, and self-esteem) in turn to mental disorder. A secondary concern in these chapters, but a primary objective in Chapters 8 through 10, was the determination of the extent to which each of these variables might be used as an intervening variable to explain variations in yield of mental disorder among different community subgroups (age groups, socioeconomic status groups, mobility groups, etc.).

Establishing these social-psychological variables as intervening variables necessitates that they be related to sociological factors on one hand (independent variables) and to mental illness on the other (dependent variable). Data presented in Chapters 3 through 7 determined the linkage of these social-psychological study variables to mental illness, and Chapters 8 through 10 evaluated the relationship between these study variables and the sociological factors. A number of questions still remain to be investigated and discussed before an evaluation of the theoretical framework of the total study is possible.

Implicit in the discussion in earlier chapters was the assumption that each of the study variables could be treated independently of the others. No such implication was intended—these variables were treated as if they were independent of one another only for ease of data presentation. The theoretical point of view summarized in Chapter 1 did include two hypotheses concerning the relationship between self-esteem, and both goal-striving stress and reference group discrepancy (Hypotheses 4 and 5). The present chapter will explore these relationships more directly.

Data presented on the yield issue indicate that the study variables may be used as intervening variables between mental illness and some sociological factors, but not with others. There are two possible explanations of our partial success in using the study variables as intervening variables. (1) The study variables may not really be related to the sociological factors and to mental illness at all. (2) The study variables may relate to mental illness, as the data suggest, but the sociological factors may not. For example, although illness rates vary by socioeconomic status, these variations may not be a function of status per se, but of other variables associated with status (e.g., migratory status, social mobility). If this is the case, the lack of significant relationships between status and our study variables is not surprising.

Since previous analyses involved statistics based primarily on group characteristics, the present chapter will explore these inconsistencies in greater detail by means of correlation techniques which relate the variables to one another *within the individual himself*. Hopefully, such analyses will clarify the reasons for these inconsistencies.

Even if we discover why the social-psychological variables cannot always be applied successfully as intervening variables, we must determine how the sociological factors which are related to the study variables relate to one another. This question will also be discussed in the present chapter.

Summary of Prior Analyses

WE HAVE SHOWN that our mentally ill and community populations differ with respect to perception of the opportunity structure, goal-striving stress and its components, reference group behavior, and self-esteem. Findings presented in earlier chapters confirmed Hypotheses 1, 2, and 3 and their corollaries. Although these prior analyses indicated differences between these two populations on the social-psychological study variables, they did not tell us whether these differences were antecedent or consequent conditions of illness.

As a first means of resolving this problem, subgroups within the community population differing in rates or yield of mental disorder were compared with respect to the study variables. We reasoned that if individuals in high and low yield community subgroups, who were not themselves mentally ill, differed from each other in the same ways as the ill differed from the community sample, the observed differences could not be regarded as consequences of illness. (We should note that once the illness process begins, there is undoubtedly a continuing interaction among all factors, including illness itself.)

Community subgroups defined in terms of sex, age, migratory status, socioeconomic status, and mobility type were analyzed in this effort. The goal-striving stress scores discriminated as expected between high and low yield age, migratory status, and occupational mobility groups. The self-ideal discrepancy, our major measure of self-esteem, discriminated between age and occupational mobility groups but did not discriminate between migratory status groups. Blue/white-collar occupational preferences (considered as a measure of reference group behavior) differentiated between age, migratory status, and educational mobility groups. The reference group discrepancy (between position of self and "close friends" on the striving scale) did not reveal any systematic differences between high and low yield community subgroups. None of the social-psychological study variables could consistently account for variations in illness rates among sex or socioeconomic status groups (defined in terms of occupation, income, or education). Later in this chapter we shall discuss the reasons for these inconsistencies.

Interaction of Study Variables

THE CORRELATIONS to be reported in the discussion of the interrelationship of our social-psychological variables were derived from the procedures used in computing the multiple correlation coefficients (described in Chapter 3). This computer program considered only cases for which information was available on all of the thirty-four variables used in the multiple correlation analysis, a prerequisite which reduced the size of the study population from 2912 to 1995 cases. We should remind the reader that correlation coefficients were computed using both the linear and the nonlinear assumptions.[1] The differences between the two kinds of assumptions were also described in Chapter 3. We reemphasize that these correlations reflect the extent of interdependence of particular variables within the individual.

SELF-ESTEEM AND GOAL-STRIVING STRESS

Hypothesis 4 states: *The degree of deviation from the optimum level of goal-striving stress (in either direction) will be inversely related to level of self-esteem.* We expect the self-ideal discrepancy to increase as goal-striving stress deviates from an optimum level (especially as it exceeds the optimum level). This hypothesis is based on the premise that the individual's inability to reduce or raise his level of stress to the optimum level will be psychologically threatening and will contribute to a loss of self-esteem.

The nature of the predicted relationship leads us to expect a significant correlation when the nonlinear assumption is made. Whether the linear or nonlinear assumption is made, however, no significant correlations between the self-ideal discrepancy and either the occupation or the income stress scores are obtained. These nonsignificant coefficients suggest that the factors directly related to self-ideal discrepancy scores are not related to goal-striving stress in either of these specific content areas.

When the self-ideal discrepancy measure is correlated with the striving scale stress score and a nonlinear relationship is assumed, a significant coefficient is obtained (.10, $P = < .01$). There are two possible interpretations of this finding: either the self-ideal discrepancy scores increase as striving scale stress deviates from the optimum level, as predicted, or else stress scores have to increase to certain magnitudes before changes in self-esteem are noted. The low absolute correlation between the two variables also provides evidence for relatively low interdependence between them. In addition, since the striving scale stress score discriminated more consistently than the self-ideal discrepancy between community subgroups differing in yield of mental illness, this stress score may therefore be considered a likely antecedent to changing self-esteem as well as to mental illness.

Why do the occupation and income stress scores fail to correlate with the self-esteem measure, in contrast to the striving scale stress score? The

1. Computing correlations based both on the linear and nonlinear assumptions allows us to determine which assumption best fits the data. If correlations based on the two assumptions are significant, the conclusion rests on a more secure foundation.

reader should remember that the specific content areas in which stress was measured were selected by the investigators, who assumed that these areas were important and salient to the respondents. The nonsignificant correlations indicate that this assumption may not have been enirely correct. In the striving scale area, the respondent himself determined what goal-striving areas he would use to estimate his position on the ten-step scale. Logically, he would evaluate himself in terms of those striving areas most important to him. This assumption may account for the significant correlation between self-esteem and the striving scale stress score: the striving areas on which the respondent based these responses were meaningful to him and therefore strongly influenced his self-esteem.

SELF-ESTEEM AND REFERENCE GROUP DISCREPANCY

Hypothesis 5 states: *The degree of negative discrepancy from reference group will be inversely related to self-esteem.* We therefore expect the self-ideal discrepancy to increase as negative reference group discrepancy increases. Previous chapters have treated these two variables as if they functioned independent of each other. We have established a significant relationship between each of these study variables and mental illness. It only remains to establish a relationship between the self-esteem measure and reference group discrepancy. A significant correlation between these variables is obtained whether the linear or nonlinear assumption is made (.12 and .14, respectively, $P = <.01$ for both). Hypothesis 5 is clearly confirmed; negative reference group discrepancy and the self-ideal discrepancy increase together.

Although there is a significant interdependence between the two factors, we cannot be sure which variable is antecedent to the other. The fact that the self-esteem measure discriminated between some high and low yield community groups, and the reference group discrepancy did not, suggests that self-esteem is the antecedent variable.

Also, although they appear to be conceptually independent, we must ask whether the reference group and self-ideal discrepancies are really measuring the same phenomenon, rather than two different but positively related phenomena. Since the correlations between these variables are relatively low (but significant), and since previous evidence showed that one of these variables might be considered an antecedent of illness and the other variable not, it seems unlikely that these discrepancies are measuring the same thing.

These intercorrelations indicate that one's perception of his achievement relative to that of his reference group(s) is a significant factor for self-esteem. This particular point is related to Festinger's "social comparison theory" (1954) and to reference group theory (Hyman, 1942; Merton, 1957: 225–386). These theoretical approaches maintain that individuals need to evaluate their abilities and achievements. Since no objective criteria for such evaluation exist, self-evaluation must depend on how the individual compares himself to others he uses as a point of reference. Both theories emphasize in particular the importance of such informal reference groups as "close friends."

SELF-ESTEEM AND DISCREPANCY BETWEEN LEVEL OF ASPIRATION AND ACHIEVEMENT

We made no formal prediction about a relationship between the self-ideal discrepancy and aspiration-achievement discrepancies in various substantive content areas, but we did entertain the notion that these discrepancies would increase together (i.e., a decrease in self-esteem as the perceived distance to one's goal increases). This view was based on studies which have discussed the level of aspiration and self-esteem as interdependent factors (Escalona, 1940; Lewin, 1944; Escalona, 1948; Atkinson, 1957; Mahone, 1960).

The self-ideal discrepancy was correlated with the aspiration-achievement discrepancy in the areas of occupation, income, and the striving scale. Regardless of whether the linear or nonlinear assumption is made, self-esteem does not correlate significantly with the occupation or the income aspiration-achievement discrepancy. At least in these two content areas there is little justification for assuming an interrelationship between the aspiration-achievement discrepancy and self-esteem. These low correlations also suggest that these specific goal-striving areas are not the most salient determinants of self-evaluation. Perhaps significant relationships between self-esteem and discrepancy scores would emerge if we were sufficiently sophisticated in defining specific psychologically meaningful content areas.

It is also possible to view self-esteem as a composite of several subidentities, each corresponding to a different goal-striving content area. Degree of self-esteem, then, becomes a function of the degree of esteem inherent in each subidentity, and of the relative salience or weight of each subidentity in one's total self-esteem. Subidentities associated with low self-esteem in specific areas may not be individually related to mental illness. Such a relationship may emerge only when there is a cumulative effect of several low self-esteem subidentities. This point of view is similar to that proposed by French (1962) and Miller (1963).

The occupation and income aspiration-achievement discrepancies did differentiate between high and low yield community subgroups, suggesting that these discrepancies are antecedents of illness. However, their psychological implications may be determined largely by their salience to the individual, their cumulative effects, the relative influence of reference groups, historical factors, and even the nature of the interview situation itself.

Correlating the self-esteem measure and the striving scale aspiration-achievement discrepancy presents a somewhat different pattern. Regardless of whether the linear or the nonlinear assumption is made, the correlation between the self-ideal and the striving scale discrepancy is significant (.20 in each case, $P = < .001$). As the striving scale discrepancy increases, the self-ideal discrepancy also increases (i.e., self-esteem decreases).

Again we must ask whether these variables are measuring aspects of the same thing, or different but interdependent factors. The striving scale discrepancy discriminates more efficiently than the self-esteem measure between high and low yield community subgroups and the relatively low (but significant) correlation between the two variables also indicates that they are not measuring the same thing. Based on the differential ability of these variables to discriminate between high and low yield community subgroups, we suggest that the striving scale discrepancy is antecedent to the self-ideal discrepancy as well as to mental illness.

We reiterate our consideration of all three aspiration-achievement discrepancies as antecedents of illness. Since the individual *himself* determines what criteria are used in making aspiration and achievement judgments on the striving scale, however, we expect this discrepancy to show the most significant correlations with the other study variables (which, in fact, it does).

One final point about the striving scale discrepancy should be made. This discrepancy is larger in high than in low yield community subgroups, and on the basis of the yield issue, we predict that it will increase progressively as we move along the mental health continuum from the low symptom group to the psychotics, unlike the occupation and income discrepancies which decrease. But why should respondents with a large aspiration-achievement discrepancy on the striving scale and comparatively few symptoms increase this discrepancy even further as illness becomes more severe, thus provoking additional feelings of failure and adding to the burden of illness?

This situation resembles Mowrer's description of the "neurotic paradox" (1945; 1950: 418–530). Mowrer attempted to explain in learning theory terms why the individual continued to respond to anxiety-provoking stimuli in ways that not only maintained, but intensified the anxiety. He conceived of the individual as conflicted (Mowrer and Ullman, 1945): a person gave responses that elicited pain or anxiety if he anticipated future reward that would be more satisfying than immediate pain avoidance. Later, Mowrer reinterpreted the problem (1950: 418–530). He said that the fear which was reduced by these pain- or anxiety-producing responses was more gratifying than satisfaction obtained through pain avoidance. He attributed this behavior to deficiencies in learning—the individual never learned whether his fears were real and therefore continued in his pain-producing behavior. If the raising of the goal on the striving scale was intended to boost or maintain the threatened self-esteem as a defensive mechanism, the self-esteem of the psychotics should be more comparable to the healthier groupings than is the case. In addition, self-esteem should correlate inversely with the aspiration-achievement discrepancy scores (i.e., as a given discrepancy gets larger, the self-ideal discrepancy should also increase, thus raising or maintaining self-esteem), but an opposite trend is noted. This question is particularly difficult to resolve, if we assume that the striving scale discrepancy involves goal-striving areas of central importance to the individual.

The progressive lowering of occupational and income aspirations with increasing severity of illness seems to be a logical effect of failure in these specific areas, and of loss of self-esteem. Earlier we suggested that this tendency to lower occupational and income goals might be a function of (1) the individual's concessions to his failure, reflecting a loss of self-esteem which increases with severity of illness; or (2) the individual's desire to lower his goals and thereby maximize the possibilities of success, in an effort to sustain his falling self-esteem. The nonsignificant correlations between self-esteem and the discrepancies in these specific content areas indicate that this latter alternative is untenable. The data tend to support the former possibility—that patients admit failure as a limited manifestation of low self-esteem. This is not to say that the patients come to terms with their failures and accept them psychologically. The fact that the psychotics are characterized by the highest goal-striving stress scores and the highest reference group discrepancies indicates that they do not accept lowering of goals in these specific areas.

It is also possible that such "material" areas of goal striving as occupation and income diminish in importance as severity of illness increases.

Nonmaterial values may increase in importance, and this changing emphasis is reflected in the striving scale discrepancy. Data on "best" and "worst" way of life do in fact indicate a greater emphasis on moral goals among the patients than among the community subjects. This shifting emphasis may also be a defensive maneuver to avoid the reality of failure in "material" areas of striving and to boost or maintain threatened self-esteem levels. The progressive lowering of self-esteem with increasing severity of illness argues against this "defensive" interpretation, however.

REFERENCE GROUP DISCREPANCY AND DISCREPANCY BETWEEN
LEVEL OF ASPIRATION AND ACHIEVEMENT

In Chapter 1 we considered whether the concept of the aspiration-achievement discrepancy was really the same as the discrepancy between one's own achievement and that of his reference group. We felt that level of aspiration had many more determinants than how one evaluated his achievements relative to a current reference group (e.g., "close friends"). If the two types of discrepancy do, in fact, overlap to a great degree, we should find near-perfect interdependence between these variables—that is, correlations close to 1.00.

The correlations between the reference group discrepancy and the occupation, income, and striving scale discrepancies yield a somewhat complicated pattern. When the linear assumption is made, no significant correlations between reference group discrepancy and either the occupation or income discrepancy are obtained. Significant correlations are obtained in these content areas when the nonlinear assumption is made ($-.08$ in both areas, $P = < .01$). We conclude that as the discrepancy scores in these content areas increase, the reference group discrepancy decreases, but at an uneven rate. In more general terms, as the aspiration-achievement discrepancy decreases, there is relatively little effect on the reference group discrepancy. As one's aspiration-achievement discrepancy continues to decrease, however, the discrepancy between his own and his reference group's achievement begins to increase. We have already reported a decrease in the occupation and income discrepancies and a concomitant increase in reference group discrepancy along the mental health continuum from the low symptom group to the psychotics. This pattern clearly suggests a growing concern over how one compares with his reference group as severity of illness increases.

The striving scale discrepancy relates to the reference group discrepancy in a different manner than the occupation and income discrepancies. A significant correlation is obtained between striving scale discrepancy and reference group discrepancy, regardless of whether the linear or nonlinear assumption is made. We shall base our discussion only on the correlation which assumes a linear distribution of scores for these two variables (.57, $P = < .001$). As the discrepancy between aspiration and achievement on the striving scale increases, the reference group discrepancy also increases.

Since the striving scale discrepancy differentiates between high and low yield community subgroups and the reference group discrepancy does not, we suggest that the striving scale discrepancy occurs prior (antecedent) to the reference group discrepancy (consequent). The fact that these variables showed different degrees of discrimination in the yield analysis also indicates that they are not merely measuring aspects of the same thing. The high correlation between the two factors clearly demonstrates their interdependence, however.

The correlation between self-esteem and the striving scale discrepancy is only .20, in contrast to the correlation of .57 between the reference group discrepancy and the striving scale discrepancy. A person's aspiration-achievement discrepancy is apparently more dependent on how he perceives his achievements relative to his reference group than on his self-esteem, which is probably influenced by historical and idiosyncratic experiences as well as by current factors.

REFERENCE GROUP DISCREPANCY AND GOAL-STRIVING STRESS

Our formal hypotheses did not include predictions about the relationship between goal-striving stress and the reference group discrepancy. We assumed that each of these variables was probably related to self-esteem, which, in turn, was related to mental illness. Nevertheless, we should see whether goal-striving stress and reference group discrepancy do intercorrelate.

In Chapter 1, and in discussions of the aspiration-achievement discrepancies in various content areas, we noted that one's reference group(s) correlated with selection of his goals, with his estimates of the probability of success or failure attached to these goals, and with the degree of importance various goals had for him. All of these components of the goal-striving stress score should therefore correlate significantly with the reference group discrepancy, assuming one's close friends are important sources of influence on these issues. This trend should be particularly evident with the striving scale stress score—the type of relationship expected between these two variables is logically derivable. Since this stress score showed a significant nonlinear correlation with

self-esteem, and since the reference group discrepancy showed a significant linear correlation with self-esteem, we expect a nonlinear correlation between this stress score and the reference group discrepancy.

In the areas of occupation and income, regardless of whether the
linear or nonlinear assumption is made, reference group discrepancy
fails to correlate significantly with the stress scores. The reference group
discrepancy did correlate with the aspiration-achievement discrepancies
in each of these content areas; including the probability and valence elements of the stress scores negate these correlations. Apparently, then,
"close friends" influence one's goals in these areas, but do not necessarily
affect the probability and valence values attached to these goals.

When a nonlinear relationship is assumed, the striving scale stress
score correlates significantly with the reference group discrepancy ($.33$,
$P = < .001$). There are two possible interpretations of this finding:
(1) as the stress score continues to deviate from an optimum stress level
in either direction, the reference group discrepancy increases; or (2) the
stress score must manifest a certain amount of change before the reference group discrepancy begins to change.

The relationship between these two variables, as stated, implies that
the stress score changes are antecedent to changes in the reference group
discrepancy. The justification for this assumption rests on the ability of
this stress score to discriminate between high and low yield community
subgroups, thereby establishing it as a possible antecedent to illness. The
reference group diescrepancy has no discriminatory power with respect to
the yield issue, suggesting that this variable is a concomitant or consequence of illness.

The correlation between the reference group discrepancy and the
striving scale stress score is significantly larger than the correlation between our self-esteem measure and this same stress score ($.33$ and $.10$,
respectively, $P = < .001$).

Although the reference group discrepancy correlates with the stress
score and aspiration-achievement discrepancy based on the striving scale
and with self-esteem, it does not discriminate between high and low yield
community subgroups. The striving scale stress score and aspiration-
achievement discrepancy and the self-esteem measure *are* able to differentiate between high and low yield subgroups. One explanation for this
inconsistency suggests that if the higher stress, and/or larger discrepancies, and/or lower self-esteem characteristic of a high yield subgroup
persist over time and are subject to continuous evaluation, such high
yield individuals begin to manifest symptoms and to perceive their

achievements as lower than those of their "close friends." A process of interaction is then initiated in which the symptoms lead to larger reference group discrepancies, which in turn lead to increased symptoms, etc.

It is also possible that high and low yield respondents are characterized by reference group discrepancies of equal magnitude, but that this discrepancy has different implications for each group. For example, high yield subjects may be less satisfied than low yield subjects with the achievements of their "close friends," or less attracted to their "close friends." Support for these two possibilities is inferred from our second and less direct measure of reference group orientation, blue/white-collar occupation preference.

Each of the three blue/white-collar choices discriminated between high and low yield community subpopulations. If we treat this measure only as an alternate index of reference group discrepancy, we must account for the different results obtained with the two measures. However, taking each blue/white-collar choice situation as a measure of aspired status seems to support our suggestion that high yield individuals are less attracted to their "close friends" or to their achievements than are low yield respondents. Since the overwhelming majority of our respondents occupy blue-collar occupations, the high yield subject who aspires to white-collar occupations which are higher than those of his "close friends" is indicating that their status achievements have limited appeal for him. The low yield respondent who aspires to blue-collar occupations is expressing greater satisfaction with, or attraction to, the status achievements of his "close friends." Although we have no direct measure of the strength of attraction to achievement of "close friends," our assumptions about a choice of a blue- or white-collar occupational alternative, if valid, account for the differences between this measure and the reference group discrepancy measure in predicting yield.

CUMULATIVE EFFECTS OF MAJOR SOCIAL-PSYCHOLOGICAL VARIABLES

Earlier chapters have shown that each of the three stress scores, reference group discrepancy, and self-esteem discriminate between the mentally ill and community populations. Up to this point in the present chapter, most of the intercorrelations we have reported among these variables have been low, although sometimes statistically significant. If each of these variables is related to mental illness, and each has a high degree of independence from the others, it should follow that the greater the number of variables on which a given respondent shows pathology-linked characteristics, the greater the probability of his being mentally ill. Stating the proposition in another way: the proportion of individuals manifesting multiple problems should increase along the four-step mental health continuum from the low symptom group to the psychotics.

Three different cumulative models were analyzed, all of which considered self-esteem and reference group discrepancy. The first model included in addition the occupation goal-striving stress score for the self, the second included the income goal-striving stress score for the self, and the third the striving scale stress score.

Cases were selected for these analyses on the following basis. Arbitrarily determined limits to the low, middle, and high sections of the distribution of each of these variables were defined. Only respondents whose scores fell in the low or high sections on all variables were included in the analyses; those with middle-range scores were eliminated.

SELF-ESTEEM, REFERENCE GROUP DISCREPANCY, AND THE OCCUPATION GOAL-STRIVING STRESS SCORE

As one moves from the low symptom group to the psychotics, the proportion of individuals with three pathology-linked characteristics increases (see Table 11.1). The proportion of those showing pathology-linked characteristics on two of the three factors also increases from the low symptom group to the psychotics. As one moves along the continuum

Table 11.1—Cumulative Effect of Pathology–Linked Characteristics,
by Illness Status in Percentages

	Psychotics	Neurotics	High Symp.	Low Symp.
High Reference Group Discrepancy Low Self Esteem High *Occupational* Stress-Self	5	4	3	0
Any two of above	38	30	23	7
Any one of above	43	47	47	41
None of the above	14	19	27	52
	100	100	100	100
High Reference Group Discrepancy Low Self-Esteem High *Income* Stress-Self	4	5	2	2
Any two of above	35	23	28	7
Any one of above	47	54	39	39
None of the above	14	18	31	52
	100	100	100	100
High Reference Group Discrepancy Low Self-Esteem High *Striving-Scale* Stress-Self	12	7	3	1
Any two of above	35	34	28	13
Any one of above	43	43	42	39
None of the above	10	16	27	47
	100	100	100	100

in this same direction, the percentage of individuals with *no* pathology-linked characteristics decreases.

SELF-ESTEEM, REFERENCE GROUP DISCREPANCY, AND
INCOME GOAL-STRIVING STRESS SCORE

When the income stress score replaces the occupation stress score in the cumulative model, the proportions of individuals with three and two pathology-linked characteristics again increases (see Table 11.1). Individuals with none of these characteristics decrease from the low symptom group to the psychotics.

SELF-ESTEEM, REFERENCE GROUP DISCREPANCY, AND THE
STRIVING SCALE GOAL-STRIVING STRESS SCORE

When the striving scale stress score is incorporated into the model, the predicted sequences appear in three of the four rows (see Table 11.1). The proportion of those who manifest pathology-linked characteristics on all three variables increases from the low symptom group to the psychotics. The percentage of respondents showing two of these characteristics also increases along the continuum. The proportion of subjects with none of these characteristics decreases from the low symptom group to the psychotics.

Clearly, the greater the number of pathology-linked characteristics, the greater the probability of falling into the "sickest" group on the illness continuum (the psychotics). Conversely, the fewer the number of these characteristics, the lower the probability of falling into this category. The distributions of the number of pathology-linked characteristics in the four mental health groupings differ significantly for the three cumulative models ($P = < .001$).

When the high and low symptom groups are combined into the community sample, and the psychotics and the neurotics into the ill sample, we find for each model an increased likelihood of appearing in the ill sample as the number of one's pathology-linked characteristics increases.

Sociological Factors, Goal-Striving Stress,
and Mental Illness

WE HAVE EXPLORED the possibilities of using perception of the opportunity structure, goal-striving stress, reference group discrepancy, blue/white-collar occupational preference, and self-esteem as intervening variables to explain variations in illness rates among different social groupings. These social groupings have been defined by (1) sex; (2) age; (3) migratory status; (4) socioeconomic status; and (5) social mobility status.

The ability of the social-psychological variables to act as intervening variables in accounting for rate differentials among these social groupings only appeared with age, migratory status, and social mobility groups. Our study variables could not account for rate differentials in sex and socioeconomic status groups. Therefore, although our study variables have been linked to mental illness on one hand, they are not linked to sex or socioeconomic status on the other, despite the fact that these factors seem to be independently linked to mental illness.

There are two possible interpretations of these inconsistent findings. (1) The bases for defining the social groupings may be related to mental illness, as shown, but the social-psychological variables may not be related, thereby explaining the inconsistent results when such factors are offered as explanatory variables. However, since all the social-psychological variables have been linked to mental illness, and to some extent to age, migratory status, and mobility status, this alternative seems unlikely. (2) The links already established may be valid, except for those relating sex and socioeconomic status to illness. The rate differentials may be more apparent than real—that is, sex and socioeconomic status may not be related to illness at all. If these considerations are correct, there is little reason to expect our social-psychological variables to relate either to sex or to socioeconomic status.

One of our purposes is to investigate the appropriateness of this alternative. We shall utilize goal-striving stress as the social-psychological intervening variable in this effort, since it has been the most efficient variable in accounting for rate variability.

We must also investigate the interrelationship of these demographic and sociological factors (especially those variables for which goal-striving stress showed high and low yield differences—i.e., age, migratory status, and social mobility). The variability of illness rates may be attributable to only one of these three factors. Perhaps the other variables only *seem* to be related to illness and are superfluous in accounting for rate differentials.

Our earlier attempts to explore the utility of these social-psychological factors as intervening variables employed yield analyses based on group characteristics, comparing, for instance, the mean goal-striving stress scores of high and low yield community subgroups. This type of analysis is limited in two respects.

(1) It does not allow us to determine whether a given respondent's position on a particular variable, such as socioeconomic status, is also related to his particular position on the illness continuum.

(2) In several instances the analysis of group characteristics necessitated the collapsing of certain categories in order to obtain a sufficient number of cases for statistical evaluation. Originally, for example, the occupational scale had seven steps, but when we analyzed the stress scores and controlled for occupational status, individuals at occupation levels 4 through 7 were considered as a single group. Collapsing groups in this way may possibly distort the actual relationships between stress, status level, and position on the illness continuum. In effect, we ignored whatever differences might have existed with respect to illness among occupation levels 4, 5, 6, and 7.

Consequently, correlations derived from the multiple correlation procedure will be considered in the present context. Since these types of data deal with the individual level of analysis, they avoid limitation (1). These correlations also take into account the full spread of positions on the seven-step occupational, income, and educational scales. In this way, the loss of sensitivity through collapsing of groups is resolved. The major disadvantage of utilizing correlations instead of group data is the diminution in size of the total sample. As noted earlier, the prerequisites of the multiple correlation computer program reduced the number of usable cases from 2912 to 1995.

SEX, GOAL-STRIVING STRESS, AND MENTAL ILLNESS

On the group level of analysis, our data indicated a higher illness rate for males than for females. Consequently, we expected males to manifest higher stress scores than females, and the higher stress scores in turn to be associated with mental illness. With respect to the former expectation, males did tend to have higher stress scores than females in all three self-related striving areas, but the evaluations were usually not significant. A relationship between each of the goal-striving stress scores and mental illness has already been demonstrated.

On the individual level of analysis, we must examine the correlation between sex and illness status. If *this* correlation is not significant, we have no basis for expecting stress to discriminate between the sex groups. A person's sex, then, would not allow prediction of his position on the illness continuum, whereas his stress scores would. The correlations between sex and both the two- and four-step illness continua are small and not significant (−.01 in both cases). Clearly, sex does not allow us to predict position on either of the illness continua, and therefore it is not surprising that the stress scores do not discriminate between the sex groups.

AGE, GOAL-STRIVING STRESS, AND MENTAL ILLNESS

We have reported higher rates of illness for the young group (twenty to thirty-nine years of age) in the community population than for the older group (forty to sixty years of age). To establish goal-striving stress as an intervening variable, we must demonstrate that the young have higher stress scores than the older subjects, and that those respondents with higher stress scores fall into the ill sample on the two-step illness continuum and into the pychotic grouping on the four-step continuum.

Previous analyses on a group level revealed a relationship between each of the three stress scores and yield of illness. Comparable analyses also showed higher goal-striving stress scores for the young than the older group. On the individual level of analysis, one's age correlates significantly with his position on the two- and four-step continua (−.21 and −.22, respectively, $P = < .001$ for both). These negative correlations indicate that the younger the respondent, the greater the likelihood of his falling into the ill sample or into the "sickest" mental health grouping. These correlations clearly illustrate the interdependence of age, goal-striving stress, and mental illness.

MIGRATORY STATUS, GOAL-STRIVING STRESS, AND MENTAL ILLNESS

Of the three migratory status groups, the natives showed the highest rate of illness and the southern migrants the lowest. The northern migrants fell between these two groups. All three stress scores (whose relationship with mental illness has been established) also related to migratory status in the manner expected from a consideration of variations in illness rates: the higher the rates, the higher the stress scores.

On the individual level of analysis, we expect high correlations between an individual's migratory status and his position on the two- and four-step illness continua. Both of these correlations are significant (.16 in each case, $P = < .001$ for both), clearly demonstrating the interconnection and interdependence of migratory status, goal-striving stress, and mental illness.

SOCIOECONOMIC STATUS, GOAL-STRIVING STRESS,
AND MENTAL ILLNESS

We shall discuss each of the three different measures of status individually. We have already shown that rates of mental disorder vary by occupational status, and that all three goal-striving stress scores are related to illness status. In Chapter 9 we reported that none of the stress scores varied in the four occupational status groups in the manner predicted on the basis of their differential rates of illness. Therefore, in the present context we do not expect to obtain a significant correlation between the full seven-step occupational status scale and mental illness. Correlations between occupation and the two- and four-step continua are small and not significant ($-.04$ in both cases). Since a person's occupational status does not correlate with his position on either of the continua, the inability of the three stress scores to discriminate in accordance with status-associated rates of illness becomes understandable.

In Chapter 9 rates of mental illness were shown to decrease as income status increased. Presumably, the three stress scores should also have decreased with higher position on the income scale. The data showed the opposite pattern, although the differences among the income status groups were not significant. Again we ask whether income status on the seven-step scale correlates with illness position, at the individual level of analysis. The correlations between income position and the two- and four-step illness continua are small and not significant ($-.04$ and $-.05$, respectively).

The educational status groups also varied in their yield or rates of mental disorder (Chapter 9). The variation in average goal-striving stress scores from one educational status group to the next was discrepant from predictions based on differential illness yield in these groups. The treatment of educational status presents problems similar to those encountered with occupational status, and therefore, we do not expect a respondent's educational status to predict his position on either of the illness continua. The correlations between education and the two- and four-step illness continua are small and not significant ($-.02$ and $-.03$, respectively). In this case, too, the failure of the three stress scores to discriminate among the educational status groups according to predictions based on status-linked illness rates in these groups becomes understandable. Since an individual's goal-striving stress correlates with his position on each illness continuum, and his educational status position does not, we cannot expect a significant correlation between educational status and stress.

Although there were significant variations in status-associated illness rates for each of the three status measures, a respondent's status position does not correlate in any instance with his position on either of the illness continua. The complete failure of stress to discriminate among the status groups in the community, regardless of the definition of status, is not surprising. If status is not related to illness, there is no reason to expect stress to intervene between the two.

The reader may raise the following question about our correlation approach to relating status and illness: since the curve of illness rates for occupational status was U-shaped, and for educational status W-shaped, how are we justified in making the linear assumption with the correlation techniques? This objection is well taken and should be considered in subsequent analyses. It should be reemphasized that the rate curves involved status groups obtained by collapsing sections of the seven-step scales. Computing the correlations with the *total* spread of occupational or educational status groups allows us to determine any possible correlation with illness position, at least with the linear assumption. The above objection does not apply to the income status measure, since illness rates decreased as status position increased—there was no evidence to indicate a rate curve other than linear, or nearly linear. But even with this measure of status, no significant correlation with illness status emerged.

In Chapter 9, we suggested that the variability in illness rates among the socioeconomic status groups might be partly a function of the representation of natives, northern migrants, and southern migrants in these groups, rather than completely a function of status position itself. The high rate of mental illness at the upper occupational status positions may be a function of the greater concentration of natives (with a high illness rate) than of northern or southern migrants at these levels. The increase in rates in the highest educational groups may also be accounted for by the greater concentration of natives in these categories. In support of this reasoning, migratory status correlates significantly with occupational and with educational achievement (.11 and .26, respectively, $P = < .001$ for both). As position in the occupational or educational status hierarchy increases, the likelihood of being a native also increases.

SOCIAL MOBILITY, GOAL-STRIVING STRESS, AND MENTAL ILLNESS

Chapter 10 analyzed data on occupational and educational mobility. Rates of illness varied both by direction of mobility (i.e., upward or downward), and by one's current position on the status scale. If, for example, the upwardly mobile subjects at the high end of the status scale manifested a higher illness rate than the stable respondents at that level, we also expected the upwardly mobile to show higher goal-striving stress scores. Similarly, if the downwardly mobile at the low end of the status scale had a higher illness rate than the stable subjects at that position, we expected the downwardly mobile group to manifest higher stress scores.

All three stress scores tended to parallel the variations in illness rates in occupationally mobile and nonmobile groups (Chapter 10). A particular mobility group with a higher illness rate than other mobility groups at that same status position also tended to be characterized by higher stress scores in the three self-related content areas. Occupational mobility was significantly related to rates of illness and to goal-striving stress scores in the expected manner. Unfortunately, we were unable to include occupational mobility as one of the conditions in the multiple correlation analysis. Complete information on occupational mobility was unavailable for a large enough number of cases to necessitate omitting this variable from the multiple correlation computer program. Therefore, we cannot indicate at this time whether one's occupational mobility status correlates with his position on the illness continuum.

Variations in average stress scores among the educational mobility groups did not parallel the variations in rates of mental illness. For this reason, we do not expect a significant correlation between one's position in the educational mobility complex and his position on either of the illness continua. The multiple correlation procedure considered both direction and amount of mobility from parental level. The correlations between educational mobility and the two- and four-step continua are small and not significant (.05 in both cases). The absence of a systematic relationship between educational mobility and goal-striving stress is apparently related to the fact that goal-striving stress is associated with mental illness, but educational mobility is not.

INTERACTION OF DEMOGRAPHIC AND
SOCIOLOGICAL VARIABLES

Both age and migratory status correlated with goal-striving stress and mental illness. To what extent do age and migratory status correlate with each other? The correlations reported earlier between these variables and illness may be completely explainable in terms of one *or* the other variable. The two factors correlate significantly with each other $(-.32, P = < .001)$, indicating that as age increases, the likelihood of being in the native group decreases. If the two variables showed close to complete interdependence (i.e., a correlation close to 1.00), age could be assumed to account for all the findings obtained with migratory status, and conversely. The absolute magnitude of the correlation does not warrant this conclusion, however.

In this volume we have made limited use of the multi-status social class index (see Appendix D), since each of its three components (occupation, income, and education) showed a different pattern of illness rates as status position varied. We should note that the three status measures intercorrelated with one another significantly (education with occupation, .44; education with income, .20; occupation with income, .28; $P = < .001$ for all correlations). As noted in Chapter 10, these measures intercorrelate in the same *manner* as in studies of white populations, but the absolute magnitudes of these correlations are considerably lower than correlations among comparable measures in the white community. These data tend to support the basic assumption made in Chapter 1 of an opportunity structure that is relatively closed to the Negro population with which we have been concerned.

Predictive Value of All Variables Considered Simultaneously

DURING THE DISCUSSION of the data in this volume, we have been partly concerned with the correlation between each of our sociological and social-psychological variables and position on the mental health continuum: the higher the correlation value between a particular variable and illness, the greater the possibility of predicting a subject's illness status from his score on that variable. We have discussed the intercorrelations of thirty-four variables,[2] each of which has its own correlation (or its own predictive value) with illness. The multiple correlation procedure to which we have often referred yields a correlation coefficient or value indicating the predictive power of all thirty-four variables considered simultaneously.

This single value is not the sum of each of its correlations. If it were, it would imply that the study variables were completely independent of

2. Because of the information requirements of the multiple correlation computer program, two variables discussed in earlier chapters had to be omitted from this model: the education-hypothetical son goal-striving stress score, and occupational mobility from parental level.

one another, which we have shown not to be the case. For example, the reference group discrepancy correlates with the aspiration-achievement discrepancy on the striving scale, indicating that these variables are probably to some degree a function of each other. The multiple correlation program was so constructed, however, that it made no difference which of these variables was considered first—whenever the second of these variables entered the model, its contribution to the predictive value of the multiple correlation coefficient was automatically reduced by the amount of contribution it shared with the previously admitted variable. In general, then, the multiple correlation procedure determined the specific contribution of each of the thirty-four variables to the final coefficient.

Two multiple correlation values were computed: one related to predicting position on the two-step illness continuum, and the other to predicting position on the four-step continuum. The values of these two coefficients are .61 and .64, respectively. These values allow us to account for 37 and 41 per cent of the variance of positions on the two illness continua. Since these correlations are based on the assumption that all thirty-four variables are linearly related to illness, they may underestimate the predictive value of the thirty-four variables to a certain extent. We have shown that the linear assumption does not apply with the stress scores. If the nonlinear assumption could have been made with these scores, the two multiple coefficients would probably have been higher.

Summary

THIS CHAPTER has been primarily concerned with:

(1) the interaction and intercorrelation of our sociological and social-psychological variables, in order to determine how these variables are linked to one another and how they relate to broader theoretical issues.

(2) the correlation between the sociological variables and mental illness, in order to ascertain why our expectations based on the yield analyses were not always supported, even with variables showing significant variations in rates of mental illness.

Our theoretical point of view predicted that both goal-striving stress and the reference group discrepancy would correlate with self-esteem (Hypotheses 4 and 5). These expectations were based on the assumption that self-esteem, which is related to mental illness, acts as the inter-vening variable between each of these variables and mental illness. We expected to find a nonlinear relationship between the stress scores and self-esteem—we predicted that as deviations in stress increased from the optimum level (in either direction) self-esteem would decrease. We also predicted that as discrepancy between one's perceived position and that of his "close friends" increased, self-esteem would decrease. Both expecta-tions are supported by the data, although only the stress score based on the striving scale correlates with self-esteem. Analyses based on the yield issue indicate that stress may be antecedent to self-esteem, but that the reference group discrepancy is not.

It is generally assumed that a decrease in self-esteem is associated with an increased tendency to set either very high or very low levels of aspiration. We tested this assumption by comparing groups differing in self-esteem on the variance of their aspiration-achievement discrepancy scores. Our data do not strongly support the degree of interdependence usually assumed between self-esteem and goal level.

Aspiration-achievement discrepancy scores in the areas of occupation and income were correlated with the reference group discrepancy in order to determine how strongly level of aspiration is influenced by the achievements of one's "close friends." Although the correlations are significant, their absolute magnitudes are low, suggesting that the achievements of a reference group such as "close friends" do not play an important role in *goal-setting*.

The reference group discrepancy correlates significantly with the striving scale aspiration-achievement discrepancy, with the striving scale stress score, and with self-esteem. These correlations indicate the gen-eralized importance of "close friends" in *goal oriented* and *evaluative* behavior. The fact that the reference group discrepancy correlates more highly than self-esteem with the striving scale discrepancy and stress score suggests that "close friends" are more important in such behavior than the factors measured by the self-esteem index.

On the basis of comparatively low intercorrelations among goal-striving stress scores, reference group discrepancy, and self-esteem, we hypothesized the existence of a cumulative model in which an increase in the number of pathology-linked characteristics for a given individual was associated with a greater probability of his being in the diagnosed ill population (on the two-step illness continuum) or in the psychotic grouping (on the four-step continuum). The data confirm these expecta-tions.

Early analyses of the relationship between community population subgroups and rates of mental illness revealed significant rate variations among sex and socioeconomic status groups. However, our social-psychological study variables could not explain these variations either for sex or status. Correlation coefficients show that a respondent's sex or socioeconomic status does not help in predicting his illness status. Therefore, the failure of our social-psychological variables to explain the variations in illness rates among sex and status groups becomes understandable.

12
REVIEW AND NEW
PERSPECTIVES

Viewed in terms of the larger questions raised in this study and the many possible lines of inquiry, ours is only an initial effort. We pause at this point to discuss this effort—to highlight for the reader some of the major findings of this study and to speculate about their meaning and significance. Our attempts to interpret the empirical data presented in this volume necessitate the selection of explanations that seem most consonant with this and other studies, most intellectually economic and precise, and even most esthetic.

Essentially, we have considered the utility of several social and psychological concepts for understanding the complex entity known as "mental illness." These concepts were derived mainly from level-of-aspiration formulations and from a general theory of anomie and deviant behavior. We do not intend to deny or minimize other facets of the study, such as the methodological problems of measuring the total strength of goal-striving behavior, a better understanding of Negro life, and some psychological consequences of the "American dream" of success. The points of greatest interest must depend on the reader's values.

We do not claim that a social-psychological approach to understanding the phenomenon of mental illness is the only or even the most fruitful approach. As social scientists we have chosen to work at this level of conceptualization. What is currently designated as "mental illness" probably involves processes that must be considered from the vantage point of such disciplines as biochemistry, psychiatry, and genetics. The types of explanations most valuable in the ultimate control of mental illness are, at this point, mere speculation.

From a review of the clinical literature and recent large-scale epidemiological studies, it appears pointless to search for a single cause of mental disorder. Rather, we look for configurations of social and psychological factors and patterned sequences of behavior that seem to provide the climate for the development of illness. It has already been noted that all the variables of this study considered simultaneously yield a multiple correlation coefficient of .64, which allows us to explain only 41 per cent of the variance associated with mental disorder. This suggests a highly complex etiology. It also indicates that the psychotherapist or community organizer must consider many more sociological and social-psychological factors than are usually taken into account.

The decision to concentrate on goal-striving behavior and related factors arose from some empirical findings and a "hunch" that the theory of deviant behavior (associated with Durkheim and Merton) would be particularly relevant for understanding psychological stress and possibly mental illness among Negroes.

Hypotheses: Review of Findings
and New Issues

AT THIS POINT we shall restate our formal hypotheses, summarize the relevant findings, and discuss some of the theoretical and methodological problems and implications generated by these data.

Hypothesis 1. *Goal-striving stress will be significantly higher in the mentally ill population than in the community population.*

Hypothesis 1a. *Within the mentally ill population, goal-striving stress will be significantly higher among patients diagnosed as psychotic than among those diagnosed as neurotic.*

Hypothesis 1b. *Within the community population, goal-striving stress will be significantly higher in a subgroup having a low yield of psychoneurotic symptoms than in a subgroup having a high yield of such symptoms.*

Data relevant to the individual's goal-striving stress were analyzed in the areas of occupation, income, and generalized striving scale. Tests of Hypothesis 1 were made for total populations, as well as for sex, age, three measures of social status, migratory status groups, and types of socioeconomic mobility. The data analyzed for each of these three stress scores strongly supported Hypothesis 1.

In considering Hypothesis 1a, the psychotics and the neurotics on our mental health continuum were compared, for the total groupings and for each of three socioeconomic status controls. In evaluating Hypothesis 1b, the high and low symptom groups in the community population were compared, using the same status controls. The findings supported the prediction of higher stress for the psychotics than the neurotics, when stress scores for the self and for a hypothetical son were considered. There was also a consistent trend for the high psychiatric symptom group to manifest lower stress scores than the low symptom group. No significant differences emerged between the two psychiatric symptom groupings when stress scores for self-related content areas were considered, but stress scores for a hypothetical son were significantly lower for the high symptom group, as predicted.

Almost all the nonsignificant differences between the ill and community samples with respect to Hypothesis 1 and its corollaries occurred at the higher status levels. This could mean that goal striving in general was less important, or less potentially pathological at these higher status levels. However, later analyses revealed that high goal striving in the upper occupational and educational status groups was associated with high illness rates.

The stress score derived from the self-anchored striving scale provided the most consistent support for our predictions concerning stress. No erratic results at the upper status levels emerged with this stress score. Since respondents defined their own salient striving areas for this measure, they presumably selected goals that could not be arranged on a hierarchical status continuum. In an earlier paper relating ethnic identification to status and social mobility (Parker and Kleiner, 1964), we demonstrated increasing ambivalence in relationships with the Negro *and* white communities, and decreasing attraction to the Negro community, as one moved up the status ladder. The problems of horizontal mobility, psychological orientation toward the Negro and white communities, and the relevance of these issues to mental illness are areas for further investigation. Such research may also account for the inability of our stress variable to discriminate significantly in certain instances.

In Chapter 3 occupational and educational stress scores for a hypothetical son were considered, in addition to stress scores in areas related to self-striving. We assumed that the respondent projected his own goal striving onto a hypothetical son. The pattern of these scores in the four mental health groupings on our illness continuum was somewhat complicated. The low symptom individuals were characterized by moderate stress for themselves and high stress for a hypothetical son. High symptom subjects showed low stress scores for themselves as well as for a hypothetical son. The neurotics showed essentially the same pattern as the high symptom group, which initially led us to suspect that these groupings might have many common characteristics. The psychotics manifested high striving levels for themselves and for a hypothetical son. These patterns were interpreted as different modes of adaptation to the goal-striving situation by individuals in the four mental health groupings. These varying response patterns also indicate that analyses of semi-projective questions are more complicated than is generally assumed.

Many laboratory experiments attempting to relate personality variables and mental health have defined their sample "pathological" populations as: (1) high anxiety individuals; (2) individuals characterized by high fear of failure; (3) mildly disturbed persons; (4) neurotic individuals; etc. In such experiments an analogy has been assumed between respondents with a particular characteristic (e.g., high fear of failure) and mentally ill individuals. In our analyses, the low occupation and income stress scores of the high symptom group were mainly attributable to high perceived probabilities of failure, a pattern not characteristic of the neurotics or the psychotics. This finding implies that the assumption of a parallel between the mentally ill and high-anxiety or high fear-of-failure respondents is a tenuous one—laboratory subjects may deviate considerably from a diagnosed mentally ill population. In the present study comparisons of high symptom and low symptom (presumably the healthiest) respondents revealed patterns of differences unlike those uncovered by neurotic–psychotic comparisons.

Our predictions about the effect of deviations in either direction from an optimum stress level suggested a nonlinear relationship between goal-striving stress and mental disorder. The evidence supporting this assumption raises two considerations that warrant further attention. First, theory construction in the behavioral sciences should devote greater attention to the possibility of nonlinear relationships between the variables under consideration. Formal hypotheses are usually stated in a manner that assumes a linear relationship. Second, when nonlinear relationships *are* predicted, more attention should be paid to statistical methods appropriate to this assumption, as well as to methods of precise determination of relationships between variables.

Although the aspiration-achievement discrepancy provided the point of departure for the theoretical orientation of this study, the incorporation of the discrepancy measure into the stress score permitted the consideration of several variables interacting simultaneously. Subsequent analyses indicated that this was a valuable procedure, and one that will become more necessary as our awareness of the interaction effects of different social and psychological variables increases. Most laboratory studies of goal-setting behavior have focused on the aspiration-achievement discrepancy, or on subjects' expectations of failure. These emphases may be appropriate to the particular problems involved, but more attention should be directed to a simultaneous consideration of several variables. Such efforts may eventuate in better predictions of behavioral outcomes in various situations. As an illustration, in this study analyses which utilized only the discrepancy concept had much less predictive power than those involving the goal-striving stress score.

Hypothesis 2.   *The degree of negative discrepancy from a reference group will vary directly with the severity of mental illness.*

Hypothesis 2a. *Within the mentally ill population, negative discrepancy from a reference group will be higher for the psychotics than for the neurotics.*

Hypothesis 2b. *Within the community population, negative discrepancy from a reference group will be larger for a high symptom group than for a low symptom group.*

Chapter 6 considered Hypotheses 2, 2a, and 2b in terms of three measures of reference group behavior, with particular emphasis on the perceived distance between one's own achievements and those of his "close friends." Findings on this reference group discrepancy measure, analyzed for both total samples, the diagnostic groups, and the psychiatric symptom groups confirmed Hypotheses 2 and its corollaries.

The reference group measure based on blue/white-collar occupational preference was analyzed only for the total ill and community samples. At all multi-status control levels except the highest, more ill than community subjects preferred white-collar occupations, despite the wage penalties arbitrarily attached to these jobs. Since all subjects at the two lowest multi-status positions and a large portion of those at the next higher level actually held blue-collar jobs, the selection of white-collar alternatives was taken as a measure of the discrepancy between one's current achievement and that of an aspired reference group. These data also confirmed Hypothesis 2.

The third measure of reference group behavior utilized was intended primarily to explore the extent of a respondent's orientation toward the Negro and white communities. The community respondents manifested conflicted or mixed feelings about their identification. Within the ill population, young subjects increased the intensity of their Negro identification, and older subjects were more concerned with their status in the white community.

These findings on reference group behavior have implications for theory and research. Our analyses of this phenomenon involved such different reference points as "close friends," aspired occupational status level, and orientation toward the Negro and white communities. Since people have multiple reference groups, our analyses reflect some of the complexity of reference group behavior in real life situations. The fact that all our reference group measures, including those used in an explanatory manner, revealed differences between the ill and community populations indicates the value of reference group theory as a means to a more thorough investigation of mental illness. These analyses also show that the specific reference points utilized here are potentially useful for more intensive analyses.

In Chapter 6 we evaluated whether our respondents perceived "being a Negro" as a barrier to goal achievement. This question also relates to their perception of the opportunity structure. As reported in Chapter 3, the patients tended to perceive a more open opportunity structure, and to set higher probability-of-success estimates than individuals in the general community. Significantly more ill subjects also denied that "being a Negro" had been a barrier to achievement; the larger Negro community believed the contrary. Despite their crudity, the measures used to determine perception of the opportunity structure have provided important insights into this phenomenon. However, their lack of sensitivity made it difficult to tell whether the consistent but nonsignificant differences between high and low yield community subgroups were real or apparent. Consequently, a more adequate index or measure of the perception of the opportunity structure must be developed.

Hypothesis 3.   *Self-esteem will vary inversely with the severity of mental illness.*

Hypothesis 3a. *Within the mentally ill population, self-esteem will be lower for the psychotics than for the neurotics.*

Hypothesis 3b. *Within the community population, self-esteem will be lower for the high symptom group than for the low symptom group.*

Three of the four measures used as indices of self-esteem (including the self-ideal discrepancy, our major measure) showed lower self-esteem for the ill than the community respondents, a finding consistent with clinical impressions and systematic research findings. The supporting evidence for Hypothesis 3a is weak: only one of these measures supported the predicted difference between the psychotics and the neurotics. Two of the four measures, including the self-ideal discrepancy, confirmed expectations about the high and low symptom community groups providing somewhat stronger evidence for Hypothesis 3b. The findings confirmed each of the predictions to some degree. The difference in the weight of evidence supporting Hypotheses 3a and 3b illustrates the ever-present scaling problem and the nature of the scale units used to measure social and psychological variables.

Hypothesis 4. *The degree of deviation from the optimum level of goal-striving stress (in either direction) will be inversely related to level of self-esteem.*

A nonlinear correlation between the variables in Hypothesis 4 was predicted and confirmed. In the chapter dealing with the interrelationship of the social-psychological variables (Chapter 11), we pointed out that Hypothesis 4 was logically derived from the two hypotheses relating mental illness to goal-striving stress and to self-esteem.

Hypothesis 5. *The degree of negative discrepancy from reference group will be inversely related to self-esteem.*

The correlation between negative discrepancy and self-esteem was statistically significant in the predicted direction. Reference group theory emphasizes the importance of reference groups in one's self-evaluation. The confirmation of Hypothesis 5 supports this point of view. If the individual evaluates himself in terms of different reference groups, as suggested earlier, we should be able to determine the salience of each of these reference groups for different individuals and the relative influence of each group on self-esteem.

We have presented the general findings with respect to the relationship between the social-psychological variables and mental illness, diagnosis, psychoneurotic symptoms, and the relationship of these factors to one another. We have also indicated the degree of support obtained for each of our formal hypotheses and have discussed a number of implications for further investigation. These implications are not intended to be all-inclusive, but only to suggest new research directions with respect to our study variables.

An Evaluation of the Yield Procedure

OUR FORMAL HYPOTHESES were concerned with differences between the diagnosed mentally ill and the community populations, and between groupings within each of these larger populations (i.e., psychotics and neurotics, high and low symptom groups). Now we consider the procedure utilized to isolate possible antecedent conditions of illness. We predicted that the social-psychological variables would explain the variations in rates of yields of mental illness associated with different subgroups within the community population. Variables of specific interest were perception of the societal opportunity structure, the three stress scores in the self-striving content areas, the reference group discrepancy, the three blue/white-collar paired choices, and the self-ideal discrepancy.

MIGRATORY STATUS

Native Negroes (those socialized in Philadelphia) had higher rates of mental illness than migrants from the South (those socialized in the South) or from the North (those socialized somewhere in the North other than in Philadelphia), although the differences between the natives and northern migrants were inconsistent. In addition, rates for the northern migrants were generally higher than those for the southern migrants. The incidence of high symptom individuals in the community also paralleled the variation in rates obtained for the migration groups. We therefore expected our variables to account for the rate difference between the natives and southern migrants, and between the northern and southern migrants.

Before we could consider the explanatory value of the social-psychological variables, however, we had to determine whether these rate variations among the migratory status groups persisted when measures of status, sex, age, diagnosis, and chronicity were applied. The expected rate differences were obtained in all these analyses. The migratory status groups were also compared with respect to referral source and treatment disposition to see whether the rates could have been selectively influenced by these factors—no significant differences emerged. We concluded that the differences among the migration groups were stable and reliable. Perception of the opportunity structure, each of three goal-striving stress scores, and the three paired blue/white-collar occupation choices were able to account for variations in rates. Reference group discrepancy and self-ideal discrepancy showed no consistent association with rate variations.

SOCIOECONOMIC STATUS

Analysis of illness rates for each measure of status (occupation, income, and education), for group totals only, revealed different patterns of rate variations. Rates were high for the lowest and highest occupational status groups. Illness rates for educational groups were high at the lowest, middle, and highest status positions. Position on the income hierarchy increased as rates of mental illness decreased. Rates of psychiatric high symptoms in the community for each status dimension did not yield curves similar to those obtained for occupational and educational status, but they did show the same pattern as the rate curve for the income status measure. The stability of these three status curves was also determined by controlling for sex, age, chronicity, and diagnosis. Since the shape of these curves persisted in these analyses, rate variations were considered to be reliable and stable.

Attempts to utilize our social-psychological variables to explain rate variations did not meet with the same success noted for migratory status. Perception of the opportunity structure, the three self-related stress scores, and the three blue/white-collar occupational choices showed no correlation with any of the three rate curves. Although mean reference group discrepancy scores varied in the same way as illness rates, no significant variations were obtained for any of the status measures. The mean self-ideal discrepancy scores manifested the same pattern of variations as the rate curves for occupation and income, but there were no significant differences between any of the occupational, income, or educational status groups. Clearly, there was very little evidence that the social-psychological variables underlying this study could explain variations in status-linked rates of illness.

SOCIAL MOBILITY

Chapter 10 was primarily concerned with occupational and educational mobility (in both cases, relative to parental achievement level). When we compared group totals without considering the status achievements of each type of mobility group, the occupationally downwardly mobile showed the highest illness rate, the stable, or nonmobile, respondents the next highest rate, and the upwardly mobile the lowest rate. This pattern was also evident for the incidence of high symptom scores.

When educational mobility was considered, we found the highest illness rate for the downwardly mobile and the lowest rate for the stable respondents. The upwardly mobile fell between these two groups. This pattern reappeared when the incidence of high symptom individuals in the three mobility groups was considered. Analysis of mobility groups controlling for status level altered these impressions, in the areas of occupation and education. At the lowest status position on both the occupational and educational scales, the downwardly mobile showed a higher rate of mental illness than their nonmobile status peers. On the other hand, the upwardly mobile at the highest status level had a higher rate than the stable subjects at that level. It should be noted that with increasing position on the status hierarchy, the illness rate for the upwardly mobile increased and the rate for the downwardly mobile decreased.

At each status level we attempted to fit our social-psychological variables to rates of illness. Some of our variables (perception of the opportunity structure, the self-related goal-striving stress scores, and the self-ideal discrepancy) were able to account for the mobility-associated illness rates. White-collar occupations in each of the three choices were most preferred by educational mobility groups with the highest illness rates, and blue-collar occupations were selected most often in groups with the lowest rates. The reference group discrepancy was the only variable to show no fit whatsoever with illness rates.

SEX GROUPS

Males had a higher rate of mental illness than females when the total populations were considered. These differences persisted at the different status levels, but there were a number of inconsistencies. No sex differences emerged with respect to perception of the opportunity structure, the reference group discrepancy, or the self-ideal discrepancy. Each of the three stress scores was higher for males than for females, but these differences were not significant. There was little evidence to support a consistent relationship between the social-psychological variables underlying this study and variations in sex-linked rates of mental illness.

AGE GROUPS

The young subjects were characterized by a higher illness rate than the older subjects. These differences persisted when comparisons were made at each status level. The three measures of stress, the three blue/white-collar occupational choices, and the self-ideal discrepancy yielded differences between the age groups consistent with the variations in rates. The perception of the opportunity structure and the reference group discrepancy failed to distinguish between the age group dichotomy.

IMPLICATIONS OF YIELD ANALYSES

Throughout this study we have entertained the assumption that the yield procedure would help identify the antecedent conditions to mental illness. The sociological and social-psychological variables that emerged as possible antecedents to illness were age, goal-striving stress, reference group orientation, self-esteem, migratory status, and social mobility. Analyses of aspiration-achievement discrepancies in various content areas also fulfilled the criterion for consideration as antecedents.

We have emphasized in all discussions of this issue that the social-psychological variables were only *possible* antecedents. This cautionary note was injected since the data were collected at one point in time, and the logic of the procedure necessitated the inference of a time sequence. Longitudinal studies must ultimately be conducted to determine whether, and to what degree, these variables are in fact antecedent conditions. Community population subgroups, with no history of psychiatric treatment but differing with respect to pathology-linked characteristics will have to be studied over time to see whether they eventually manifest an increase in psychiatric symptoms and develop mental illness. These studies could be carried out over periods of five to ten years, since disorders like schizophrenia occur primarily among young people.

The validity of the yield analyses might be questioned on the basis of two points. In predicting more pathology-linked characteristics for a high than for a low yield group, we used statistics based on group characteristics (means, variances, etc.). These analyses showed that the social-psychological variables could be utilized as variables intervening between mental illness and either age, migratory status, or status mobility, but could not be said to intervene between illness and socioeconomic status or sex. These inconsistencies might have cast doubt on the explanatory value of our variables, but when correlational techniques were applied to our findings (on the individual level of analysis), these apparent inconsistencies became fully understandable. A given individual's sex or status position did not correlate significantly with his position on the two- or four-step mental health continuum, whereas his age, migratory status, and mobility type did. A significant correlation between any sociological variable and illness status was taken as a basis for expecting our social-psychological variables to account for the rate variations— which, in fact, they did.

It might be maintained that the yield analyses merely contrasted groups containing a different number of noninstitutionalized patients. This possibility is highly unlikely. Of the 1588 interviews obtained in the Philadelphia Negro community, ninety-nine respondents who had been in treatment during the year preceding the study were placed in our mentally ill population. This left in the community sample only fifty-six cases with some prior contact with a psychiatric facility, a sample too small to have affected the analyses carried out between high and low yield community subgroups. In addition, the mentally ill sample included patients from all types of facilities. All noninterviewed eligible respondents were accounted for and considered a part of the total incidence ill population, and therefore could not have been included in the community population.

In predicting high stress scores for groups with high illness rates, we did not consider that stress scores below the optimum level (i.e., inferred from the scores of the low symptom group) were also associated with psychoneurotic symptoms. Consequently, respondents with lower-than-optimum levels of goal-striving stress in high yield subgroups lowered the mean stress scores of these subgroups. Since there was less of a tendency for individuals with lower-than-optimum stress levels to appear in low yield subgroups, the average stress scores of these subgroups were little, if at all, influenced by these respondents. In other words, the difference between the mean stress scores of the high and low yield groups was possibly diminished by the greater proportion of high symptom individuals with lower-than-optimum stress levels who fell into the high yield subgroups.

There are a few questions raised by the findings which cannot be answered at this time. The reference group discrepancy clearly discriminated between the ill and community populations, as well as among the four mental health groupings. It also correlated significantly with goal-striving stress, the aspiration-achievement discrepancy on the striving scale, and the self-ideal discrepancy. On the basis of these data and the belief that individuals evaluate themselves relative to reference groups (in this context, their "close friends"), we expected this discrepancy to be antecedent to self-esteem and mental illness. The evidence did not support these expectations: the reference group discrepancy did not discriminate between high and low yield community subgroups, leaving an unresolved question for future consideration.

The self-ideal discrepancy appeared to discriminate between high and low yield subgroups for age and social mobility, but not for the migratory status. If this discrepancy is a measure of self-esteem, and if changes in self-esteem are antecedent to manifestations of illness, we must ask why the discrepancy did not fit this sociological variable. In the present study, we did not investigate the usefulness of other measures of self-esteem because we felt that the self-ideal discrepancy was the most powerful measure. These other measures will be utilized in subsequent analyses, but if they are not more successful than the self-ideal discrepancy, this problem will remain unresolved.

Finally, we reaffirm that more sensitive measures of perception of the opportunity structure must be utilized. The primary measure used in this investigation was crude but still showed consistent, although nonsignificant, findings in the yield analysis.

Theory Reconsidered

WE NOW CONSIDER the theory of deviant behavior introduced in Chapter 1. This general theoretical orientation influenced the selection of the social-psychological variables utilized in this study. How successfully do our findings fit the underlying theory? This question has already been partially answered in the review of hypotheses and findings. This review not only clearly indicated the utility of the individual variables in predicting mental disorder, but also strongly suggested the relevance of the theoretical framework from which these variables were derived.

Both Durkheim and Merton clearly stated that theirs were sociological approaches to understanding anomie and deviant behavior. However, their writings do indicate the embodiment of the structural and psychological interests of sociology. To understand fully the nature of anomie is to understand the *interaction* of the two levels of conceptualization. For example, Durkheim's explanation of anomic suicide (Durkheim, 1951) rested on his implicit assumption that the individual's perception of the structural aspects of the situation and its consequent effect on his behavior were inconsistent with the actual nature of the situation. The social regulatory forces (norms, rules, laws, etc.) were no longer effective in restraining the individual in his quest for need satisfaction and goal attainment. There occurred as a result a weakening of his integration with the group.

Merton, on the other hand, defined anomie in terms of a disjunction between socially valued goals and the socially provided means to attain these goals. The individual concomitants of the disjunctive process or anomic situation remained implicit in his formulation (Merton, 1957: 131–160). In his discussion of reference group theory (Merton, 1957: 281–326), he clearly discussed the social-psychological concomitants of the anomic situation. Here, too, he elaborated on Durkheim's notion of the importance of understanding the individual's ties with significant social groups for determining his behavior.

In order to move from the sociological concept of disjunction to the individual's alienation from the group, we must know whether he experiences a disjunction between *his own* socially valued goals and his subjective estimate of the means available to him for achieving these goals. Such a disjunctive process (individually defined) causes shifts in reference group behavior, anticipatory socialization, and possibly disturbed relationships with membership groups. Alienation from group ties and resultant deviant behavior increase the degree to which goal attainment is anticipated and valued in a situation that severely interferes with its attainment. The issues raised in this brief discussion of Durkheim and Merton were also developed, apparently independently, in the theorizing of social psychologists working in the laboratory.

In the present study the configuration of the social-psychological variables for the mentally ill, compared to the general population, provide some evidence for the above characterization of the preconditions of deviant behavior. Despite the relatively closed nature of the opportunity structure for the Negro in American society (as shown by data in Chapter 10 and in other research), the patients were more prone than the community respondents to perceive the system as open. Along with this perception, they rigidly maintained high levels of goal-striving stress. The existing disjunction (as we use the term) involved high levels of goal-striving orientation in the context of an objectively limited opportunity structure. The disjunction was maintained by the perception of an open opportunity structure. The accompanying high levels of perceived discrepancy from reference group among the mentally ill presumably reflected a weakening of ties with their membership group, in turn leading to disturbed relations with peers and low self-esteem, a phenomenon also predominating among the patients. Merton described this process in his essay on reference group behavior (Merton, 1957: 225–280).

In terms of this theory we are now in a position to understand why Negro migrants from the South had a lower illness rate than Negroes native to Philadelphia. The migrants, who were socialized in the semi-caste system of the South, reflected this experience in a lower propensity to perceive the opportunity structure as open and in significantly lower levels of goal-striving stress.

With respect to social mobility, the highest rates of mental disorder were found among the downwardly mobile at the low end of the status hierarchy and among the upwardly mobile at the high end of the scale. Although our data were not perfectly consistent, in general these two groups had also experienced the greatest amounts of mobility. Durkheim (1951) pointed out that individuals who had been downwardly or upwardly mobile were most prone to anomic suicide because they were not subject to the "restraints" imposed by the social system. The downwardly mobile could not restrain their ambitions and realistically lower their aspirational levels. The upwardly mobile were also unable to limit their aspirations realistically, and they continued to strive regardless of their actual achievements. In our consideration of mental disorder as the deviant phenomenon, the predictions were supported by the perception of a more open opportunity structure and higher goal-striving stress scores among low-status downwardly mobile and high-status upwardly mobile subjects, compared to their nonmobile status peers.

It is interesting that Durkheim's description of anomic suicide fits our pathological population. However, he went to considerable lengths to demonstrate that suicide and psychopathology were different phenomena. This puzzling situation might be explained by the fact that most mental illness occurs among younger people, and suicide is more common among older persons. In addition, affective disorders are more prevalent among those age groups which show high suicide rates, and suicide is frequently accompanied by depression. From these observations we suggest that the depression of the suicidal individual and the suicidal act itself are manifestations of mental illness among older people. Durkheim used age differences and the prevalence of depression among older people as indices to support his argument that mental disorder and suicide were different problems. We suggest that his evidence may reflect different manifestations of the same conditions.

Finally, our study linked mental disorder with the status inconsistency profile of relatively high education and low occupation. We assumed that those individuals at a particular occupational level with higher educational achievements than their occupational status peers would also have higher aspirational levels and higher status reference groups. If these assumptions are valid (and the data suggest that they are) the high rates of mental disorder associated with this type of status inconsistency can be explained by the above formulation of anomie and alienation from group ties.

Further Issues of Consideration

A FEW ISSUES REMAIN to be considered. Previously, we assumed that the low symptom group, the high symptom group, the neurotics, and the psychotics constituted a continuum of increasing severity of illness. If this assumption was valid, we expected individuals in these groupings to manifest a progressively increasing prevalence of those study variables highly associated with the mentally ill. In a sense, the evaluation of our predictions concerning the ordering of these pathological variables along the continuum constituted a test of the validity of this assumption.

Let us first consider goal-striving stress scores among these four mental health groupings. Although these scores were significantly higher for patients than community respondents, our assumption of an optimum level did *not* lead us to predict progressively higher levels of goal-striving stress as one moved from the healthiest to the sickest position on the continuum. The data supported our expectations.

The findings with respect to the reference group discrepancy were in the expected direction. This discrepancy increased progressively as we moved along the continuum from the low symptom group to the psychotics. We also predicted that the self-ideal discrepancy would increase (i.e., self-esteem would decrease) from the low symptom group to the psychotics. This progressive increase did in fact occur, but only from the low symptom group to the neurotics. The psychotics did not show the expected increase in this discrepancy.

In evaluating the assumption about the existence of an illness-severity continuum, we should note the patterning of the social-psychological variables in the four mental health groupings. The low symptom individuals had moderate stress scores, saw themselves as close to the position of their reference group, and had high self-esteem. The high symptom individuals showed lower goal-striving stress, perceived themselves as further below their reference group, and had lower self-esteem than the low symptom individuals. The neurotics also had low goal-striving stress, were still further below their reference groups and had even lower self-esteem than either of the other two groupings. The psychotics were characterized by the highest goal-striving stress, the largest perceived discrepancy from their reference group, and the lowest self-esteem. The patterning of these variables suggests progressively greater dissatisfaction with one's situation as severity of mental illness increases.

Finally, we note that for all three self-related goal-striving stress scores, for the reference group discrepancy, and for the self-ideal discrepancy, the variability (i.e., the variance) of the responses increased progressively from the healthiest to the most severely ill position on the continuum. Our findings strongly support the assumption that the four mental health groupings do form a continuum of increasing severity of illness, as defined by these pathology-linked social-psychological variables. The striking consistency of these findings invites interpretive comments. It is possible that extreme stress scores relative to a group mean in either direction represent a psychologically defensive maneuver. The very low extreme insures the individual against failure and/or provides the rationale for refusal to take risks. On the other hand, setting very high goals, with a high probability of failure, provides him in advance with an excuse for anticipated failure. Clinical and experimental evidence, at least with respect to goal setting, indicates that "normal" subjects are more prone than others to select intermediate goal levels.

Another possible interpretation of the variability of scores is based on the concept of alienation discussed above. If an important precondition of mental illness is alienation from group ties, as severity of illness increases the individual is less likely to have adequate feedback from his social environment to permit realistic evaluations and choices. Under these conditions idiosyncratic tendencies become important in determining perceptions of the social environment and in goal-striving behavior.

Before making such assumptions, we must consider data reported in Chapter 6 and 7 which indicated that variability between ill and community subgroups virtually disappeared when perception of the opportunity structure and occupational achievement were controlled. The reader may recall that psychotics with extremely high self-esteem perceived a relatively closed opportunity structure and had relatively high occupational achievements. Those psychotics with low self-esteem perceived a relatively open structure and had relatively low occupational achievements. When the psychotic and low symptom respondents with the same perception of the system and the same occupational achievement level were compared, differences in variability (i.e., variance) disappeared. Since our investigation of this point was largely exploratory, however, the reasons for the relationship between greater variability and increasing severity of illness merit more intensive research.

Although this study has treated mental disorder as one form of deviancy, we should see whether our variables and findings are applicable to other forms of deviant behavior. We have theorized that the particular configuration of the variables with which we were concerned reflected alienation from societal restraints, which finally resulted in mental disorder. Are other forms of deviant behavior, such as crime and delinquency, also characterized by similar configurations?

Merton felt that the anomic disjunction (defined sociologically) was a general antecedent to various forms of deviant behavior, but that the particular configuration of psychologically valued goals and perceived means to goal attainment might determine the form of deviancy. We were interested in variables within the person's phenomenological field. The only social-structural factor which entered our theoretical framework was the existence of a relatively closed or severely limited opportunity structure available to the Negro. Is the particular configuration of variables observed here also associated with other forms of deviant behavior? Our findings did not clarify this problem, but research currently being conducted by one of the authors and his colleague (Robert Kleiner and Jack V. Buerkle) on delinquent youths suggests some interesting deviations from the present findings. These investigators noted that a sample of delinquent Negro youths in Philadelphia were more prone than a community sample of nondelinquent youths (and more prone than the mentally ill males in the present study) to perceive a closed opportunity structure. These delinquent youths also had lower goal-striving stress scores and lower probability-of-success estimates. At this point such comparisons are preliminary—it would be premature to overstate their implications, but they do suggest possible areas of further research, ultimately leading to a general theory of deviant behavior.

New Research Areas

SOME OF THE MAJOR IMPLICATIONS of our findings for further research have been discussed. In the course of this investigation many related theoretical questions arose with which we could not deal. They should be stated briefly to enable the reader to see the type of theoretical issues suggested by this research.

(1) A considerable number of studies have focused on the stresses and strains of geographical movement. Presumably the migration experience suddenly thrusts the individual into a new environment which makes different demands upon him than those he experienced in his place of origin. This explanation is congruent with those studies in which migrants manifested high rates of illness, but it is inapplicable to studies where this finding was not observed. Further research into the relationship between rate of cultural change and rates of illness is necessary. More often than not, rate of change is assumed to operate in this situation. Research is also necessary on the psychological reactions associated with situations which vary in this way.

(2) Similar approaches characterize discussions of social mobility. If the individual shifts suddenly from one status level to another, he is presumably faced with expectations and demands which he is unprepared to meet. Studies showing lower rates of illness among socially mobile groups might be understood more clearly if rate of change and its psychological concomitants were considered.

(3) Our analyses of migration data controlled for status achievement in order to determine whether the same relationship between migration and mental illness occurred at all levels in the status hierarchy. Analyses of the social mobility data controlled for status achievement for the same reasons. At no time, however, did we examine the interrelationship of migration and social mobility. For example, is the movement of the southern migrants associated with upward mobility, downward mobility, or status stability? Or is it merely a change of place of residence? The success of the yield analyses for migration and mobility may be attributed to the possibility that southern migrants have the social mobility characteristics of groups with low rates of illness, whereas the natives show those mobility characteristics associated with high illness rates. Further research will provide more definitive answers to this question.

(4) The multi-status or social-class index was used sparingly in the presentation of our findings. Because the shape of the rate curves differed

from one status dimension to another, we were not sure that anything would be gained by combining these indices into a single measure. The pattern of social-psychological characteristics predicted for status position did not correspond to expectations. Further research on status and class measures will contribute to our understanding of problems associated with using single measures of status and multi-status measures specifically, and the interrelationship of stratification and social-psychology in general.

(5) In Chapter 1 we explicitly stated that the theoretical orientation of this volume was a general approach to mental illness which should apply to any type of population. The present study was conducted in a Negro community because of our initial interest in migration and mental illness. It was limited to this community because the Negro population has shown such large shifts during the past twenty years. Consequently, we do not believe that the dynamics of illness presented in this volume are specific to this population. The validity of this assumption rests on future research efforts to test its applicability in other communities or other societies.

What are some of the implications of these findings for the larger "Negro problem" in American society? Do our data enlarge our understanding of this problem and some of the measures taken to alleviate it? The values and orientations of the lower-status Negro have often been characterized as "the culture of poverty." As currently used, this concept conjures up an image of individuals with low aspirations coupled with a lethargic acceptance of their fate. Social welfare planning, involving social educational and retraining programs, often implicitly assumes the above characterization. This culture and its members are sometimes seen as qualitatively (not only quantitatively) different from the more "respectable" elements of society.

Our data suggest that for the lower-status Negro this characterization is too sharply drawn and may sometimes cause welfare workers to misunderstand the motivation of their clients. Although our data do indicate that low-status Negroes have low levels of goal-striving stress, other findings suggest that their adjustment is not modally as apathetic as it might superficially appear. These individuals perceive themselves as furthest below their reference group, have the lowest self-esteem, and are more likely than others to be conscious of having lowered their ambitions from a previously higher level. The facts do not suggest a passive acceptance of fate, but rather a painful compromise. This is not to deny, of course, that apathy may be more prevalent among low-status than high-status Negroes, nor that the "culture of poverty" is not an actual phenomenon. We suggest that the characterization may be overdrawn, that the individuals so characterized may be too sharply differentiated from the larger community, and that the number of people involved may be exaggerated. If so, failure to appreciate these facts may hinder the full realization of welfare programs.

We must consider, too, the effects of the current upsurge of the civil rights struggle on the mental health of the Negro. Will the movement result in an increase or decrease of mental disorder among Negroes in the immediate future? No simple answer is possible, but our findings suggest certain possibilities. Analyses in different content areas consistently showed that Negroes who perceived the opportunity structure as open, and who had relatively high levels of goal-striving stress, were most prone to mental illness. This relates to the notion that a disjunction between goals and means is psychopathogenic. This idea was strongly confirmed by the lower correlation between educational achievement and occupational and/or income achievement for the patients than for the community respondents. Furthermore, comparing individuals with the same educational achievement also revealed lower occupational achievements for the ill than for the community subjects. Here we assume that uneven advances in important areas of striving provide the climate for anomie, alienation, and mental disorder.

With respect to the possible short-term effects of the civil rights movement, one immediate consequence of the demand for equality and "freedom now" will probably be a further rise in aspirational levels among Negroes. If opportunities for goal attainment are not expanded concomitantly, mental disorder may increase. Another immediate consequence of increased pressure from the Negro civil rights movement may be an uneven opening of different segments of the opportunity structure, permitting more mobility in one area of striving than in another. In this event, we again predict an increase in mental disorder. Whether this occurs depends partly on the ability of the civil rights movement to maintain its momentum and on the astuteness of its leaders in pursuing advantages that are not merely apparent gains. Token progress may actually increase mental illness.

Some of our findings also suggest that the fight for equal rights may *decrease* mental illness. Our analyses have revealed that the nature of an individual's ties with significant social groups has important implications for his mental health. If the impact of the civil rights movement increases cohesion and positive identity within the Negro community and creates a more positive group identification (as it appears to be doing), mental disorder may decrease. Which way the balance will tip is difficult to predict. Of this we are sure: given the nature of the American ethos with its emphasis on goal striving, the only viable way to reduce the anomic disjunction and the accompanying stresses experienced by the Negro is to insure for him greater opportunities in many areas of goal striving and social participation.

GENERAL BIBLIOGRAPHY

Adams, W. A. "The Negro Patient in Psychiatric Treatment," *American Journal of Orthopsychiatry*, 20 (1950), 305–310.

Alexander, C. N., and E. Q. Campbell. "Peer Influences on Adolescent Educational Aspirations and Attainments," *American Sociological Review*, 29 (1964), 568–575.

Alexander, L. E., L. B. Macht, and B. P. Karon. "The Level of Aspiration Model Applied to Occupational Preference," *Human Relations*, 12 (1959), 163–171.

Alper, T. G. "Memory for Completed and Incompleted Tasks as a Function of Personality: Correlation between Experimental and Personality Data," *Journal of Personality*, 17 (1948), 104–137.

Altrocchi, J., O. A. Parsons, and H. Dickoff. "Changes in Self-Ideal Discrepancy in Repressors and Sensitizers," *Journal of Abnormal and Social Psychology*, 61 (1960), 67–72.

Astrup, C., and Ø. Ødegaard. "Internal Migration and Mental Disease in Norway," *Psychiatric Quarterly Supplement*, 34 (1960), 116–130.

Atkinson, J. W. "Explorations Using Imaginative Thought to Assess the Strength of Human Motives," in M. R. Jones (ed.), *Nebraska Symposium on Motivation*, pp. 58–112. Lincoln: University of Nebraska Press, 1954.

Atkinson, J. W. "Motivational Determinants of Risk-Taking Behavior," *Psychological Review*, 64 (1957), 359–372.

Atkinson, J. W. (ed.). *Motives in Fantasy, Action, and Society: A Method of Assessment and Study*. Princeton, N.J.: D. Van Nostrand Co., Inc., 1958.

Atkinson, J. W., J. R. Bastian, R. W. Earl, and G. H. Litwin. "The Achievement Motive, Goal Setting, and Probability Preferences," *Journal of Abnormal and Social Psychology*, 60 (1960), 27–36.

Atkinson, J. W., and G. H. Litwin. "Achievement Motive and Test Anxiety Conceived as Motive to Approach Success and Motive to Avoid Failure," *Journal of Abnormal and Social Psychology*, 60 (1960), 52–63.

Ausubel, D. P. "Ego Development among Segregated Negro Children," *Mental Hygiene*, 42 (1956), 362–369.

Becker, J. "Achievement Related Characteristics of Manic-Depressives," *Journal of Abnormal and Social Psychology*, 60 (1960), 334–339.

Berlyne, D. E. *Conflict, Arousal, and Curiosity*. New York: McGraw-Hill Book Co., Inc., 1960.

Berlyne, D. E. "New Directions in Motivation Theory," in *Anthropology and Human Behavior*, pp. 150–173. Washington, D.C.: The Anthropological Society of Washington, 1962.

Bernard, V. "Psychoanalysis and Members of Minority Groups," *American Psychoanalytic Journal*, 1 (1953), 256–267.

Birch, H. G. "The Relation of Previous Experience to Insightful Problem Solving," *Journal of Comparative Psychology*, 38 (1945) 367–382.

Blau, P. M. "Social Mobility and Interpersonal Relations," *American Sociological Review*, 21 (1956), 290–295.

Block, J., and H. Thomas. "Is Satisfaction with Self a Measure of Adjustment?" *Journal of Abnormal and Social Psychology*, 51 (1955), 254–259.

Bremer, J. "A Social Psychiatric Investigation of a Small Community in Northern Norway," *Acta Psychiatrica et Neurologica*, Supplementum 62 (1951).

Brown, M. C. "The Status of Jobs and Occupations as Evaluated by an Urban Negro Sample," *American Sociological Review*, 20 (1955), 561–566.

Butler, J. M., and G. V. Haigh. "Changes in the Relation between Self-Concepts and Ideal Concepts Consequent upon Client Centered Counseling," in C. R. Rogers and R. F. Dymond (eds.), *Psychotherapy and Personality Change*, pp. 55–75. Chicago: University of Chicago Press, 1954.

Cade, J. F. J. "The Aetiology of Schizophrenia," *Medical Journal of Australia*, 2 (1956), 135–139.

Calvin, A. D., and W. H. Holtzman. "Adjustment and the Discrepancy between Self-Concept and Inferred Self," *Journal of Consulting Psychology*, 17 (1953), 39–44.

Chance, J. E. "Personality Differences and Level of Aspiration," *Journal of Consulting Psychology*, 24 (1960), 111–115.

Chapman, L. F., L. E. Hinkle, and H. G. Wolff. "Human Ecology, Disease, and Schizophrenia," *American Journal of Psychiatry*, 117 (1960), 193–204.

Chodorkoff, B. "Self-Perception, Perceptual Defense, and Adjustment," *Journal of Abnormal and Social Psychology*, 49 (1954), 508–512.

Clark, R. E. "The Relationship of Schizophrenia to Occupational Income and Occupational Prestige," *American Sociological Review*, 13 (1948), 325–330.

Clark, R. E. "Psychosis, Income, and Occupational Prestige," *American Journal of Sociology*, 54 (1949), 433–440.

Clausen, J. A. "Mental Disorders," in R. K. Merton and R. A. Nisbet (eds.), *Contemporary Social Problems*, pp. 127–180. New York: Harcourt, Brace and World, Inc., 1961.

Clausen, J. A., and M. L. Kohn. "Relation of Schizophrenia to the Social Structure of a Small City," in B. Pasamanick (ed.), *Epidemiology of Mental Disorder*, pp. 69–95. Washington, D.C.: American Association for the Advancement of Science, Publication Number 60, 1959.

Clausen, J. A., and M. L. Kohn. "Social Relations and Schizophrenia: A Research Report and a Perspective," in D. D. Jackson (ed.), *The Etiology of Schizophrenia*, pp. 295–320. New York: Basic Books, Inc., 1960.

Cohen, L. D. "Level-of-Aspiration Behavior and Feelings of Adequacy and Self-Acceptance," *Journal of Abnormal and Social Psychology*, 49 (1954), 84–86.

Combs, A., and D. Syngg. *Individual Behavior*. New York: Harper and Row, Publishers, 1959.

Cowen, E. L. "The Negative Self-Concept as a Personality Measure," *Journal of Consulting Psychology*, 18 (1954), 138–142.

Cowen, E. L., and E. Beir. "The Influence of 'Threat Expectance' on Perception," *Journal of Personality*, 19 (1950), 85–94.

Dai, B. "Some Problems of Personality and Development among Negro Children," in C. Kluckhohn and H. A. Murray (eds.), *Personality in Nature, Society, and Culture*, pp. 437–458. New York: Alfred A. Knopf, 1950.

Davids, A., and A. A. White. "Effects of Success, Failure, and Social Facilitation on Level of Aspiration in Emotionally Disturbed and Normal Children," *Journal of Personality*, 26 (1958), 77–93.

Davis, A. "Socialization and Adolescent Personality," in T. M. Newcomb and E. L. Hartley (eds.), *Readings in Social Psychology*, pp. 139–150. New York: Henry Holt and Co., 1947.

Dayton, N. A. *New Facts on Mental Disorders*. Springfield, Illinois: Charles C. Thomas, 1940.

Dell, P. C. "Some Basic Mechanisms of the Translation of Bodily Needs into Behaviour," in G. E. W. Wolstenholme and C. M. O'Connor (eds.), *Ciba Foundation Symposium on the Neurological Basis of Behaviour*, pp. 187–203. Boston: Little, Brown and Co., 1958.

Dreger, R., and K. S. Miller. "Comparative Studies of Negroes and Whites in the United States," *Psychological Bulletin*, 57 (1960), 361–402.

Dunham, H. W. *Sociological Theory and Mental Disorder*. Detroit: Wayne State University Press, 1959.

Durkheim, E. *Suicide,* Translated by J. A. Spaulding and G. Simpson. Glencoe, Illinois: The Free Press, 1951.

Eisenstadt, S. M. "Reference Group Behavior and Social Integration: An Explorative Study," *American Sociological Review*, 19 (1954a), 175–185.

Eisenstadt, S. M. "Studies in Reference Group Behavior," *Human Relations,* 7 (1954b), 191–216.

Eitinger, L. "The Incidence of Mental Disease among Refugees in Norway," *Journal of Mental Science,* 105 (1959), 326–338.

Ellis, E. "Social-Psychological Correlates of Upward Social Mobility among Unmarried Career Women," *American Sociological Review*, 17 (1952), 558–563.

Escalona, S. K. "The Effect of Success and Failure upon the Level of Aspiration and Behavior in Manic-Depressive Psychoses," in *University of Iowa Studies in Child Welfare: Studies in Topological and Vector Psychology I*, Volume 16, Number 3, pp. 199–302. Iowa City: University of Iowa Press, 1940.

Escalona, S. K. *An Application of the Level of Aspiration Experiment to the Study of Personality*. Teachers College, Columbia University Contributions to Education Number 937. New York: Bureau of Publication, Teachers College, Columbia University, 1948.

Eysenck, H. J. "The Measurement of Motivation," *Scientific American*, 208 (May 1963), 130–140.

Eysenck, H. J., and H. T. Himmelweit. "An Experimental Study of the Reactions of Neurotics to Experiences of Success and Failure," *Journal of General Psychology*, 35 (1946), 59–75.

Faris, R. E., and H. W. Dunham. *Mental Disorders in Urban Areas*. Chicago: University of Chicago Press, 1939.

Ferguson, E. D. "The Effect of Sibling Competition and Alliance on Level of Aspiration, Expectation, and Performance," *Journal of Abnormal and Social Psychology*, 56 (1958), 213–223.

Festinger, L. "Wish, Expectation, and Group Standards as Factors Influencing the Level of Aspiration," *Journal of Abnormal and Social Psychology*, 37 (1942), 184–200.

Festinger, L. "A Theory of Social Comparison Processes," *Human Relations,* 7 (1954), 117–140.

Festinger, L. *A Theory of Cognitive Dissonance*. Evanston, Illinois: Row, Peterson and Co., 1957.

Festinger, L., K. Back, S. Schachter, H. H. Kelley, and J. Thibaut. *Theory and Experiment in Social Communication*. Ann Arbor, Michigan: Research Center for Dynamics, Institute for Social Research, University of Michigan, 1950.

Festinger, L., J. Torrey, and B. Willerman. "Self Evaluation as a Function of Attraction to the Group," *Human Relations,* 7 (1954), 161–174.

Frank, J. "Individual Differences in Certain Aspects of the Level of Aspiration," *American Journal of Psychology,* 47 (1935a), 119–128.

Frank, J. "Some Psychological Determinants of the Level of Aspiration," *American Journal of Psychology,* 47 (1935b), 285–293.

Frank, J. "The Influence of Level of Performance in One Task on the Level of Aspiration in Another," *Journal of Experimental Psychology,* 18 (1935c), 159–171.

Frazier, E. F. *The Negro Family in the United States.* Chicago: University of Chicago Press, 1939.

Frazier, E. F. *Black Bourgeoisie.* Glencoe, Illinois: The Free Press, 1957.

French, J. R. P., Jr. *The Social Environment and Mental Health.* Presidential Address, American Psychological Association Convention, Philadelphia, September, 1963.

French, J. R. P., Jr., and R. L. Kahn. "A Programmatic Approach to Studying the Industrial Environment and Mental Health," *Journal of Social Issues,* 18 (1962), 1–47.

Frenkel-Brunswik, E. "Personality Theory and Perception," in R. Blake and G. V. Ramsey (eds.), *Perception, an Approach to Personality,* pp. 356–419. New York: The Ronald Press Co., 1951.

Fried, M. A. "Transitional Functions of Working-Class Communities: Implications for Forced Relocation," in M. B. Kantor (ed.), *Mobility and Mental Health,* pp. 123–165. Springfield, Illinois: Charles C. Thomas, 1965.

Friedman, I. "Phenomenal, Ideal, and Projected Conceptions of Self," *Journal of Abnormal and Social Psychology,* 51 (1955), 611–615.

Fromm, E. *Escape from Freedom.* New York: Holt, Rinehart and Winston, Inc., 1941.

Gardner, J. W. "The Relation of Certain Personality Variables to Level of Aspiration," *Journal of Psychology,* 9 (1940), 191–206.

Glick, P. C., and H. P. Miller. "Educational Level and Potential Income," *American Sociological Review,* 21 (1956), 307–312.

Greenbaum, J., and L. I. Pearlin. "Vertical Mobility and Prejudice: A Socio-Psychological Analysis," in R. Bendix and S. M. Lipset (eds.), *Class, Status, and Power: A Reader in Social Stratification,* pp. 480–491. Glencoe, Illinois: The Free Press, 1953.

Gurin, G., J. Veroff, and S. Feld. *Americans View Their Mental Health.* New York: Basic Books, Inc., 1960.

Hatfield, J. *A Study of Self-Concept Configurations in Relation to Forms of Ego Functioning.* (Unpublished Doctoral Dissertation), Berkeley, University of California, 1958.

Hausmann, M. F. "A Test to Evaluate Some Personality Traits," *Journal of General Psychology*, 9 (1933), 179–189.

Haveman, E., and P. S. West. *They Went to College*. New York: Harcourt, Brace and World, Inc., 1952.

Hebb, D. O. *Organization and Behavior: A Neuropsychological Theory*. New York: John Wiley and Sons, Inc., 1949.

Himmelweit, H. "A Comparative Study of the Level of Aspiration of Normal and Neurotic Persons," *British Journal of Psychology*, 37 (1947), 41–59.

Hinkle, L. E., and H. G. Wolff. "Health and the Social Environment: Experimental Investigations," in A. H. Leighton, J. A. Clausen, and R. N. Wilson (eds.), *Explorations in Social Psychiatry*, pp. 105–137. New York: Basic Books, Inc., 1957.

Hinkle, L. E., and H. G. Wolff. "Ecological Investigations of the Relationship between Illness, Life Experience, and the Social Environment," *Annals of Internal Medicine*, 49 (1958), 1373–1388.

Hinkle, L. E., W. N. Christenson, F. D. Kane, A. Ostfeld, W. N. Thetford, and H. G. Wolff. "An Investigation of the Relation between Life Experience, Personality Characteristics, and General Susceptibility to Illness," *Psychosomatic Medicine*, 20 (1958), 278–295.

Hollingshead, A. B., and F. C. Redlich. "Schizophrenia and Social Structure," *American Journal of Psychiatry*, 110 (1954), 695–701.

Hollingshead, A. B., and F. C. Redlich. "Social Mobility and Mental Illness," *American Journal of Psychiatry*, 112 (1955), 179–185.

Hollingshead, A. B., and F. C. Redlich. *Social Class and Mental Illness*. New York: John Wiley and Sons, Inc., 1958.

Hollingshead, A. B., R. Ellis, and E. Kirby. "Social Mobility and Mental Illness," *American Sociological Review*, 19 (1954), 577–584.

Horney, K. *The Neurotic Personality of Our Time*. New York: W. W. Norton and Co., Inc., 1937.

Hughes, E. C., "Dilemmas and Contradictions of Status," *American Journal of Sociology*, 50 (1945), 353–359.

Hull, C. L. *A Behavior System: An Introduction to Behavior Theory Concerning the Individual Organism*. New Haven: Yale University Press, 1952.

Hyde, R. W., and L. V. Kingsley. "Studies in Medical Sociology I: The Relation of Mental Disorders to the Community Socio-Economic Level," *New England Journal of Medicine*, 231 (1944), 543–548.

Hyman, H. H. "The Psychology of Status," *Archives of Psychology*, Number 269 (1942).

Hyman, H. H. "The Relation of the Reference Group to Judgments of Status," in R. Bendix and S. M. Lipset (eds.), *Class, Status, and Power: A Reader in Social Stratification*, pp. 263–270. Glencoe, Illinois: The Free Press, 1953a.

Hyman, H. H. "The Value Systems of Different Classes: A Social Psychological Contribution to the Analysis of Stratification," in R. Bendix and S. M. Lipset (eds.), *Class, Status, and Power: A Reader in Social Stratification*, pp. 426–442. Glencoe, Illinois: The Free Press, 1953b.

Irwin, F. W. and M. G. Mintzer. "Effect of Differences in Instructions and Motivation upon Measures of the Level of Aspiration," *American Journal of Psychology*, 55 (1942), 400–406.

Jaco, E. G. "Social Stress and Mental Illness in the Community," in M. B. Sussman (ed.), *Community Structure and Analysis*, pp. 388–409. New York: Thomas Y. Crowell Co., 1959.

Jaco, E. G. *The Social Epidemiology of Mental Disorder: A Psychiatric Survey of Texas*. New York: Russell Sage Foundation, 1960.

Janowitz, M., and R. Curtis. *Sociological Consequences of Upward Mobility in a U.S. Metropolitan Community*. Working Paper One, The Fourth Working Conference on Social Stratification and Social Mobility, International Sociological Association, December, 1957.

Jost, K. C. "The Level of Aspiration of Schizophrenic and Normal Subjects," *Journal of Abnormal and Social Psychology*, 50 (1955), 315–320.

Kahl, J. A., and J. A. Davis. "A Comparison of Indexes of Socio-Economic Status," *American Sociological Review*, 20 (1955), 317–325.

Kantor, M. B. "Some Consequences of Residential and Social Mobility for the Adjustment of Children," in M. B. Kantor (ed.), *Mobility and Mental Health*, pp. 86–122. Springfield, Illinois: Charles C. Thomas, 1965.

Kaplan, B., R. Reed, and W. Richardson. "A Comparison of the Incidence of Hospitalized and Non-Hospitalized Cases of Psychosis in Two Communities," *American Sociological Review*, 21 (1956), 472–479.

Kardiner, A., and L. Ovesey. *The Mark of Oppression: A Psychosocial Study of the American Negro*. New York: W. W. Norton and Co., Inc., 1951.

Kasl, S. V., and J. R. P. French, Jr. "The Effects of Occupational Status on Physical and Mental Health," *Journal of Social Issues*, 18 (1962), 67–89.

Kephart, W. M., and T. P. Monahan. "Desertion and Divorce in Philadelphia," *American Sociological Review*, 17 (1952), 719–727.

Kleiner, R. J. *Status, Group Membership, and Schizophrenia*. Paper Presented at the American Psychological Association Convention, Cincinnati, September, 1959.

Kleiner, R. J. "The Effects of Threat Reduction upon Interpersonal Attractiveness," *Journal of Personality*, 28 (1960), 145–155.

Kleiner, R. J., and S. Parker. "Migration and Mental Illness: A New Look," *American Sociological Review*, 24 (1959), 687–690.

Kleiner, R. J., and S. Parker. *Occupational Status, Goal-Striving Behavior, and Mental Disorder*. Paper Presented at the American Psychological Association Convention, St. Louis, September, 1962.

Kleiner, R. J., and S. Parker. "Goal-Striving, Social Status, and Mental Disorder: A Research Review," *American Sociological Review*, 28 (1963), 189–203.

Kleiner, R. J., and S. Parker. "Goal Striving and Psychosomatic Symptoms in a Migrant and Non-Migrant Population," in M. B. Kantor (ed.), *Mobility and Mental Health*, pp. 78–85. Springfield, Illinois: Charles C. Thomas, 1965.

Kleiner, R. J., S. Parker, and H. G. Taylor. *Goal Striving and Psychosomatic Symptoms in a Migrant and Non-Migrant Population*. Paper Presented at the World Federation for Mental Health Convention, Paris, September, 1961.

Kleiner, R. J., J. Tuckman, and M. Lavell. "Mental Disorder and Status Based on Race," *Psychiatry*, 23 (1960), 271–274.

Klugman, S. F. "Relationship Between Performance on the Rotter Aspiration Board and Various Types of Tests," *Journal of Psychology*, 23 (1947), 51–54.

Klugman, S. F. "Emotional Stability and Level of Aspiration," *Journal of General Psychology*, 38 (1948), 101–118.

Koffka, K. *Principles of Gestalt Psychology*. New York: Harcourt, Brace and Co., 1935.

Kounin, J. S. "Experimental Studies of Rigidity," *Character and Personality*, 9 (1941), 251–282.

Langner, T. S., and S. T. Michael. *Life Stress and Mental Health: The Midtown Manhattan Study*, Volume 2. Glencoe, Illinois: The Free Press, 1963.

Lapouse, R., M. A. Monk, and M. Terris. "The Drift Hypothesis and Socio-Economic Differentials in Schizophrenia," *American Journal of Public Health*, 46 (1956), 978–986.

Last, J. M. "The Health of Immigrants: Some Observations from General Practice," *Medical Journal of Australia*, 1 (1960), 158–162.

Lazarus, R. S., and R. W. Baker. "Personality and Psychological Stress: A Theoretical and Methodological Framework," *Psychological Newsletter*, 8 (1956), 21–32.

Lazarus, J., B. Z. Locke, and D. S. Thomas. "Migration Differentials in Mental Disease: State Patterns in First Admissions to Mental Hospitals for all Disorders and for Schizophrenia, New York, Ohio, and California, as of 1950," *Milbank Memorial Fund Quarterly*, 41 (1963), 25–42.

Lee, E. S. "Socio-Economic and Migration Differentials in Mental Disease, New York State, 1949–1951," *Milbank Memorial Fund Quarterly*, 41 (1963), 249–269.

Leighton, D. C., J. S. Harding, D. B. Macklin, C. C. Hughes, and A. H. Leighton. "Psychiatric Findings of the Stirling County Study," *American Journal of Psychiatry*, 119 (1963), 1021–1026.

Leighton, D. C., J. S. Harding, D. B. Macklin, A. M. Macmillan, and A. H. Leighton. *The Character of Danger.* New York: Basic Books, Inc., 1963.

Lemert, E. M. "An Exploratory Study of Mental Disorders in a Rural Problem Area," *Rural Sociology,* 13 (1948), 48–65.

Lenski, G. "Status Crystallization: A Non-Vertical Dimension of Social Status," *American Sociological Review,* 19 (1954), 405–413.

Lerner, M. *America as a Civilization: Life and Thought in the United States Today.* New York: Simon and Schuster, 1957.

Lewin, K. *A Dynamic Theory of Personality: Selected Papers by Kurt Lewin,* Translated by D. K. Adams and K. E. Zener. New York: McGraw-Hill Book Co., Inc., 1935.

Lewin, K. "Psychology of Success and Failure," *Occupations,* 14 (1936), 926–930.

Lewin, K. "Formalization and Progress in Psychology," in *University of Iowa Studies in Child Welfare: Studies in Topological and Vector Psychology I,* Volume 16, Number 3, pp. 9–42. Iowa City: University of Iowa Press, 1940.

Lewin, K. *Resolving Social Conflicts: Selected Papers on Group Dynamics.* New York: Harper and Brothers, 1948.

Lewin, K. *Field Theory in Social Science: Selected Theoretical Papers by Kurt Lewin,* Edited by D. Cartwright. New York: Harper and Brothers, 1951.

Lewin, K., T. Dembo, L. Festinger, and P. S. Sears. "Level of Aspiration," in J. McV. Hunt (ed.), *Personality and the Behavior Disorders: A Handbook Based on Experimental and Clinical Research,* Volume 1, pp. 333–378. New York: The Ronald Press Co., 1944.

Lewis, H. B. "An Experimental Study of the Role of the Ego in Work. I. The Role of the Ego in Cooperative Work," *Journal of Experimental Psychology,* 34 (1944), 113–126.

Lewis, H. B., and M. Franklin. "An Experimental Study of the Role of the Ego in Work. II. The Significance of Task-Orientation in Work," *Journal of Experimental Psychology,* 34 (1944), 195–215.

Likert, R. "A Technique for the Measurement of Attitudes," *Archives of Psychology,* Number 140 (1932).

Lin, Tsung-yi. "A Study of the Incidence of Mental Disorder in Chinese and Other Cultures," *Psychiatry,* 16 (1953), 313–336.

Lipset, S. M., and R. Bendix. *Social Mobility in Industrial Society.* Berkeley and Los Angeles: University of California Press, 1963.

Listwan, I. A. "Mental Disorders in Migrants: Further Study," *Medical Journal of Australia,* 1 (1959), 566–568.

Little, S. W., and L. D. Cohen. "Goal Setting Behavior of Asthmatic Children and of Their Mothers for Them," *Journal of Personality,* 19 (1951), 376–389.

Litwak, E. *Conflicting Values and Decision Making.* (Doctoral Dissertation), New York, Columbia University, 1956.

Locke, B. Z., M. Kramer, and B. Pasamanick. "Immigration and Insanity," *Public Health Reports,* 75 (1960), 301–306.

Lystad, M. H. "Social Mobility Among Selected Groups of Schizophrenic Patients," *American Sociological Review,* 22 (1957), 288–292.

MacLean, P. D. "Psychosomatic Disease and the 'Visceral Brain,'" *Psychosomatic Medicine,* 11 (1949), 338–353.

Macmillan, A. M. "The Health Opinion Survey: Technique for Estimating Prevalence of Psychoneurotic and Related Types of Disorder in Communities," *Psychological Reports,* 3 (1957), 325.

Macmillan, A. M. "A Survey Technique for Estimating the Prevalence of Psychoneurotic and Related Types of Disorders in Communities," in B. Pasamanick (ed.), *Epidemiology of Mental Disorder,* pp. 203–228. Washington, D.C.: American Association for the Advancement of Science, 1959.

Mahone, C. H. "Fear of Failure and Unrealistic Vocational Aspiration," *Journal of Abnormal and Social Psychology,* 60 (1960), 253–261.

Malzberg, B. *Social and Biological Aspects of Mental Disease.* Utica, New York: State Hospitals Press, 1940.

Malzberg, B. "Mental Disease Among the Native and Foreign-Born White Population of New York State, 1939–1941," *Mental Hygiene,* 39 (1955), 545–563.

Malzberg, B., and E. S. Lee. *Migration and Mental Disease: A Study of First Admissions to Hospitals for Mental Disease, New York, 1939–1941.* New York: Social Science Research Council, 1956.

Marrow, A. J. "Goal Tensions and Recall: I," *Journal of General Psychology,* 19 (1938a), 3–35.

Marrow, A. J. "Goal Tensions and Recall: II," *Journal of General Psychology,* 19 (1938b), 37–64.

McClosky, H., and J. H. Schaar. "Psychological Dimensions of Anomy," *American Sociological Review,* 30 (1965), 14–40.

McGinnies, E., and J. Adornetto. "Perceptual Defense in Normal and in Schizophrenic Observers," *Journal of Abnormal and Social Psychology,* 47 (1952), 833–837.

Merton, R. K. *Social Theory and Social Structure,* Revised Edition. Glencoe, Illinois: The Free Press, 1957.

Miller, D. "The Study of Social Relationships: Situation, Identity, and Social Interaction," in S. Koch (ed.), *Psychology: A Study of a Science,* Volume 5, pp. 639–737. New York: McGraw-Hill Book Co., Inc., 1963.

Miller, N. E. "Experimental Studies of Conflict," in J. McV. Hunt (ed.), *Personality and the Behavior Disorders: A Handbook Based on Experi-*

mental and Clinical Research, Volume 1, pp. 431–465. New York: The Ronald Press Co., 1944.

Miller, N. E., and J. Dollard. *Social Learning and Imitation.* New Haven: Yale University Press, 1941.

Morris, J. N. "Health and Social Class," *Lancet,* 1 (1959), 303–305.

Mowrer, O. H. *Learning Theory and Personality Dynamics: Selected Papers.* New York: The Ronald Press Co., 1950.

Mowrer, O. H., and A. D. Ullman. "Time as a Determinant in Integrative Learning," *Psychological Review,* 52 (1945), 61–90.

Murphy, G. *Personality: A Biosocial Approach to Origins and Structure.* New York: Harper and Brothers, 1947.

Murphy, H. B. M. "Social Change and Mental Health," in *Causes of Mental Disorders: A Review of Epidemiological Knowledge, 1959,* pp. 280–329. New York: Milbank Memorial Fund, 1961.

Murphy, H. B. M. "Migration and the Major Mental Disorders: A Reappraisal," in M. B. Kantor (ed.), *Mobility and Mental Health,* pp. 5–29. Springfield, Illinois: Charles C. Thomas, 1965.

Myers, J. K., and B. H. Roberts. *Family and Class Dynamics in Mental Illness.* New York: John Wiley and Sons, Inc., 1959.

Ødegaard, Ø. "Emigration and Insanity: A Study of Mental Disease Among the Norwegian-Born Population of Minnesota," *Acta Psychiatrica et Neurologica,* Supplementum 1–4 (1932).

Ødegaard, Ø. "The Distribution of Mental Diseases in Norway: A Contribution to the Ecology of Mental Disorder," *Acta Psychiatrica et Neurologica,* 20 (1945), 247–284.

Ødegaard, Ø. "The Incidence of Psychoses in Various Occupations," *International Journal of Social Psychiatry,* 2 (1956), 85–104.

Olson, G. W. "Failure and the Subsequent Performance of Schizophrenics," *Journal of Abnormal and Social Psychology,* 57 (1958), 310–314.

Osgood, C. E. *Method and Theory in Experimental Psychology.* New York: Oxford University Press, 1953.

Osgood, C. E. "Psycholinguistics," in S. Koch (ed.), *Psychology: A Study of a Science,* Volume 6, pp. 244–316. New York: McGraw-Hill Book Co., Inc., 1963.

Ovsiankina, M. "Die Wiederaufnahme Unterbrochener Handlugen," *Psychologische Forschung,* 11 (1928), 302–379.

Parker, S., and R. J. Kleiner. "Status Position, Mobility, and Ethnic Identification of the Negro," *Journal of Social Issues,* 20 (1964), 85–102.

Parker, S., R. J. Kleiner, and H. G. Taylor. "Level of Aspiration and Mental Disorder: A Research Proposal," *Annals of the New York Academy of Sciences,* 84 (1960), 878–886.

Pasamanick, B., D. W. Roberts, P. W Lemkau, and D. B. Krueger. "A Survey of Mental Disease in an Urban Population: Prevalence by Race and Income," in B. Pasamanick (ed.), *Epidemiology of Mental Disorder*, pp. 183–201. Washington, D.C.: American Association for the Advancement of Science, 1959.

Prange, A. J., and M. M. Vitols. "Cultural Aspects of the Relatively Low Incidence of Depression in Southern Negroes," *International Journal of Social Psychiatry*, 8 (1962), 104–112.

Prange, A. J., and M. M. Vitols. "Jokes among Southern Negroes: The Revelation of Conflict," *Journal of Nervous and Mental Disease*, 136 (1963), 162–167.

Price, D. O. "Next Steps in Studying Mobility and Mental Health," in M. B. Kantor (ed.), *Mobility and Mental Health*, pp. 238–247. Springfield, Illinois: Charles C. Thomas, 1965.

Raifman, I. "Level of Aspiration in a Group of Peptic Ulcer Patients," *Journal of Consulting Psychology*, 21 (1957), 229–231.

Rasmussen, G., and A. Zander. "Group Membership and Self-Evaluation," *Human Relations*, 7 (1954), 239–251.

Reid, D. D. "Precipitating Proximal Factors in the Occurrence of Mental Disorders: Epidemiological Evidence," in *Causes of Mental Disorders: A Review of Epidemiological Knowledge, 1959*, pp. 197–216. New York: Milbank Memorial Fund, 1961.

Rennie, T. A. C. "The Yorkville Community Mental Health Research Study," in *Interrelations Between the Social Environment and Psychiatric Disorders*, pp. 209–221. New York: Milbank Memorial Fund, 1953.

Rogers, C. R. *Client-Centered Therapy: Its Current Practice, Implications, and Theory*. Boston: Houghton Mifflin Co., 1951.

Rogers, C. R. "A Theory of Therapy, Personality, and Interpersonal Relationships, as Developed in the Client-Centered Framework," in S. Koch (ed.), *Psychology: A Study of a Science*, Volume 3, pp. 184–252. New York: McGraw-Hill Book Co., Inc., 1959.

Rogers, C., and R. Dymond. *Psychotherapy and Personality Change*. Chicago: University of Chicago Press, 1954.

Rose, A. W., and M. C. Wall. "Sociological Factors in the Prestige Rankings of Occupations," *Personnel Guidance Journal*, 35 (1957), 420–423.

Ruesch, J. *Chronic Disease and Psychological Invalidism: A Psychosomatic Study*. New York: American Society for Research in Psychosomatic Problems, 1946.

Ruesch, J. "Social Technique, Social Status, and Social Change in Illness," in C. Kluckhohn, H. A. Murray, and D. M. Schneider (eds.), *Personality in Nature, Society, and Culture*, pp. 123–136. New York: Alfred A. Knopf, 1956.

Ruesch, J., A. Jacobson, and M. B. Loeb. *Acculturation and Illness*. Psychological Monographs, General and Applied, Volume 62, Whole Number 292. Washington, D.C.: The American Psychological Association, 1948.

Savitz, L. *Delinquency and Migration*. Philadelphia: Commission on Human Relations, 1960.

Sclare, A. B. "Cultural Determinants in the Neurotic Negro," *British Journal of Medical Psychology*, 26 (1953), 279–288.

Sears, P. S. "Level of Aspiration in Relation to some Variables of Personality: Clinical Studies," *Journal of Social Psychology*, 14 (1941), 311–336.

Sewell, W. H., and A. O. Haller. "Factors in the Relationship Between Social Status and the Personality Adjustment of the Child," *American Sociological Review*, 24 (1959), 511–520.

Shane, M. "Some Subcultural Considerations in the Psychotherapy of a Negro Patient," *Psychiatric Quarterly*, 34 (1960), 1–19.

Shibutani, T. "Reference Groups as Perspectives," *American Journal of Sociology*, 60 (1955), 562–570.

Simpson, R. "Parental Influence, Anticipatory Socialization, and Social Mobility," *American Sociological Review*, 27 (1962), 517–522.

Snedecor, G. W. *Statistical Methods*, Fourth Edition. Ames, Iowa: The Iowa State College Press, 1946.

Srole, L., T. S. Langner, S. T. Michael, M. K. Opler, and T. A. C. Rennie. *Mental Health in the Metropolis: The Midtown Manhattan Study*, Volume 1. New York: McGraw-Hill Book Co., Inc. 1962.

Stein, L. " 'Social Class' Gradient in Schizophrenia," *British Journal of Preventive Medicine*, 11 (1957), 181–195.

Sullivan, H. S. *Conceptions of Modern Psychiatry*. Washington, D.C.: The William Nanson White Psychiatric Foundation, 1947.

Thomas, D. S., and B. Z. Locke. "Marital Status, Education, and Occupational Differentials in Mental Disease: State Patterns in First Admissions to Mental Hospitals for all Disorders and for Schizophrenia. New York and Ohio, as of 1950," *Milbank Memorial Fund Quarterly*, 41 (1963), 145–160.

Tietze, C., P. Lemkau, and M. Cooper. "Schizophrenia, Manic-Depressive Psychosis, and Socio-Economic Status," *American Journal of Sociology*, 47 (1941), 167–175.

Tietze, C., P. Lemkau, and M. Cooper. "Personality Disorder and Spatial Mobility," *American Journal of Sociology*, 48 (1942), 29–39.

Tuckman, J., and R. J. Kleiner. "Discrepancy Between Aspiration and Achievement as a Predictor of Schizophrenia," *Behavioral Science*, 7 (1962), 443–447.

Turner, R. H., and R. H. Vanderlipp. "Self-Ideal Congruence as an Index of Adjustment," *Journal of Abnormal and Social Psychology*, 57 (1958), 202–207.

Tyhurst, L. "Displacement and Migration: A Study in Social Psychiatry," *American Journal of Psychiatry*, 107 (1951), 561–568.

Vogel, W., R. W. Baker, and R. S. Lazarus. "The Role of Motivation in Psychological Stress," *Journal of Abnormal and Social Psychology*, 56 (1958), 105–113.

Vogel, W., S. Raymond, and R. S. Lazarus. "Intrinsic Motivation and Psychological Stress," *Journal of Abnormal and Social Psychology*, 58 (1959), 225–234.

Walker, H. W., and J. Lev. *Statistical Inference*. New York: Henry Holt and Co., 1953.

Warner, W. L. "The Society, the Individual, and his Mental Disorders," *American Journal of Psychiatry*, 94 (1937), 275–284.

Weinberg, A. A. "Problems of Adjustment of New Immigrants to Israel," *World Mental Health*, 5 (1953a), 57–63.

Weinberg, A. A. "Problems of Adjustment of New Immigrants to Israel," *World Mental Health*, 5 (1953b), 129–135.

Weinberg, A. A. "Problems of Adjustment of New Immigrants to Israel," *Bulletin of the World Federation of Mental Health*, 5 (1953c), 1–13.

Weinberg, A. A. "Mental Health Aspects of Voluntary Migration," *Mental Hygiene*, 39 (1955), 450–464.

Weinberg, S. K. "A Sociological Analysis of a Schizophrenic Type," in A. M. Rose (ed.), *Mental Health and Mental Disorder*, pp. 240–257. New York: W. W. Norton and Co., Inc., 1955.

Weinberg, S. K. "Social-Psychological Aspects of Schizophrenia," in L. Appelby, J. M. Scher, and J. Cumming (eds.), *Chronic Schizophrenia*, pp. 68–88. Glencoe, Illinois: The Free Press, 1960.

Wolff, H. G. "Stress and Adaptive Patterns Resulting in Tissue Damage in Man," in *The Medical Clinics of North America: Basic Sciences in Medical Practice*, pp. 783–797. Philadelphia: W. B. Saunders and Co., 1955.

Wolff, H. G. "A Concept of Disease in Man," *Psychosomatic Medicine*, 24 (1962), 25–30.

Zander, A., and H. Medow. "Individual and Group Levels of Aspiration," *Human Relations*, 16 (1963), 89–105.

Zander, A., and R. Quinn. "The Social Environment and Mental Health: A Review of Past Research at the Institute for Social Research," *Journal of Social Issues*, 18 (1962), 48–66.

Zeigarnik, B. "On Finished and Unfinished Tasks," in W. D. Ellis (ed.), *A Source Book of Gestalt Psychology*, pp. 300–314. London: Kegan Paul, Trench, Trubner, and Co., Ltd., 1938.

APPENDIX A

Sampling Plan for the
Community Population

The sample consists of a five-stage, self-weighting sample designed to yield 1500 interviews with native-born, adult Negroes 20–60 years of age residing in Philadelphia. This will result in approximately four interviews per block. There are 59 voting wards divided into a total of 1573 divisions. These are sampled in Stages I and II of the following detailed sample design. Stage III consists of identifying the selected districts and drawing a sample of blocks from the block statistics data for Philadelphia. Stages IV and V consist of identifying the sample household and the respondent within the household.

The overall sampling rate is one in 200. Therefore, the sampling rate used for Stage V will depend on the selections made in the other four stages. This is explained in a detailed flow chart giving every possible combination of selections in the different stages.

The five stages of sampling are:

Stage I: Selection of Wards

The wards are selected with PPS[1], sampling interval 1200. Included with certainty are any wards with Negro voters numbering 800 or more. The measure of size of the ward is the number of Negro voters within a ward, unless this number is less than six, in which case six will be used. Let w_h = probability of selection of h-th ward and W_h = number of Negroes within h-th ward.

Stage II: Selection of Divisions

The divisions are selected with PPS, sampling interval 400. *Included with certainty are any divisions with Negro voters numbering 300 or more. Also*

---

1. Probability in Proportion to Size.

included with certainty are all divisions in a ward for which $w_h = 1/200$. The measure of size is Negro voters, unless this is less than $2/w_h$; otherwise, measure of size is $2/w_h$. Let d_{hi} = probability of selection of i-th division and D_{hi} = number of Negroes within the i-th division.

Stage III: Selection of Blocks

The blocks are selected with PPS, using H_{hij}, number of nonwhite dwelling units (1950), as a measure of size and sampling interval $360w_h d_{hi}$ with the following exceptions:

a) Blocks are selected with certainty if H_{hij} is $360w_h d_{hi}$ or more.

b) Measure of size $H'_{hij} = 2$ if $H_{hij} =$ one or less.

Omitted from further work is any division for which $w_h d_{hi} = 1/200$, but these were listed separately.

Let b_{hij} = probability of selection of j-th block and B_{hij} = number of Negroes within the j-th block.

Stage IV: Selection of Households

All Negro households are listed (i.e., households including any Negroes). Households are selected with a sampling rate $f_{hij} = 9/H_{hij}$; provided that this is less than or equal to one. Otherwise, the whole black is included ($F_{hij} = 1$).

Stage V: Selection of Respondents

All eligible persons are listed and sampled one (1) in five (5) or at the rates listed in the following table based on the previous combination of selected stages. Let k_{hij} = probability of selection of the respondent.

Table 1 (Appendix A)—Sampling Rate for Stage V

for All Possible Combinations of Stages so That:

$$w_h d_{hi} b_{hij} f_{hij} k_{hij} = 1/200$$

Stage II Code	Stage III Code	Stage IV Code	Stage I w_h	Stage II d_{hi}	Stage III b_{hij}	Stage IV f_{hij}	Stave V k_{hij}
					PROBABILITY OF SELECTION		
1	1	1	1	1	1	1	impossible
1	1	2	1	1	1	1/40	1/5
1	2	1	1	1	H/360	1	1.8/H
1	2	2	1	1	H/360	9/H	1/5
2	1	1	1	D/400	1	1	2/D
2	1	2	1	D/400	1	9/H	2H/9D
2	2	1	1	D/400	400H/360D	1	1.8/H
2	2	2	1	D/400	400H/360D	9/H	1/5
3	1	-	1	1	1	1	1
4	1	1	W/1200	1	1	1	6/W
4	1	2	W/1200	1	1	9/H	2H/3W
4	2	1	W/1200	1	10H/3W	1	1.8/H
4	2	2	W/1200	1	10H/3W	9/H	1/5
5	1	1	W/1200	D/400	1	1	2400/WD
5	1	2	W/1200	D/400	1	9/H	800H/3WD
5	2	1	W/1200	D/400	12000H/9WD	1	1.8/H
5	2	2	W/1200	D/400	12000H/9WD	9/H	1/5

APPENDIX B

The Interview Schedule

National Analysts, Inc.   Study #1-754
Philadelphia 7, Pa.   February-March, 1960

HEALTH, OCCUPATION AND EDUCATION STUDY

Segment #	
D.U. #	
Line #	

Time Interview Started:

_____ A.M. _____ P.M.
....
Time Interview Ended:

_____ A.M. _____ P.M.

SUGGESTED INTRODUCTION: I am _____ from National Analysts, Inc., a research
company. At this time we are doing a study in Philadelphia. (SHOW RESPONDENT LETTER)
We are talking to people like yourself about the attitudes and feelings they have regarding
their education, occupation and their health. We are talking to a cross section of people,
and you were selected as part of this cross section.

1. In what community (city, town, village) and state was your mother born?

_____   _____
(Community, city or town)   (State)

2. In what community (city, town, village) and state was your father born?

_____   _____
(Community, city or town)   (State)

3. In what community (city, town, village) and state were you born?

_____   _____
(Community, city or town)   (State)

4. How many years have you lived in Philadelphia?

| # Years | |

5. Altogether, how many different addresses have you yourself had within Philadelphia city limits during the last three years?

| Number | |

6. Where did you live during the first seventeen years of your life? Starting with the place where you were born, please give me the town or city, the state, and the number of years you lived there. What was the next place you lived? How many years? (REPEAT UNTIL FIRST 17 YEARS ARE ACCOUNTED FOR)

Town or City	State	Number of Years
		TOTAL = 17 YEARS

(RECORD EITHER MIGRANT OR NON-MIGRANT, FROM INFORMATION IN Q. 6:)

Respondent is:	(CONTINUE)	Migrant	1
	(SKIP TO Q.15)	Non-migrant	2

(A NON-MIGRANT IS ANYONE, REGARDLESS OF BIRTHPLACE, WHO SPENT ANY 9 OF HIS FIRST 17 YEARS OF LIFE IN PHILADELPHIA. ALL OTHERS ARE TO BE REGARDED AS MIGRANTS.)

- 1 -

7. (IF BORN IN SOUTH) How old were you when you first moved north of Washington, D.C.?

(coded only for Southern migrants)

Age in years	

8. How many years have you lived in the "North?"

(omitted from Community sample, coded for III sample)

Number of years	

9. When you came to Philadelphia, with whom did you come? (ENTER IN COL. 1, TABLE BELOW)

(coded only for migrants)

10. (IF "ALONE") Did any of your friends or relatives come to Philadelphia within a period of 3 months before or 3 months after you did?

(omitted from both samples)

	Yes	1
(SKIP TO Q.12)	No	2

11. (IF "YES", Q.10) Who was it? (ENTER IN COL. 2, TABLE BELOW)

12. During your first 3 months in Philadelphia, with whom did you live? (ENTER IN COL. 3)

(omitted from both samples)

13. Did you have any friends or relatives already in Philadelphia with whom you regularly got together soon after you arrived?

(omitted from both samples)

	Yes	1
(SKIP TO Q.15)	No	2

14. (IF "YES") With whom did you regularly get together? (ENTER IN COL. 4)

(omitted from both samples)

15. (ASK EVERYONE) With whom do you live now? (ENTER IN COL. 5)

	Col. 1 (Q.9) Come With	Col. 2 (Q.11) Came After	Col. 3 (Q.12) Lived With	Col. 4 (Q.14) Get Together With	Col. 5 (Q.15) Live With Now
Parent(s) - Brother(s) - Sister(s)	1	1	1	1	1
Husband - Wife - my children	2	2	2	2	2
Other relatives	3	3	3	3	3
Friends	4	4	4	4	4
Alone (no one)	5	5	5	5	5
Other	6	6	6	6	6

- 2 -

16. Supposing you received $5,000 unexpectedly, how would you spend this money? What would be your first choice, what would be second choice? What would be third choice?

	First choice	Second choice	Third choice
a. Money for vacation for family	1	2	3
b. Money for a car	1	2	3
c. Money for a new house or pay off mortgage on present house	1	2	3
d. Money for education for family	1	2	3
e. Money for new clothes	1	2	3
f. Money for a saving fund	1	2	3
g. Money for life and health insurance	1	2	3
h. Money for medical and dental expenses	1	2	3
i. Money to pay off debts	1	2	3
j. Money for furniture and/or repairing the house	1	2	3

17. What was the highest grade that you completed in school?

None	0							
Grade school	1	2	3	4	5	6	7	8
High school	1	2	3	4				
College or University	1	2	3	4	5 or more			

18. Since you left the _(READ RESPONSE IN Q.17)_ grade, have you had any further schooling?

	Yes	1
(SKIP TO Q.20)	No	2

19. (IF "YES") What kind(s) and how long attended?

(omitted from both samples)

Type of School	Number of months

20. When you were in school, what was the highest education you wanted to get?

(CIRCLE HIGHEST GIVEN)	Complete elementary school education	1
	Complete vocational training	2
	Complete high school education	3
	Complete college education	4
	Graduate - Professional education	5
	Cannot specify any level	6

21. How do you feel now about having left school when you did?

(omitted from both samples)

Very satisfied	1
Somewhat satisfied	2
Don't feel very strongly one way or another	3
Somewhat sorry	4
Very sorry	5

22. What are your reasons for feeling this way about it?

(omitted from both samples)

- 3 -

23. Are you going to school now?

	Yes	1
	No	2

24. Do you plan to continue your education in the future?

	Yes	1
	No	2

25. If you had a son, of at least normal intelligence, starting school now, how much education would you like him to have?

	Complete elementary school education	1
	Complete vocational training	2
(CIRCLE	Complete high school education	3
HIGHEST	Complete college education	4
GIVEN)	Graduate - Professional education	5
	Cannot specify any level	6

26. I am going to show you a picture of a ladder. Each step up represents a better chance of reaching the goal. The top step of the ladder stands for an "excellent" chance of reaching the goal, i.e., 100 chances out of a 100. The bottom step of the ladder stands for "no chance at all." The higher the step the better the chance -- the lower the step the poorer his chance. Pick out which step on the ladder best describes his chances of getting this much education. (HAND RESPONDENT GREEN CARD)

Record number of step	

27. In your opinion, what could prevent him from getting this much education?

(omitted from Community sample, coded for III sample)

28. How would you feel if he did not reach this level of education? (REFERS TO ANSWER IN Q.25)

Very disappointed	1
Fairly disappointed	2
Slightly disappointed	3
Not disappointed at all	4

29. Now that you have told me how much education you would want your son to have -- will you please tell me how much education you would really expect him to get?

(omitted from Community sample coded for III sample	Complete elementary school education	1
	Complete vocational training	2
	Complete high school education	3
	Complete college education	4
	Graduate - Professional education	5
	Cannot specify any level	6

30. What kind of work have you done most of your life? Please give me the title and a full description of the job.

31. Did you work at all the past 12 months?

(SKIP TO Q.36)	Yes	1
	No	2

32. How come you didn't work at all during the past 12 months?

(SKIP TO Q.50)	Housewife	1
	Retired or permanently disabled	2
(ASK Q's.33, 34 & 35)	Sick or unemployed and/or looking for work	3
(CHANGE 31 TO "YES" AND SKIP TO Q.36 - RECORD ARMED SERVICES IN Q.37)	Armed Services	4

33. What was the last full-time occupation you had? Please give me the title and a full description of the job?

34. In what year was this?

Year	

35. What was your average weekly take-home pay for that year?

Insert line number	

- 5 -

(ASK Q's. 36 TO 39 ONLY IF "YES" TO Q.31 --
THAT IS, RESPONDENT WORKED LAST YEAR.
OTHERWISE SKIP TO Q.40)

36. (IF "YES" TO Q.31) Altogether how many
weeks during 1959 did you work at least
4 days or 30 hours?

*(omitted from Community sample, coded for III
sample)*

Number of weeks:	

37. What was your major occupation outside
of the home during last year? Please
give me the title and a full description
of the job.

38. In your major occupation during the past
12 months, did you work for someone else
or were you self-employed -- that is,
have you your own business or practice?

Worked for someone else	1
Self-employed	2

39. Have you had any part-time job(s) or
second full-time job(s) in addition to
your regular job last year?

Yes	1
No	2

(ASK EVERYONE)
40. What kind of an occupation would you like
to have?

41. Pick out the step on the ladder which
best describes your chances of obtaining
this occupation.

Record number of step	

42. How would you feel if you found out that
you could never have this occupation?

Very disappointed	1
Fairly disappointed	2
Slightly disappointed	3
Not disappointed at all	4

- 6 -

43. What three things do you like about
   " ?"
   (REFER TO JOB GIVEN IN Q.40)
   (RANK IN ORDER OF IMPORTANCE TO YOU)

Good wages or income	1	2	3
Skilled job	1	2	3
Feeling of being of service to others	1	2	3
Job security - steady work	1	2	3
Unusual or different kind of work	1	2	3
Chance to meet and socialize with nice people	1	2	3
Chance to supervise others	1	2	3
Chance to be independent	1	2	3
Nice clean job	1	2	3
Like the work itself	1	2	3

44. What possible reasons could you give that would prevent you from getting this kind of occupation?

45. Please tell me what you are doing or have done to help you get this occupation? (REFERS TO JOB OR OCCUPATION MENTIONED IN Q.40)

   (omitted from both samples)

46. At any time in the future, do you expect to be in a better job than you now have? (IF RESPONDENT IS NOT WORKING NOW, THE REFERENT SHOULD BE HIS LAST JOB)

	Yes	1
(SKIP TO Q.50)	No	2
	Undecided	3

47. (IF "YES" OR "UNDECIDED") What kind of job do you expect this to be? (PROBE IF NECESSARY: What type of job would this be?)

(IF DON'T KNOW, SKIP TO Q.50)

- 7 -

48. At any time in the past, after you left school, did you <u>expect</u> to get a better job than this one? <u>(REFER TO JOB MENTIONED IN Q.47)</u>

	Yes	1
(SKIP TO Q.50)	No	2

49. (IF "YES") How much have you lowered your job expectations?

	Very much	1
	Somewhat	2
	Very little	3

(ASK EVERYONE)
50. At the present time, are you....

	Married	1
(CIRCLE	Single	2
CURRENT	Widowed	3
STATUS)	Divorced	4
	Permanently Separated	5

51. What was your father's main occupation?

52. (IF CURRENTLY MARRIED) What was your father-in-law's main occupation?

53. (IF MARRIED) Does your husband (wife) work now?

Yes - full-time	1
Yes - part time	2
No	3

54. Who is head of this household?

(Q's. 55 - 77 ARE ASKED OF ALL RESPONDENTS WHO ARE <u>NOT</u> HEAD OF HOUSEHOLDS.)
(IF RESPONDENT IS HEAD OF HOUSEHOLD, SKIP TO Q.78)

55. What kind of work has ___ (HEAD OF HOUSE-HOLD) done, most of <u>his</u> (her) life? Please give me the title and full description of the job.

56. What was the major occupation of
(HEAD OF HOUSEHOLD) during the past year?
(IF HEAD OF HOUSEHOLD IS NOT HUSBAND,
REFER TO INDIVIDUAL MENTIONED IN Q.54,
e.g., FATHER, UNCLE, ETC.)

Working: (title and description)	1
Housewife	2
Sick or unemployed and/or looking for a job	3
In Armed Services	4
Retired or permanently disabled	5

57. (IF "SICK OR UNEMPLOYED") What was
the last full-time occupation that he
(she) had? Please give me the title
and a full description of the job?

58. Has he (she) had any part-time job(s)
or second full-time job in addition to
his (her) regular job during this period?
(REFERS TO JOB MENTIONED IN Q. 56 OR Q.57)

(omitted from both samples)

| Yes | 1 |
| No | 2 |

59. What kind of occupation would you <u>like</u>
him (her) to have?

60. Pick the step on the ladder which best
describes his (her) chances of obtaining
this occupation.

| Record number of step | |

61. How would you feel if you found that he
(she) could never have this occupation?

Very disappointed	1
Fairly disappointed	2
Slightly disappointed	3
Not disappointed at all	4

62. What reasons could you give that would
possibly prevent him (her) from obtaining
this occupation?

63. What <u>three</u> things do you like about
    "   ?"
    (REFER TO RESPONSE GIVEN IN Q.59)
    (RANK IN ORDER OF IMPORTANCE TO YOU)
    *(omitted from Community sample, **coded for III***
    sample)

Good wages or income	1	2	3
Skilled job	1	2	3
Feeling of being of service to others	1	2	3
Job security - steady work	1	2	3
Unusual or different kind of work	1	2	3
Chance to meet and socialize with people	1	2	3
Chance to supervise others	1	2	3
Chance to be independent	1	2	3
Nice clean job	1	2	3
Like the work itself	1	2	3

64. Do you expect him to get a better job
    than he has now?

	Yes	1
(SKIP TO Q.66)	No	2
	Undecided	3

65. (IF "YES" OR "UNDECIDED") What kind
    of job do you expect this to be?
    (PROBE: "What <u>type</u> job would this
    be?")

(omitted from Community sample, coded for III
sample)

66. What was his (her) total gross earnings
    for the last year he (she) worked?

    (omitted from
    both samples)

Insert line number	

67. What was his (her) average weekly take-
    home pay when he (she) worked during
    that year?

Insert line number	

68. Has he (she) ever had a higher average
    weekly take-home pay in any previous
    year?

	Yes	1
(SKIP TO Q.70)	No	2

69. (IF "YES") What was his (her)
    average weekly take-home pay for the
    highest previous year?

Insert line number	

70. What average weekly take-home pay would
    you like him (her) to have?

Insert line number	

71. Pick out the step on the ladder which
    best describes his (her) chances of
    earning this income.

Record number of step	

72. How would you feel if you found out
    that he (she) could never earn this
    income?

Very disappointed	1
Fairly disappointed	2
Slightly disappointed	3
Not disappointed at all	4

Q's. 73 - 77 ARE TO BE ASKED ONLY OF THOSE WHO DID NOT WORK AT ALL DURING THE LAST 12 MONTHS, AND WHO ARE NOT HEADS OF HOUSEHOLD. ("NO" TO Q.31)

73. Would you want a full-time paying job sometime in the future?

Yes	1
No	2
Undecided	3

74. Do you think you actually will have a full-time paying job in the future?

	Yes	1
(SKIP TO Q.78)	No	2
	Undecided	3

75. (IF "YES" OR "UNDECIDED") What kind of work would you like this to be?

76. Pick the step on the ladder which best describes your chances of doing this work.

| Record number of step | |

77. How would you feel if you found out that you could never do this work? (REFERS TO ANSWER IN Q.75)

Very disappointed	1
Fairly disappointed	2
Slightly disappointed	3
Not disappointed at all	4

78. If you had a son, of at least normal intelligence, what kind of occupation would you like him to have when he gets out of school?

79. Pick out the step on the ladder which best describes his chances of getting this occupation?

| Record number of step | |

80. How would you feel if he could never have this occupation?

Very disappointed	1
Fairly disappointed	2
Slightly disappointed	3
Not disappointed at all	4

81. In your opinion, what could prevent him from obtaining this occupation?	(ASK Q's. 83 - 86 ONLY OF THOSE WHO WORKED LAST YEAR. OTHERWISE, SKIP TO Q.87)
	
	83. What were your own total <u>gross</u> earnings last year?
	   (omitted from both samples) Insert line number ☐
	
	84. What was your average weekly take-home pay when you worked during the last year?
	   Insert line number ☐
	
	85. Have you ever had a higher average weekly take-home pay in any previous year?
	   Yes 1
	   (SKIP TO Q.87) No 2
	
	86. (IF "YES") Give your average weekly take-home pay for the highest previous year?
	   Insert line number ☐
	
	87. What average weekly take-home pay would you like to have?
	   Insert line number ☐

82. When you were in school, what sort of work did you expect to do when you left school?	88. Pick out the step on the ladder which best describes your chances of earning this income.
	   Record number of step ☐
	
	89. How would you feel if you found out that you could never earn this income?
	
	   Very disappointed 1
	   Fairly disappointed 2
	   Slightly disappointed 3
	   Not disappointed at all 4

90. What reasons could you give that would possibly prevent you from earning this salary?

1. *(omitted from Community sample, coded for III sample)*

2.

91. What is the smallest average weekly take-home pay you need to have for the "basic" needs of life?

Insert line number	

92. What is the highest average weekly take-home pay you expect to earn in the future?

Insert line number	

93. In each of the following pairs, pick the job that you think is the better one.

1.	Bricklayer	@ $120 per wk.	1	or	Teacher	@ $90 per wk.	2
2.	Machine Operator	@ $100 per wk.	1	or	Gov't Clerk	@ $80 per wk.	2
3.	Factory Worker	@ $ 80 per wk.	1	or	Sales Person (Dept. Store)	@ $60 per wk.	2

Now, I am going to read you some statements that people sometimes use in describing themselves. People differ, however, in the degree to which they apply these statements to
themselves. As I read each statement would you please tell me which choice in the booklet
best describes you. Don't think about your choices too long, but give me the first thing
that comes to your mind.

I am a person who:	Almost Never	Occasionally	Usually	Almost Always	
94. -takes an active part in organizations	1	2	3	4	
95. -blames myself when things go wrong	1	2	3	4	
96. -tries harder to win an argument with a White person than with a Negro person	1	2	3	4	
97. -welcomes criticism of myself	1	2	3	4	
98. -thinks about whether other people like me	1	2	3	4	
99. -keeps my anger to myself when a White person gets me angry	1	2	3	4	
100.-asks others for help	1	2	3	4	
101.-lives "the good life"	1	2	3	4	
102.-likes to be with a group of people	1	2	3	4	
103.-expresses my opinion freely with White persons	1	2	3	4	
104.-thinks about how he compares with others	1	2	3	4	
105.-pays special attention to his appearance	1	2	3	4	
106.-feels sensitive or "touchy" about being a Negro	1	2	3	4	
107.-(Not Applicable If Not Married) Makes the decisions on money and other important family matters	1	2	3	4	N.A.
108.-(Not Applicable If Not Married) Shares the responsibility of financially supporting the household with my wife (husband)	1	2	3	4	N.A.
109.-(Not Applicable If Not Married) Shares the responsibility of training my children	1	2	3	4	N.A.
110.-(Not Applicable If Not Married) Talks to my wife (husband) about things that bother me	1	2	3	4	N.A.

The following are some general questions about your health. Everyone is bothered, to some extent, by some of the things listed below. In answering these questions you will give us an idea of the state of your health during the past year. Remember there are no right or wrong answers to any of these....it is just a question of how you feel about them.

	Almost never, rarely	Sometimes, occasionally, a little	Fairly often, usually, a good deal	Very often, almost always, etc.
111. How often do you have a poor appetite?	1	2	3	4
112. How often do you have dizzy spells?	1	2	3	4
113. How often are you bothered by difficulty in getting to sleep or staying asleep?	1	2	3	4
114. How often are you troubled by headaches?	1	2	3	4
115. How often do you feel tired even though you have been doing no hard work?	1	2	3	4
116. How often are you bothered by itching or skin rashes on any part of your body?	1	2	3	4
117. How often do you have pains in your chest, shortness of breath, or difficulty with breathing?	1	2	3	4
118. How often are you bothered by stomach trouble? (constipation, diarrhea, etc.)	1	2	3	4
119. How often are you bothered by nervousness (on edge, fidgity, depressed, cannot stay put, etc.)	1	2	3	4
120. How often are you bothered by your heart beating fast?	1	2	3	4
121. How often are you bothered by numbness in any part of your hands or feet?	1	2	3	4
122. How often are you bothered by general aches and pains in all parts of your body?	1	2	3	4
123. How often are you bothered by your hands trembling?	1	2	3	4

124. Have you been told by a doctor at anytime in your life that you have had....

		Yes	No
1.	Tuberculosis?	1	2
2.	High blood pressure?	1	2
3.	Nervous or mental trouble?	1	2
4.	Stomach ulcer?	1	2
5.	Migraine headaches?	1	2
6.	Asthma?	1	2

(SKIP Q.125 IF "NO" TO #3 ABOVE)

125. (IF "YES" TO "3", REPEAT FOR EACH "YES" CONDITION GIVEN IN Q.124)
     Please give me the period or periods of treatment for __(CONDITION IN Q.124)

1. (Tuberculosis)	
2. (High blood pressure)	
3. (Nervous or mental trouble)	
4. (Stomach ulcer)	
5. (Migraine headaches)	
6. (Asthma)	

Now, I am going to read you some statements that people sometimes use in describing them-selves. People differ, however, in the degree to which they apply these statements to themselves. As I read each statement would you please tell me which choice in the booklet best describes the kind of person you would like to be. Don't think about your choices too long, but give me the first thing that comes to your mind.

I would like to be a person who:	Almost never	Occasionally	Usually	Almost always
126. -takes an active part in organizations	1	2	3	4
127. -blames myself when things go wrong	1	2	3	4
128. -tries harder to win an argument with a White person than with a Negro person	1	2	3	4
129. -welcomes criticism of myself	1	2	3	4
130. -thinks about whether other people like me	1	2	3	4
131. -keeps my anger to myself when a White person gets me angry	1	2	3	4
132. -asks others for help	1	2	3	4
133. -lives "the good life"	1	2	3	4
134. -likes to be with a group of people	1	2	3	4
135. -expresses my opinion freely with White persons	1	2	3	4
136. -thinks about how he compares with others	1	2	3	4
137. -pays special attention to his appearance	1	2	3	4
138. -feels sensitive or "touchy" about being a Negro	1	2	3	4
139. -makes the decisions on money and other important family matters	1	2	3	4
140. -shares the responsibility of financially supporting the household with my wife (husband)	1	2	3	4
141. -shares the responsibility of training my children	1	2	3	4
142. -talks to my wife (husband) about things that bother me	1	2	3	4

143. If you had a son (daughter) growing up, to what degree would you like him (her) to be like you?

(CIRCLE ONLY ONE)

Exactly like me	1
Pretty much like me	2
Slightly like me	3
Not like me at all	4

144. In what way(s), if any, would you like him (her) to be like you?

145. In what way(s), if any, would you like him (her) to be different from you?

I will read several questions one at a time. After each question I will give you a number of possible answers -- select one. There are no right or wrong answers, and everybody has his own feelings about these matters.

146. How would you describe the neighborhood you live in now?

Almost all White	1
Mixed - mostly White	2
Mixed - mostly Negro	3
All Negro	4

147. If you decided to buy a house and had money for it, what kind of neighborhood would you like to have it in?

Almost all White	1
Mixed - mostly White	2
Mixed - mostly Negro	3
All Negro	4
No preference	5
	6

148. In picking "
 (READ ANSWER SELECTED IN
 " give me some of your reasons
Q.147)
for your answer.

149. How important is this to you?

(CIRCLE ONLY ONE)	Very important	1
	Fairly important	2
	Slightly important	3
	Not important at all	4

150. Suppose you were in a position to join any organized social group you wanted, what type of membership would you like it to have?

Almost all White	1
Mixed - mostly White	2
Mixed - mostly Negro	3
All Negro	4
No preference	5
	6

151. What are some of the reasons why you picked "＿＿＿＿＿?"
     (READ RESPONSE IN Q.150)

152. How strongly do you feel that it should have this type of membership?

Very strong	1
Fairly strong	2
Not too strong	3
No strong feelings one way or another	4

153. What type of membership does the organized social group you belong to (or have belonged) have? (REFERS TO ORGANIZATION MOST ACTIVE IN)

Almost all White	1
Mixed - mostly White	2
Mixed - mostly Negro	3
All Negro	4
Not applicable	5
	6

154. If you had children and could choose any school of equal quality for them, which of the following would you pick?

(omitted from both samples)

Almost all White	1
Mixed classes - mostly White	2
Mixed classes - mostly Negro	3
All Negro	4
No preference	5
	6

155. In picking "＿＿＿＿＿
     (READ ANSWER SELECTED IN
     ＿＿＿＿," give me some of your reasons
     Q.154)
     for your answer.

(omitted from both samples)

- 19 -

156. How important is this to you?

(omitted from both samples)

Very important	1
Fairly important	2
Slightly important	3
No importance at all	4

157. What kind of school(s) did you go to? (RESPONSE REFERS TO MOST TYPICAL OF ELEMENTARY OR SECONDARY SCHOOLS ATTENDED, -- ONLY ONE ANSWER)

Almost all White	1
Mixed classes - mostly White	2
Mixed classes - mostly Negro	3
All Negro	4
Separate classes for Negroes and Whites	5
	6

158. If you picked up a newspaper and saw the headlines "Negro Seized in Camden," which of the following would best describe your first reaction?

Very uncomfortable	1
Fairly uncomfortable	2
Slightly uncomfortable	3
Would not feel one way or another	4

159. What reasons do you have for feeling this way?

160. When you are working at a job, whom would you like to have as a foreman or boss....

(CIRCLE		
	Negro foreman or boss?	1
ONLY	White foreman or boss?	2
ONE)	No preference	3

161. How strongly do you feel about your answer? (REFERS TO Q.160)

Very strong	1
Fairly strong	2
Not too strong	3
No feelings one way or another	4

162. What are some of the reasons why you picked " ?" (READ ANSWER SELECTED IN Q.160)

163. (If you had children and) If you could pick your children's close friends, whom would you prefer?

(omitted from both samples)	Negro only	1
	White only	2
	Negro and White	3

164. How strongly do you feel about your answer?

(omitted from both samples)	Very strong	1
	Fairly strong	2
	Not too strong	3
	No strong feelings one way or another	4

165. What type of close friends does (do) your child(ren) have?

(omitted from both samples)	All Negro	1
	All White	2
	Negro and White	3
	Respondent has no children	4

166. If you had a Negro friend who told you that he wanted to "pass" for the advantages that it would give him, which of the following choices best describes how you would feel?

Glad for him	1
Mixed feelings toward him	2
Angry with him	3
	4

167. Why do you feel this way?

- 21 -

I'm going to present you with a number of situations and ask you to make some choices based on them. Remember, there are no right or wrong answers -- it's a matter of your own judgment.

(omitted from III sample, coded for Community sample)

168. Suppose a neighbor came to you and asked your advice about her husband who, for the past six weeks, has been staying in his room, refuses to talk to anyone and talks to himself. What kind of a problem, in your own opinion, would you say he has?

(CIRCLE ONLY ONE)

Probably nothing is really wrong with him	1
Probably emotionally upset	2
Probably physically run down or sick	3
Probably insane or crazy	4
Probably lazy or weak-willed	5

169. What would you recommend she do? Select from the list below, the choice you think is best. Remember it's your own opinion that is important. There is no right or wrong answer.

(omitted from III sample, coded for Community sample)

Have her talk it over with her minister (priest)	1
Call the police	2
Call in her family or local doctor	3
Take him to a clinic or hospital for nervous or mental problems	4
Call in a psychiatrist or "nerve" specialist	5
Take him to a medical clinic	6
Have her family handle the problem	7
Other (SPECIFY)	
	8

170. Suppose a neighbor came to you and asked your advice about her husband who, for the past six weeks, has been having dizzy spells, pains in his chest, and nose bleeds. What kind of a problem, in your own opinion, would you say he has?

(omitted from both samples)

(CIRCLE ONLY ONE)

Probably nothing is really wrong with him	1
Probably emotionally upset	2
Probably physically run down or sick	3
Probably insane or crazy	4
Probably lazy or weak-willed	5

171. What would you recommend she do? Select from the list below, the choice you think is best. Remember it's your own opinion that is important. There is no right or wrong answer.

(omitted from both samples)

Have her talk it over with her minister (priest)	1
Call the police	2
Call in her family or local doctor	3
Take him to a clinic for nervous or mental problems	4
Call in a psychiatrist or "nerve" specialist	5
Take him to a medical clinic	6
Have her family handle the problem	7
Other (SPECIFY)	
	8

172. Suppose a neighbor came to you and asked your advice about her husband who, for the past six weeks, has been accusing her of all kinds of horrible things and gets violent over unimportant matters. What kind of a problem, in your own opinion, would you say he has?

(omitted from III sample, coded for Community sample)

(CIRCLE ONLY ONE)

Probably nothing is really wrong with him	1
Probably emotionally upset	2
Probably physically run down or sick	3
Probably insane or crazy	4
Probably lazy or weak-willed	5

173. What would you recommend she do? Select from the list below, the choice you think is best. Remember it's your own opinion that is important. There is no right or wrong answer.

(omitted from III sample, coded for Community sample)

Have her talk it over with her minister (priest)	1
Call the police	2
Call in her family or local doctor	3
Take him to a clinic or hospital for nervous or mental problems	4
Call in a psychiatrist or "nerve" specialist	5
Take him to a medical clinic	6
Have her family handle the problem	7
Other (SPECIFY)	
	8

174. Suppose a neighbor came to you and asked your advice about her husband who, for the past six weeks, talks about committing suicide. What kind of a problem, in your own opinion, would you say he has?

(omitted from III sample, coded for Community sample)

(CIRCLE ONLY ONE)

Probably nothing is really wrong with him	1
Probably emotionally upset	2
Probably physically run down or sick	3
Probably insane or crazy	4
Probably lazy or weak-willed	5

175. What would you recommend she do? Select from the list below, the choice you think is best. Remember it's your own opinion that is important. There is no right or wrong answer.

(omitted from III sample, coded for Community sample)

Have her talk it over with her minister (priest)	1
Call the police	2
Call in her family or local doctor	3
Take him to a clinic or hospital for nervous or mental problems	4
Call in a psychiatrist or "nerve" specialist	5
Take him to a medical clinic	6
Have her family handle the problem	7
Other (SPECIFY)	
	8

- 23 -

176. Suppose a neighbor came to you and asked your advice about her husband who, for the past six weeks, tells us he talks with God, and always talks about the sins of man. What kind of a problem, in your own opinion, would you say he has?

(omitted from III sample, coded for Community sample)

(CIRCLE ONLY ONE)

Probably nothing is really wrong with him	1
Probably emotionally upset	2
Probably physically run down or sick	3
Probably insane or crazy	4
Probably lazy or weak-willed	5

177. What would you recommend she do? Select from the list below, the choice you think is best. Remember it's your own opinion that is important. There is no right or wrong answer.

(omitted from III sample, coded for Community sample)

Have her talk it over with her minister (priest)	1
Call the police	2
Call in her family or local doctor	3
Take him to a clinic or hospital for nervous or mental problems	4
Call in a psychiatrist or "nerve" specialist	5
Take him to a medical clinic	6
Have her family handle the problem	7
Other (SPECIFY)	
	8

I am going to show you a picture representing the possible steps in a person's life. The top step stands for the "best possible way of life" and the bottom step the "worst possible way of life." Try to picture these steps in terms of a person like yourself. (HAND RESPONDENT SALMON CARD)

178. When you think of the "best way of life" for you -- what are the things that come to your mind? Before answering take a moment to think about it.

179. When you think of the "worst way of life" for you -- what are the things that come to your mind? Before answering take a moment to think about it.

180. Keeping in mind that step 10 represents the best way of life and step 1 the worst way of life, will you look at the diagram again and tell me the step number that best describes where you are now?

Indicate step number	

181. Will you please tell me the step number that best describes where you were a few years ago?

Indicate step number	

182. Will you please tell me the step number that best describes where you expect to be a few years from now?

Indicate step number	

183. Will you please tell me the step number that best describes where you would like to be a few years from now?

Indicate step number	

184. Which step on the ladder best describes your chances of reaching this position? (REFER TO STEP SELECTED IN Q.183)

Indicate step number	

185. How disappointed would you be if you found out that you could never reach this step?

Very disappointed	1
Fairly disappointed	2
Slightly disappointed	3
Not disappointed at all	4

186. Which of the following things, if any, do you feel may be keeping you from where you would like to be a few years from now? (REFER TO STEP GIVEN IN Q.183)

Lack of ability	1
Lack of training and education	2
Lack of opportunity; not getting right breaks in life	3
Lack of any clear and positive aim in life	4
Family background	5
Class I am in	6
Race I am part of	7
My religion	8
Own ambitions and high goals I have set for myself	9
Other (SPECIFY)	10
None	11

187. We have just spoken about a "few years from now" -- could you tell me how many years you had in mind?

Record number of years	

188. (IF RESPONDENT REPLIES TO Q.186) What are you doing now, or what plans have you to get around these things? (REFERS TO THINGS MENTIONED IN Q.186)

(omitted from both samples)

- 25 -

189. We asked you before to pick the step which best describes your position in life; now pick the step which best describes the position of your close friends as compared to where you are now?

Indicate step number	

190. What are the things that you had in mind when you compared the position of your close friends to yourself?

191. If you picked up a newspaper and saw the headline "Negro Received Major Award", which of the following best describes your first reaction?

Very proud	1
Fairly proud	2
Slightly proud	3
No feelings one way or another	4
Slightly annoyed	5

192. What are your reasons for feeling this way?

193. Which of the following terms most accurately describes you?

Colored	1
Negro	2
Indian	3
Afro-American	4
Mulatto or Creole	5
Other (SPECIFY:)	
	6

194. In your opinion, has being a(n) _____ prevented you from (RESPONSE IN Q.193) getting the things you wanted?

Yes - very much	1
Yes - to some degree	2
Yes - slightly	3
No	4

195. On the basis of your experience so far, to what degree would you say you have been "successful" in life?

Very successful	1
Fairly successful	2
Slightly successful	3
Not successful	4

196. Which of the choices below best describes how your present ambitions compared with those you had in the past?

	Present ambitions higher	1
(SKIP TO Q.198)	Present ambitions about the same	2
	Present ambitions lower	3

197. (OMIT IF RESPONDENT ANSWERS "ABOUT THE SAME") To what degree have your ambitions changed?

Very much	1
Somewhat	2
Very little	3

198. It has been said that if a man works hard, saves his money, and is ambitious, he will get ahead. How often do you think this really happens?

Very often	1
Often	2
Occasionally	3
Hardly at all	4

199. What things do you think of when you decide what social class a person belongs to? Choose three from the list in order of importance.

Education	1	2	3
Neighborhood in which a person lives	1	2	3
Income	1	2	3
Family background	1	2	3
Kind of work a person does	1	2	3
Color of skin	1	2	3
Organizations he's a member of	1	2	3
Influence in the community	1	2	3
Other (SPECIFY)			
	1	2	3

200. Taking into account the things you just told me, which of these choices best describes where you are?

Much above average	1
Somewhat above average	2
Average	3
Somewhat below average	4
Much below average	5

201. What is your religious preference? (CIRCLE ONE)

Protestant	1
What denomination?	
Catholic	2
Hebrew	3
Other	4
None	5

202. How much education did your mother have; what was last grade of school she completed?

None   0

Grade school 1 2 3 4 5 6 7 8

High school   1 2 3 4

College or   1 2 3 4 5 or more
University

203. How much education did your father have; what was last grade of school he completed?

None   0

Grade school 1 2 3 4 5 6 7 8

High school   1 2 3 4

College or   1 2 3 4 5 or more
University

204. Have you raised any children (not including foster children)?

Yes	1
No	2

205. (IF "YES") Have any of them completed school?

Yes	1
No	2

206. (IF "YES") For each child, specify sex, age, and last grade completed.

	Age	Sex	Last grade completed
a.			
b.			
c.			
d.			
e.			
f.			

Name of
Respondent_____

Address_____

City_____State_____

Interviewer_____

Date:_____

APPENDIX C

Occupational Prestige Scale

The major occupational scales in use today are based on the norms of all white, or predominantly all white, samples. The applicability of these scales to a Negro population is questionable; research on this issue is limited to too few studies of representative samples of employed Negroes. One study, which used the National Opinion Research Council (NORC) scale with a Negro sample, found general conformity with the original NORC rating. Some differences, however, did emerge (Brown, 1955). In another study, the rankings of selected occupations and the reasons for these rankings among Negro high school students did not correspond with those found for a sample of white respondents (Rose and Wall, 1957). In the present study, we had to determine how a sample of urban Negroes perceived various occupations with respect to the prestige associated with these jobs. Since we knew of no scale applicable to an adult, all Negro population, one had to be constructed.

PROCEDURE

Occupations listed in the United States Census (1950) were classified into fifteen categories, on the basis of the education and skill required for each occupation. Three representative occupations were selected from each of ten of these fifteen categories. The selection was based on the applicability of these occupations to our population, and how well these occupations represented their particular category. Three alternate lists of occupations were prepared—the order of presentation of occupations on each list was determined by the use of random numbers.

A modified five-step Likert-type scale was used for the prestige rankings (Likert, 1932). The continuum ranged from "Very high" prestige (ranked as "1") to "Very low" prestige (ranked as "5"). Descriptive labels were not applied to the three intermediate points. The respondent encircled the

prestige position on the continuum that corresponded to his evaluation of a
given occupation. The three alternate lists of occupations are presented below.

Form A	Form B	Form C
Medical Technician	X-ray Technician	Dental Technician
Painter	Paperhanger	Plasterer
Chemical Engineer	College Professor	Physician
Foreman in Factory	Foreman in Factory	Foreman in Factory
Social Worker	Registered Nurse	Elementary School Teacher
Machinist	Carpenter	Electrician
Manager of Corporation (75 employees)	Manager of Corporation (75 employees)	Manager of Corporation (75 employees)
Waiter-Waitress	Construction Laborer	Messenger
Cashier	Post Office Clerk	Stenographer
Owner of Candy Store	Owner of Tailor Shop	Owner of Grocery Store
Manager of Company (25 employees)	Manager of Company (25 employees)	Manager of Company (25 employees)
Professional Athlete	Musician	Dancer
Supervisor in Bank	Supervisor in Bank	Supervisor in Bank
Office Manager	Office Manager	Office Manager
Shoe Salesman	Dept. Store Salesman	Brush Salesman

The occupation lists were presented to a sample of employed adult Negroes
in Philadelphia, including college students and housewives ($N = 101$). The
occupations of respondents in this sample represented all but three of the
fifteen classification groups listed. The sex and age breakdown of this sample
was as follows: Males: $N = 63$, mean age $= 32.9$ years; Females: $N = 38$,
mean age $= 27.1$ years.

The frequency of choices at each point on the five-step scale was tabulated.
The resulting frequency distribution showed some slight negative skewness,
suggesting that respondents in this sample tended to rate the occupations
toward the more prestigious end of the continuum.

Weights were assigned to each of the five steps on the prestige scale. Each
rating of "1" ("Very high" prestige) was multiplied by five, each rating of
"2" by four, etc., up to a rating of "5" ("Very low" prestige), which was
multiplied by one. The weighted score for each occupation was obtained by
multiplying the number of its ratings at each point by the assigned weight
and summing the scores for the five points. The total weighted score for each
of the fifteen categories was the sum of the weights for that category, including
the three alternate forms. The total weighted scores ranged from 186 (unskilled occupations) to 461 (college professor, chemical engineer, physician).

Before the total weighted scores of the three occupational lists could be
combined, the reliability of the forms had to be determined. The rank order
correlation procedure was used for this purpose. Only two of the three occupational lists had been presented to a sufficient number of subjects to be
utilized. The correlation between these two forms was .84 ($P = <.01$), indicating a reasonable degree of comparability.

The numerical differences between adjacent occupational ranks showed considerable variability, ranging from a difference of 2 to a difference of 55; the average numerical difference was 18.3 points.

An additional sample was obtained ($N = 21$) as a crude check on the stability of the rankings. This sample was incorporated into the original sample, and new rankings were determined. The new rankings indicated a few changes from the original ones; however, these shifts in position involved only those ranks which had previously showed minor numerical differences in weighted scores. Ranks which were characterized by large numerical differences were not appreciably affected.

This analysis indicated that we had a partially ordered scale—that is, some of the ranks evidenced considerable overlap with adjacent ranks, and others were numerically discrete. Since a scale with the formal properties of an ordinal scale was desirable, some combination or reduction of the fifteen ranks was necessary. The use of standard deviation for grouping was inappropriate for our data, and groupings based upon the range using ten or twelve categories showed too much shifting of occupations *between* classes. The method finally utilized combined those occupations whose total weighted scores tended to cluster together, resulting in a seven-step occupation scale. The final seven-step scale, with weighted scores, is presented in Table 1.

Table 1 (Appendix C)—Fifteen - and Seven-Step Occupation Scales

OCCUPATION	WEIGHTED SCORE	15-STEP RANK	7-STEP RANK
Laborer, Waitress, etc.	217	15	1
Painter, Semi-Skilled Trades	264	14	2
Sales – Retail	279	13	
Stenographer, etc.	322	12	
Foreman in Factory	338	11	3
Plumber, Skilled Trades, etc.	356	10	
Owner of Small Retail Business	359	99	
Office Manager	418	7.5	4
Manager of Company (25 employees)	4.8	7.5	
Technicians: Medical, X-ray, etc.	450	6	
Supervisor: Bank, etc.	451	5	5
R.N., Social Worker, Teacher, etc.	458	4	
Professional Athlete, Entertainer, etc.	459	3	
Manager of Corporation (75 employees)	478	2	6
College Professor, Physician	568	1	7

FINAL SEVEN-STEP OCCUPATION SCALE

A general, descriptive occupational scale was formulated on the basis of this seven-step scale, so that occupations similar in kind but not formally evaluated could be classified.

Step 1: Unskilled workers: (requires little or no formal technical training) —janitors, laborers, messengers, waiters, and waitresses, etc.

Step 2: Sales Personnel (retail) and Semi-skilled Workers: (requires no special educational requirements, but some technical skills)—includes painters, plasterers, etc.

Step 3: Skilled Craftsmen: (requires special technical skills, apprenticeship, or licensing requirements)—plumbers, machinists, carpenters, etc.

Also: Proprietors of small stores: tailors, etc.

Also: Foreman in industrial establishments, etc.

Also: Clerical workers at skilled level: stenographers, bookkeepers, etc.

Step 4: Minor Administrative Personnel: (usually requires some formal educational training)—includes office managers, assistant managers, supervisors, etc.

Step 5: Administrative Personnel (second line management) of larger organizations.

Also: Technicians (requires special educational and technical training): medical, dental, X-ray technicians, etc.

Also: Professionals (requires formal educational and technical training equivalent to a college degree or better, but less than a doctorate): social workers, public school teachers, R.N.'s.

Also: Semi-Professionals (requires specialized skills and technical training): includes musicians, dancers, athletes, etc.

Step 6: Major Administrative Personnel (may not, but usually requires formal educational training at the college level): managers, officers, and proprietors of large complex organizations.

Step 7: Major Professionals (requires formal educational requirements beyond college, usually the doctorate degree and/or requires special examinations etc., by the state): includes M.D.'s, lawyers, C.P.A.'s, judges (other than municipal), etc.

APPENDIX D

Multi-Status Position or Social Class Index

Step Number	Education (number of years)	Income (yearly)	Occupation
1	0–4	$ 500–1000	Unskilled workers (e.g., laborers, waiters, domestics, messengers, janitors, etc.).
2	5–8	$1001–2000	Semi-skilled workers, and retail sales personnel (e.g., painters, plasterers, machine operators, retail sales personnel).
3	9–11	$2001–3000	Skilled craftsmen, skilled machine operators, foremen in industrial establishments, clerical workers, minor government positions.
4	12	$3001–4000	Minor administrative personnel (requiring some formal educational training—e.g., office managers, supervisors, and minor personnel in small establishments).

5	13–15	$4001–5000	Technicians (e.g., medical, dental, semi-professionals, and minor professionals such as musicians, dancers, athletes, social workers, registered nurses, public school teachers).
6	16	$5000–6000	Major managerial personnel and business proprietors.
7	17 and over	$6001–and over	Major professionals (e.g., physicians, lawyers, university teachers, certified public accountants).

WEIGHTS

Educational position on the seven-step scale was multiplied by 4.4;
Income position on the seven-step scale was multiplied by 2.5;
Occupational position on the seven-step scale was multiplied by 1.0.
Sum of weighted positions divided by 3 = Class Score.

CLASS SCORE INTERVALS

Class 1 (lowest) = 2.6 to 6.3
Class 2   = 6.4 to 7.7
Class 3   = 7.8 to 9.6
Class 4 (highest) = 9.7 to 18.4

INDEX